PENGU

GREAT INDIAN

Stephen Alter is an American wh
where his parents worked as miss
at Wesleyan University, Connecticut. He has publish
regarded novels, *Neglected Lives*, *Silk and Steel*, and *The Godchild*, all
of which are set in India. Stephen Alter teaches at present in Cairo,
Egypt.

GREAT INDIAN
HUNTING STORIES

Edited by
Stephen Alter

PENGUIN BOOKS

Penguin Books (India) Limited, 72-B Himalaya House, 23 Kasturba Gandhi Marg,
New Delhi-110 001, India
Penguin Books Ltd., Harmondsworth, Middlesex, England
Viking Penguin Inc., 40 West 23rd Street, New York, N.Y.10010. U.S.A.
Penguin Books Australia Ltd., Ringwood, Victoria, Australia
Penguin Books Canada Ltd., 2801 John Street, Markham, Ontario, Canada L3R 1 B4
Penguin Books (N.Z.) Ltd, 182-190 Wairau Road, Auckland 10, New Zealand

First published by Penguin Books, 1988

Made and printed in India by Ananda Offset Private Limited, Calcutta.
Typeset in Times Roman by Wordtronic, New Delhi.

Dedicated to the memory of

Dil Das

shikari, friend, and raconteur

Acknowledgements

I would like to thank Dino Mazumdar, Toby Sinclair and Inderjit Singh for allowing me to pillage their private libraries for the stories included in this collection. Special thanks also to David Davidar for his encouragement and advice.

Every effort has been made to contact copyright holders; in the event of an inadvertent omission or error, the publishers should be notified.

For permission to reprint the stories and excerpts in this anthology, acknowledgement is made as follows:

George Orwell, Shooting an Elephant *from* Inside The Whale And Other Essays *to The Estate of The Late Sonia Brownell Orwell and Secker & Warburg Ltd.*

Jim Corbett, The Talla Des Man-Eater, *from* The Temple Tiger, *to Oxford University Press.*

Kenneth Anderson, The Jowlagiri Man-Eater, *from* Nine Maneaters And One Rogue, *to George Allen & Unwin Ltd.*

Hugh Allen, Eight Annas a Tail, *from* The Lonely Tiger, *to Faber & Faber Ltd.*

A Note on Style

In order to preserve the period flavour of several of these stories, some of which were written over a hundred years ago, they have been reprinted exactly as they first appeared. Spelling, punctuation, style and usage have not been 'corrected' or standardized with the result that some words (machan, nilgai etc.) are spelled differently from story to story; they should, however, be taken to mean the same thing.

Contents

Introduction

My parents used to read Jim Corbett's books aloud to me when I was a child and his stories still excite my imagination with their vivid accounts of adventure. Each night my room would become a clearing in the jungle where I sat and listened for the far off roaring of a maneater. My bed became a *machan* tied up in the branches of a mango tree and I would sit there motionless over the tiger's kill, waiting for the tell-tale sounds of his approach, the rustle of leaves, the alarm cries of jungle birds, the crunch of bones which meant that the tiger was on the kill. In my imagination, I would ease myself forward, holding a rifle to my shoulder, eyes fixed on the shadowy form below. In an instant, I would switch on the torch and fire between the gleaming eyes.

Corbett's books were some of the first unillustrated stories that I enjoyed. The descriptions were so vivid that I needed no artist to help me imagine the scenes, for the words themselves drew pictures in my mind.

It was good, old-fashioned story telling. Corbett built the tension with each word, syllable by syllable, until the forest came alive. I fell asleep to so many of these stories that they became part of one another. My father's voice would seem to dissolve as I was lifted up and taken there, to the *machan* in the mango tree where a lone Englishman sat with a rifle across his knees.

Hunting tales are probably the oldest form of storytelling; descriptions of a chase, the ferocity and bravery of both the hunter and the hunted, and the death of an animal pursued. The first nouns and adjectives which man uttered must have described the forest, the weapons, the prey and the hunter himself. Over the centuries, as hunting became less a means of survival and more of a pastime and sport, these stories evolved into a popular literature for Sunday magazines and outdoors publications.

There is a tendency to discredit hunting tales as being a less important or insignificant form of literature. No doubt, most writers who specialize in hunting tales, do not aspire to any sort of critical acclaim. They are self-styled 'rustics' and sometimes even flaunt their illiteracy to try and imitate that 'primitive' voice of the campfire

11

raconteur.

A great deal has been written about Indian literature in English but it is surprising that *shikar* stories have been almost completely ignored. This is peculiar, because the *shikar* story is one of the few distinct genres of Indian English. Naturally, the first *shikar* stories were written by Britishers, but it is interesting to see how quickly this form of literature developed as something uniquely Indian. *Shikar* stories are definitely part of the mythology and traditions of the British Raj but they are also different from most 'Raj Literature' because they describe an experience outside the strict and formal boundaries of club and bungalow. The elaborate *shikars* on elephant back, so stereotypical of the Raj, were generally looked down upon by those who met the jungle single-handed and stripped of all their imperial regalia. The lone hunter setting foot in the forest, with only his rifle in his hand, was certainly the heroic ideal of the *shikar* story and a character 'beyond the pale' of Anglo-Indian society. He was known as a 'jungle-wallah', a wild and uncivilized character.

It is interesting to note how many of the writers of *shikar* stories were 'country born,' which in the complex caste structure of the Raj, placed them on an inferior rung of the social ladder. Foremost among these writers was Jim Corbett, who was born in Nainital and grew up in the village of Kaladhungi.Though he eventually became something of a celebrity and accompanied Viceroys and other V.I.P.'s on *shikar*, Corbett was always more of a curiosity than a companion. He was never fully accepted into the narrow enclosures of British society in India. Almost half of the writers in this collection were born in India; either of British or mixed parentage. Indian writers such as Kesri Singh also continued writing *shikar* stories in the years after independence. Unlike the short story or novel, *shikar* stories are a unique form of Indian literature, distinctly 'country born'.

Despite any 'rustic' pretenses, the writing in these stories is surprisingly well polished. Many *shikar* writers achieved a wonderful, lyrical quality in their prose. One sentence from Olive Smythies, in which she describes the Ramganga river, can stand as an example:

'Through this gorge flows the river, now with its voice hushed in a long, deep, mysterious pool, now forming over boulders in a roaring cataract where the big *mahseer* lie to feed, or again swirling with a subdued mutter past occasional sandbanks, or half submerged rocks, where crocodiles love to bask and everywhere the

footmarks of sambar and of the little barking deer, of tiger and
leopard and wild dog, which lie in wait to catch and kill their prey
by the roar of the greatwaters.

(Olive Smythies, *Ten Thousand Miles on Elephants*, 1961, page
45)

In most of these stories, the narrator's voice is very conversational
and it draws you into the story with its casual, unaffected style. This is
unusual for the period since most writing during the days of the Raj
was over-blown Victorian English that always sounded as though it
were being written with a grammar book in one hand. The two
writers in this collection who are particularly colloquial in their writing are James Inglis and Col. A.I.R. Glasfurd(who becomes hilar-
iously 'talkative', to the point of rambling off in long, yet entertaining
digressions).Other writers such as Mervyn Smith and Corbett had a
very plain, 'journalistic' style, unornamented and matter of fact.
Florid, decorative language does not suit a true-life adventure.

Unlike most modern writing, whether fiction or non-fiction, the
shikar story was always written after it had first been told. These
stories came directly out of the oral tradition of the campfire and were
probably told and retold more than a dozen times before the author
actually committed them to paper. The telling of a story aloud is very
important to the texture and style of a narrator's voice. Having
already tested the story on his audience, he knows where they will
laugh, where they will express disbelief and where they will need to
have a certain incident explained. What gets written down may not be
the first breathless account of shooting a tiger which the hunter
stammered out to his companions when he came down from the
machan or even the version with which he regaled his friends at the
club, but it is definitely influenced by those who have listened to him
tell the story. If nothing else, this makes for a carefully constructed
narrative.

A number of writers attempted to turn the *shikar* story into fiction
but only with limited success. In this collection, *Mrs. Packletide's
Tiger* by H.H. Munro (Saki), and *Tiger! Tiger!* by Rudyard Kipling
are the only examples. A.G. Shuttleworth (Silver Hackle) wrote several *Romances of the Indian Jungle* but compared to his other writing, these stories were poorly conceived and full of sentimentality,
something which his non-fiction did not contain. One of his stories,
Steed of the Forest God is a lengthy, melodramatic account of a hunt
for a mystical tiger, always referred to as 'Maharaj'. Brown Saheb is

13

the English *shikari* who cannot seem to draw a bead on the tiger until he asks for the assistance of Tulshi Baiga, a tribal medicine man who offers a sacrifice at the shrine of the forest god. There is a lot of talk about evil spirits and the entire piece is hopelessly contrived. In the end Brown Şaheb is attacked by the tiger and badly mauled. He summons his faithful servant, Alla Bux:

'I am done for Alla Bux. Time is precious. Get me a pencil and paper and give what I write to the Deputy Commissioner Saheb when you reach Gurmpore. He will forward it to my *Memsaheb*. Don't weep, Alla Bux. It is only my *kismet* (fate) as you Mohammedans say. Quick, bring me the paper and pencil.'

Alla Bux did as he was bidden and with an effort the wounded and dying man wrote his short letter to the wife who, he knew, was looking out eagerly for him. These few lines are sacred and were meant for her alone. The only part of it that we shall allow our eyes to see was the last sentence. 'Bear up, it is fated that my long delayed leave cannot come off; India and the jungles have claimed me.'

(A.G. Shuttleworth, *Indian Jungle Lore and the Rifle*, 1929, page 275)

Edison Marshall, an American writer, won the O. Henry prize in 1921 with a story titled, *The Heart of Little Shikara*. It may say something about the prize itself but Marshall is almost worse than Shuttleworth and makes his 'little shikara' sound like an eastern Hiawatha: 'Little sparrow hawk,' his mother laughed at him. 'Little one of mighty words, only the great sahibs that come from afar, and Warwick Sahib himself, may hunt the tiger. So how canst thou, little worthless?'

(Edison Marshall, *The Year's Best Stories*, 1957, page 33)

Unfortunately, this kind of writing seems to have been the norm for fictional *shikar* stories, whereas the non-fictional accounts had a gripping, unpretentious style. Marshall also wrote travelogues about his hunting adventures in India and these were much more readable and had none of the over-embroidered language of his fiction. John Masters, who wrote a number of popular novels about British India, such a *Night Runners of Bengal* and *Bhowani Junction*, included *shikar* episodes in his novels but few of these are memorable. Paul Scott also has a few incidents taking place on *shikar* but these are only secondary to the much larger structure and subject of his *Raj*

Quartet. R.K. Narayan has written a novel titled, *The Maneater of Malgudi*, but it has very little to do with hunting and the maneater ends up being one of the human characters instead of a tiger. His more recent book, *A Tiger For Malgudi*, is told from the animal's point of view and though the tiger is accused of becoming a maneater, it is not a *shikar* story by any stretch of the imagination. Even Rudyard Kipling, strangely enough, wrote very little about *shikar*. Once or twice his characters take part in a hunt but it is incidental to the social intrigue and drama which was central to his stories. Kipling's *Jungle Book* does explore the forest life of India but there too, it is mostly told from the animals' perspective, or through Mowgli, the wolf child. *Tiger! Tiger!* is included in this collection not only because it describes Mowgli's hunt for Shere Khan the tiger, but also the conflict within the man-cub/wolf-child, who wants to return to the forest but knows that he does not belong there, a conflict which I believe most *shikar* writers would have recognized in themselves.

Part of the reason why *shikar* fiction is not very successful is probably due to the fact that inherent in every *shikar* story is a claim of veracity. Many of the writers describe the terrain in perfect detail so that their readers might go to the very spot and see exactly where the tiger lay and where it died. Colonel Glasfurd in his story, *Gadarene Bears*, is attacked by an enraged sloth bear and saves himself by grabbing onto a small *Bhiria* tree. He writes:

... Only nine months later, when returning with my regiment from the great Delhi Durbar of that year, I revisited the scene of the disaster, with a brother officer, a coil of rope and a camera; and I find it described in my diary as an appalling place, much worse than I had realized at the time, the position of the providential tree showing that when I struck it I was falling perpendicularly.

Should this meet the eye of somebody in a position to follow my description and sketch, and visit Chitra-Katra, it would be extaordinarily interesting to me to know whether my little patron *Bhiria* still grows there.'

(Col. A.I.R. Glasfurd in *Big Game Encounters*, editor Stanley Jepson, 1936, pages 48-49.)

Corbett goes to great lengths to mention the exact position of each boulder in a stream bed when stalking a tiger. I have visited many of the places which he writes about and found them to be exactly as he described more than fifty years after the events. For any *shikar* writer

15

it was very important to be believed. In a sense, the whole appeal of the *shikar* story lay in this one fact, that it was a 'true-to-life,' authentic adventure. For this reason fictional accounts always tend to fall flat and *shikar* fiction becomes little more than farce or fairy tale.

An example of how important it was to be believed can be seen in an incident from James Inglis' book, *Tent Life in Tigerland*.

A well known Anglo-Indian raconteur, on his first reappearance in London, was one of a dozen or more guests at a dinner party in Kensington, and among them he was delighted to see his old friend, Sir. D.M., who had retired some years previously from the bench of a provincial High Court. He recollected a startling incident connected with a tiger in which he and Sir D.M. had both shared. At a fitting opportunity he introduced the story, and feeling confidence in his old friend's memory and his readiness to vouch for the truth of every detail, gave it with all the facts, especially with one special fact that was rather hard to believe. When telling it, therefore, he laid stress upon the presence at the scene of his former colleague in the service and looked pointedly at him. The expected response did not come; but Sir D.M.'s face wore a look of perfect incredulity. ' My dear fellow,' he said at last, on direct appeal, 'I am very sorry, but I recollect nothing whatever about it.' The raconteur of course collapsed there and then. Boiling over with rage, he sought his friend as soon as he could get him in private, and remonstrated with him on his strange lapse of memory, and appealed to him whether, even if he did not fully recollect the occurrence, it might not have been possible to save his credit with the company by a less positive disclaimer. 'My dear J.,' replied the old Judge, 'I remember perfectly well the incident you were telling; but I remarked that all the people at the table considered you were lying. If, then, I had corroborated you, the only result would have been that they would have set me down as a liar too, and my regard for our host made me wish to avoid that. (Quoted from Sydney newspaper, James Inglis, *Tent Life in Tigerland*, 1888.)

It seems to have been common practice amongst hunters to have doubted each other at their word. Even today, I have met a number of people who believe that Jim Corbett never wrote his own stories and if he did, they say, he probably made most of them up. Kenneth Anderson comes in for a lot of criticism as well and in some cases his stories do seem far fetched, though he provides plenty of details to substantiate his claims. For the purposes of this collection it doesn't really matter whether any of these writers was actually telling the truth. What is important, however, is that they included such a wealth of detail that they obviously wanted the reader to accept their stories as the truth. Most *shikar* writers were able to weave their descriptions into the telling of the story, so that the exact pitch of a bird call or the precise angle at which a rock leaned out over the hillside became essential to the breathtaking momentum of the narrative.

Not only was there a wide variety of game in India but also a number of different methods of *shikar*. The Mughal emperors were probably some of the first hunters to use the system of beats, in which an area of jungle or scrub was encircled by armies of beaters and the game was driven towards the hunters who waited either on a *machan* or on the back of an elephant. In this way a large area of forest could be emptied of animals and the hunters had only to pick their targets and fire. Beats took on the dimensions of military campaigns with hundreds of beaters, as well as 'stops' who helped to funnel the escaping animals into range of the waiting guns. Part of the popularity of this form of sport seems to have come from the elaborate arrangements or 'bandobast' involved in a beat as well as the odds being very much in favour of the hunter, who had only to sit with his weapon cocked, waiting for the animals to appear. Beats were popular amongst the British as well as the Maharajahs, especially when visiting dignitaries were hosted at tiger shoots. An excellent description of a beat can be found in Olive Smythies' account of the Prince of Wales' *shikar* with the Maharajah of Nepal who had seven hundred elephants arranged to conduct the beat.

The British brought to India an obvious fondness for horses, dogs and fox-hunting. Using jackals as a substitute for foxes, they donned pink coats and rode out to the clarion notes of the horn. However, when they discovered pigsticking, jackal hunts fell by the wayside. Of all the different forms of *shikar*, pig sticking is probably the most closely associated with the British Raj. Cavalry officers were particularly obsessed with horsemanship and there seemed to have been nothing which they enjoyed more than galloping at full speed over uneven ground, through thorn thickets and over fields of ripening barley, in pursuit of a bristly, black creature with ferocious looking tushes, which curled up like a subaltern's moustache.

Pig sticking was particularly popular in the United Provinces, Punjab and of course Rajasthan, where the Maharajahs of states such as Jodhpur and Jaipur took to it with a passion. The annual Kadir cup was held in Meerut and considered the ultimate sporting event in North India. Pig-stickers from all over the country sharpened their lances and came to ride after the honour of drawing first-blood. Hunting of any kind is a cruel sport, but pig-sticking was particularly ruthless. A wild boar was pursued by three or four riders on horse-back until exhausted; it would finally turn in desperation and charge, at which time the lances were driven into its body. In most cases the boar was not killed outright and had to be speared several times before it finally died. The shooting of animals on beats may have been unsportsmanlike and callous but pig sticking was an entirely ugly and brutal form of *shikar*.

The concept of sportsmanship arises in many of these stories. The English were obsessed with the idea of 'fair play' and so, instead of simply shooting the pig with a large caliber rifle, they chose to kill it with a bamboo lance. Pig sticking obviously required riding skills and courage which were essential to being a good sportsman. The contra-diction, however, lies in another very important code of sportsman-ship, the idea that a good hunter should always make a 'clean kill' and to wound an animal was a ignoble. All of the hunters in this collection prided themselves on their 'sportsmanship' but each of them had their own interpretation of what it meant.

Some of these writers may have occasionally hunted from elephant back or even ridden after pigs, but for most of them *shikar* was a very different experience, a solitary almost ascetic pursuit. The story of a large *shikar*, like the story of a battle, often degenerates into a cata-logue of names and numbers, whereas the lone hunter following a dangerous animal has much greater fascination for the reader. Cor-bett epitomises this figure. Dressed in khaki shorts and bush shirt, a pair of light canvas shoes on his feet and a rifle tucked under one arm, he roams for hours through the forests of Kumaon. His rifle makes him a more deadly predator than the tiger but it is his senses which help him to survive. Nobody knew the forest better than Corbett and he was a firm believer in the sixth sense, that innate warning signal which we all possess. His stories describe how often his rifle was a useless defence, whether in the dark or in high grass, and his only means of protection was his acute understanding of the jungle.

The lone *shikari* such as Corbett or Hugh Allen, used one of two simple techniques for hunting. He moved through the forest on foot, usually alone, and followed game trails and pug marks. In the case of maneating tigers and leopards, he would sit up in a *machan* over a kill or live bait and wait for the tiger to come and feed. Both techniques required enormous patience and a highly developed knowledge of natural history and jungle vocabulary, as well as an undeniable dose of courage. Whatever we may think about their motives, these writers were totally attuned to their environment and though they were hunters first, they were also naturalists.

There is a memorable incident in Jim Corbett's *Maneaters of Kumaon*, when he is hunting the Chowgargh tigress. Corbett is following the maneater down a dry watercourse. As he passes a large rock, he notices the nest of a nightjar which contains a clutch of two eggs. Being an avid naturalist, he decides to take the eggs for his collection. Cradling the precious discovery in the palm of his left hand, he continues down the ravine. The tigress is obviously close at hand and Corbett releases the safety catch on his rifle as he makes his way silently over the rocks and sand. At one point, he has to slide down a smooth boulder, still holding the eggs in one hand and his rifle in the other. He accomplishes this without much difficulty but as he steps forward around a bend in the stream, there is the maneater, crouched only eight feet away, watching him with intense interest. Having only one hand free, he is forced to turn the rifle around very slowly, avoiding any sudden movement, until the barrel is in line with the tigress's body. The maneater remains transfixed and Corbett fires his rifle into her heart.She dies without moving a hair. After he has sat down and calmed his nerves, Corbett retraces his steps and puts the nightjar eggs back in their nest. He writes that the eggs probably saved his life, for if he had not been carrying them, he might have turned abruptly on the tigress and made her charge.

The incident of the nightjar eggs and the Chowgargh tigress, underlines the dilemma which confronted Corbett throughout his life, the conflict between hunter and naturalist, his obvious love and curiosity for nature and the role of exterminator which his hunting prowess bestowed on him. Holding two delicate eggs in one hand and a lightweight Martini rifle in the other, he stands in the face of death.

In his introduction to a recent anthology, Corbett's editor, R.E. Hawkins,gives a very succinct explanation of the popularity of Corbett's writings:

Maneaters of Kumaon appeared in August 1944, when the end of the war was in sight. Years of massive, indiscriminate slaughter and regimentation had eroded faith in the sighnificance of the individual. It was immensely refreshing to read of this contemporary dragon killer, who in perfect freedom roamed the countryside, cheerfully facing danger and hardship to rid the world of tigers and leopards convicted of man-eating. Sir Galahad rode again. Truth and justice had returned.'

(R.E. Hawkins, *Jim Corbett's India*, 1978, page 6.)

Hawkins' reference to the widespread slaughter of war is an important point. For the first time, man was really understanding the meaning of extinction and by 1944 that possiblity was very real, not just the extinction of a single species of animal but all living things. The first World War had raised the grotesque image of total destruction, in which the forests of Europe became mud flats, levelled by mortar fire and trenches. If anything has changed the environmental perspective of the world it was the image of trenchwarfare,the barrenness of fields laid to waste, of men dragging themselves wounded through the primordial ooze, and the evil fumes of mustard gas, altogether a vivid and frightening scenario for the end of the world. Nobody could pick up a rifle without some knowledge of the immense destruction caused by war. There was suddenly a very real sense that life of any kind was finite and threatened.

This awareness is evident in most of the shikar stories written after the first World War. Earlier writers might have mentioned briefly how the number of tigers had dwindled or that there might be a day when animals would need to be protected but it was never a particularly serious matter and usually forgotten in the thrill of shooting, 'three leopards before breakfast.' Hugh Allen describes quite clearly the changes which were taking place when he refers to the *shikar* books on his shelf, the first published around 1857 in which the author tells of shooting ninety-eight tigers, four leopards and twenty-five bears during one hot weather furlough. In the last book on the shelf, published about a hundred years later, the writer admits he was lucky and well content with two tigers and one leopard, during a shoot of about the same length of time.

It seems that most writers, including Corbett and Hugh Allen,were writing under the shadow of this knowledge. They were describing experiences which would become unknown half a century further on. They realized that the jungles of India were unlikely to survive and in a way they also realized that they themselves were responsible. This is one of the central ironies in their stories, the desire to protect wildlife and the opposing urge to hunt.

In the introduction to his book, *The Lonely Tiger*, Hugh Allen writes very honestly and eloquently of his dilemma.

Two forces were pulling me in different directions. On one side was a real love for all animals, on the other side was that old urge to hunt . . . I did not give up the rifle entirely for I still hunt for meat and still go after any animal which is better dead. Yet the urge to hunt with a rifle even after more than ten years in the jungle is as strong as ever; the only difference is that now I know the truth and that the thrill will die the moment I pull the trigger. After that, when I look down on a lifeless body, there comes a pang of remorse and the guilty thought that there but for me goes a magnificent animal.'

(Hugh Allen, *The Lonely Tiger*, 1961.)

Jim Corbett is often described as a repentant hunter, laying down his guns and taking up the cause of conservation. He did write about the pleasures of photographing animals rather than shooting them, but I do not think that Corbett's conflict was quite so simple. Much as he believed that the tiger might one day become extinct, he also felt compelled to pursue and destroy every maneater in Kumaon.

While hunting the Talla Des maneater, one of the last tigers he shot, Corbett camped in the Sarda river gorge at the foot of the Purnagiri mountain. At this spot an enormous cliff , two thousand feet of perpendicular rock, rises out of the river, converging in a pinnacle which is sacred to the Devi. One night, while he was having a last cigarette after dinner, Corbett saw a series of lights moving over the face of the mountain. He assumed at first that it was shepherds or hunters but in the morning realized that no human being could ever scale those cliffs. He later learned that these were votive lamps, set alight by the spirit of a mendicant who had fallen from the Purnagiri mountain, 'and are only visible to favoured people. This favour was accorded to me and to the men with me, because I was on mission to the hill-folk over whom the goddess watches.' (Jim Corbett, *The Temple Tiger*, 1955, page 135)

By the time he began hunting the Talla Des maneater, Corbett seems to have been consumed by a sense of responsibility to kill all tigers which became maneaters and yet which he so stongly believed were part of a peaceable kingdom, in which human beings were the only dangerous predators.

Many *shikar* writers felt the same sense of mission that Corbett writes about, as though the killing of dangerous animals was part of the 'white man's burden.' George Orwell describes something of the same feeling but in a much more immediate sense when he tells of shooting an elephant with a crowd of Burmese villagers at his back.

> I realized that I should have to shoot the elephant after all. The people expected it of me and I had got to do it; I could feel their two thousand wills pressing me forward irresistibly. And it was at this moment, as I stood there with the rifle in my hands that I first grasped the hollowness, the futility of the white man's dominion in the East. Here was I, the white man with his gun, standing in front of the unarmed native crowd—seemingly the leading actor of the piece; but in reality I was only an absurd puppet pushed to and fro by the will of those yellow faces behind.'
>
> (George Orwell, *Inside The Whale And Other Essays*, 1962, page 95)

If there is central image in these stories it is the maneater. Most of the writers included in this collection describe hunting a tiger or leopard which has killed human beings. Conservationists have argued that most *shikar* writers depicted tigers and leopards in a very inaccurate manner, as slavering, savage beasts that attack without any apparent motive. This accusation against these writers is often justified and there is no doubt that many of them got carried away in their descriptions of maneaters. Innocent readers, snuggled up by their fireplaces in wintry England, would have come to imagine the great cats of India to be the most demonic and grotesque creatures on earth, deserving of extinction.

However true this criticism may be, I do not think that the *shikar* writer's purpose was to present an image of tigers and leopards being ruthless enemies of man. There were certainly those amongst them who felt that these great animals should be eradicated, just as we today would like to eradicate the mosquito. (Unfortunately a tiger doesn't have the same resilience as the mosquito.) But each of the writers in this collection would have professed admiration for the tiger and like Corbett they would have felt that, 'A tiger is a large hearted gentleman with boundless courage and when he is exterminated — as exterminated he will be unless public opinion rallies to his support — India will be the poorer by having lost the finest of her fauna.'

(Jim Corbett, *Maneaters of Kumaon*, 1944, page XII)

But then, why this obsession with maneaters? Most of the writers acknowledged that maneaters were an aberration and took great pains to investigate the causes of their turning to human prey, whether it was old age, rotted canines, porcupine quills embedded in a paw, or more likely a crippling gunshot wound. Each of these hunters acknowledged that there had to be a clear reason why the tiger or leopard developed a taste for human flesh and that it was unnatural that they should kill human beings.

The maneater seems to represent something larger than just a crippled and desperate animal. In many of these stories, it acquires a mythical dimension. Maneaters are like any other dangerous and unknown creature. They frighten us because they move in darkness and we have no warning when they will strike. They symbolise sudden and terrible death. The hunter who killed a maneater became a heroic figure in front of whom thin brown skinned figures prostrated themselves. He became a deliverer from evil, a saviour amongst the natives.

The obsession with maneaters was carried in some cases to absurd extremes. In the story of *Seeall the Wolf Boy* Mervyn Smith describes a hunt for a maneating wolf which he succeeds in shooting. A day or so later, a wolf-child is discovered nearby and brought to his tent. According to the villagers this child had also become a maneater after feeding off the wolf's human kills. This shows how important the image had become and what kind of horror it aroused.

Here the myth of the maneater blends with a second very important jungle myth. Rudyard Kipling made the wolf-child famous with his stories about Mowgli and Mervyn Smith claims that *Seeall the Wolf Boy* was the inspiration for Kipling's character. This would be difficult to prove but it seems that a number of children were discovered in India, who it was claimed were raised by wolves or other animals. Nobody has made a particularly convincing record of whether this is at all possible, yet it remains an important part of the lore of the Indian forests. Jim Corbett wrote about 'Goongi' the wolf-child which he investigates and comes away not entirely sceptical of the possibilities of such a situation. Corbett suggests that 'Goongi' might have been raised by Himalayan bears instead of wolves. Though not directly related to *shikar*, the wolf-child does inhabit that same jungle of the subconscious where maneaters roam,

23

a slightly grotesque world of nature, in which the unusual is more familiar than the commonplace, in which the aberrations of nature multiply in the writer's imagination.

When the wolf child returns to the forest to hunt the maneater, as Mowgli does with Shere Khan, the conflict becomes almost surreal. At the end of the story, after finally killing his nemesis, Mowgli takes the Tiger's skin to the wolf pack and dances upon Shere Khan in a frenzy of victory, singing about his hunt:

'I dance on the hide of Shere Khan, but my heart is very heavy. My mouth is cut and wounded with the stones from the village, but my heart is very light, because I have come back to the jungle. Why?

These two things fight together in me as the snakes fight in the spring. The water comes out of my eyes; yet I laugh while it falls. Why?

I am two Mowglis, but the hide of Shere Khan is under my feet.

All the Jungle knows that I have killed Shere Khan. Look, look well, O Wolves!

Ahae! my heart is heavy with the things that I do not understand.' (Rudyard Kipling, *The Jungle Book*, 1946, page 71)

With a total ban on the shooting of tigers and leopards and stringent regulations on hunting of any kind in most states of India, it would appear that the *shikar* story is a closed chapter in literary history, a tradition which has no future. This is true to a certain extent but it is interesting to see how a number of contemporary writers of 'wildlife literature' owe a debt to the shikar writer both in terms of factual information and also in style. A large number of books have been written about tigers and other Indian animals in the past twenty years and though all of these have dealt with the conservation of these threatened species, they can also be read as a continuation of the shikar story genre. Arjan Singh, Suresh Vaidya , Charles McDougal, Valmik Thapar and many others obviously grew up reading authors such as Corbett. Their books, intentionally or unintentionally, contain echoes of those writers.

Ultimately, the test of a good story is whether it can be read fifty years after it was written and still enjoyed. For *shikar* stories this is an even greater test, since the experiences related in these adventures are no longer possible. Not only is hunting for big game a thing of the past in India, but it is also looked down upon as an ignoble, cruel pursuit. Hunters are no longer heroes but villains, held responsible for the near extinction of tigers and other animals.

Despite all this, these stories still hold a fascination for readers. They capture our interest and take us into the darkest reaches of our subconscious. The maneater, whether real or exaggerated continues to frighten us. The hunter who finally destroys such an animal can only be considered a hero, albeit a flawed hero, one who realizes his own guilt and wavers between a primitive urge to hunt and a modern sensibility towards conservation. Like Kipling's wolf child, he is caught between civilization and the jungle, a conflict which will probably never become outdated. As readers, we cannot escape the message of these stories that man too is a predator like the tiger.

Wild Men and Wild Beasts

Lt. Col. Gordon Cumming

In the hot season of 1856, Gordon Cumming, a young officer in the Indian Army, set off on a tour of the Central Provinces. Along the way, he hunted for tiger and other animals. In the company of the Nawab of Jowra, he was able to witness a trained hunting cheetah killing black buck. Cumming describes the method of hunting with a cheetah as well as stalking by bullock cart, two early methods of shikar. *The period in which Cumming is hunting is the year before the revolt of 1857. Cumming was stationed at Mhow at the time of the uprising and escaped into the forests with the help of his* shikaris. *This episode and his other stories of* shikar *seem to have established him as one of the best known hunters of the period. He is the hero of* Peer Bux, the Terror of Hunsur *by Mervyn Smith which is also included in this collection.*

It was proposed by the Nawab of Jowra, who had come into Indore for the Dussera festival, that some of us should go out some morning to see his cheetahs work. We accordingly made an early start, and set out for some ground which was preserved by Holkar, and on which was a good show of black buck. The Nawab, who was a stout heavy man, rode a strong hill pony, which ambled along at a great pace, and the other officers of our party were mounted on Arabs in the hope of a run at something. In the open plain we came up with the Nawab's men, about a hundred and fifty in all; men mounted on screaming horses, and men on riding camels; men on foot with guns and dogs, and men with camels laden with tents; and last, but not least, men on elephants. There were other men in attendance on the two cheetahs, each of which rode on his own platform cart; and, though hooded, were apparently aware that some amusement was in store for them. Several herds of deer were in sight, and they did not seem much disconcerted by the troop of men, horses, etc. etc. The place was not far from the town of Indore, and they were accustomed to such sights. After some talk, it was settled that one of the cheetahs should be taken up to the nearest herd; so the Nawab, leaving the main body, requested us to join him. The deer seemed to mistake us for harmless wayfarers, for they fed quietly, while we passed at a distance of about eighty yards.

A cheetah was now unhooded, and on seeing the deer he at once glided from the cart, and taking advantage of every tuft of grass and inequality in the ground, he crept towards his prey. The deer were meanwhile lazily watching us as we went on without halting, and the poor beasts were only aware of their danger when the leopard made his rush. There was a wild scurry, but the cheetah was among them, and as the herd cleared off we saw him lying with his teeth in the throat of a goodly buck. His keeper now came up with a wooden ladle and a knife, and cutting the deer's throat he caught the blood in the spoon, into which in a few minutes the cheetah thrust his nose, and while he was lapping the blood the hood was slipped over his eyes, and he was secured and replaced in the cart.

As we moved on we saw several bucks feeding singly about the plain, and the Nawab suggested that I should take my rifle and move on them with a shooting-cart. I advanced on a very black fellow with long horns. He was lying near a small bit of cultivated land, and as the ground was favourable I made sure of getting within easy shot; but when I was within about two hundred yards of him the buck rose, looked hard at us, shook his head, and trotted off to some distance, when he again lay down. We followed on slowly with the cart, and I was about to fire at him as he lay, but he again jumped up, and was shaking his head as before when I fired and dropped him. Some of the attendants ran in and cut his throat, and he was placed on the cart, with which I returned to the Nawab and one or two gentlemen who had witnessed the death from a rising ground.

One of the party proceeded to overhaul the buck, and forthwith set up a shout of derision, for on examining the horns, holes were found which had been bored in them about two inches from the tips. The natives had no doubt caught him on some former occasion, and he had been let lose with catgut nooses attached to his horns — the object being to entangle any other buck with whom he might fall in

28

and engage in combat. I got well roasted for shooting what my friends called a tame deer; but, tame deer or wild, I had dropped him by a good shot, and so could afford to be chaffed.

Notwithstanding that we were in preserved ground, the crowd of followers by whom the Nawab was accompanied had evidently scared the deer, and we were advised to go on for a mile or two, when we should be among fresh game. We accordingly mounted our horses and moved through a tract of grass land. Our company was numerous and noisy, and the chance of any addition to our bag seemed small at that moment. We were all laughing and talking as we rode along, when I observed, about sixty yards on our left, what seemed to me to be the points of a buck's horns, appearing just over the long grass. My henchman with my rifle was at my stirrup, and before any of the party were aware of what I was about, I had jumped off, and fired at the point where I imagined the horns should meet. The bullet told with a sharp crack, and the horns disappeared. On going up to the place we found a buck shot through the head. Had I not seen him, he would have lain still while the whole party of hunters — if we deserved the name — passed within a few yards of him.

At the foot of some low hills we saw a herd of deer feeding in a cornfield, and the Nawab called up the other cheetah with his attendants. The ground was very bare between us and the deer, and before the cheetah had got within distance, the herd saw him and bolted. The leopard, however, did his best, and nearly had one antelope, but, finding himself foiled, he gave in at once and was secured by his keeper. Meanwhile the deer went off to our left, where they were turned by some horsemen; on which they passed in rear of us at a distance of several hundred yards. A rapid file fire was opened, but without effect, further than perhaps to cause the deer to bound higher than usual. The last shot was fired by one of the Nawab's men, with one of his English rifles. The deer must have been nearly 500 yards off at the time, and to our astonishment one of them tumbled over. The shot was of course a fluke, but the shooter was not the less the hero of the hour.

The Nawab now suggested refreshments, and soon a string of camels was seen coming up laden with tents, tables, chairs, and all manner of kitchen arrangements. Breakfast was at once ordered, and while the tents were being pitched we went out after some quail which had been seen close by. The Nawab intimated his intention of shooting, and we had no wish to interfere with his sport, which we watched with great amusement. He was not a first-rate marksman, but one of his men could shoot very fairly, and when the Nawab fired, he also loosed his piece, but of course took no credit for any result. On breakfast being announced we returned to the tents, where we found sundry and various cooling drinks, which were gratefully swallowed. In the afternoon we rode back to the cantonment, having spent a very pleasant day, although the sporting was not of a high order. The Jowra Nawab was always most hospitable to all Europeans passing through his country. Our last meeting was in 1865, when I was his guest while on my way south from Rajpootana. Two months later he died of cholera, which was then raging at Jowra.

Towards the close of the year 1856 I accompanied the agent of the Governor-General through the Gwalior and Bundelcund states. We left Indore in October, and went north by rapid marches, so that, even had the country been favourable, we should have had little time for shooting. At this season, however, the jungles were filled with high green grass, and there was no prospect of shooting till the cold weather set in. We tried to beat a jungle near Ragoogurh, and indeed we started one large tiger, whose fresh footprints we found over our own on our way back to the tents, but we could make nothing of it, and did not again renew the attempt. At Seepree we encountered a violent thunderstorm. The ground was hard as iron, and in pitching the camp there had been a great destruction of tent-pegs. We were in the cantonment at the time, calling on some of the officers, and on returning to our camp we found it flat, with the exception of the big man's tent, which had only been kept standing by half-a-dozen men holding on to every rope.

The soil of the place was red, having a strong admixture of iron-stone, and our tents bore the marks of that storm for many a day. To add to our discomfort, cholera had broken out among a large party which had joined us from Oujein, and had been communicated to our camp.

The disease was aggravated by the wet and discomfort, and for some days we had many deaths among our people.

From Seepree we moved on Jansi, having some very good snipe-shooting on the road. At one large tank they were especially numer-ous, and sometimes we had six and seven birds lying dead around us. We also made some good bags of ducks. I had an agreeable compan-ion in Hunt, of the Bengal Lancers, who commanded the agent's escort.

At Jansi we called on the Ranee, who a few months later was destined to give so much trouble; and we also went over the old Fort, where Burgess and his gallant companions fought so well, till they were led by treacherous promises to trust themselves to their merciless assailants.

After a detour to the south, we marched to Duttiah, where the chief, hearing that we were fond of shooting, offered to send out his men with us. We knew the sport would be but tame, but having nothing better on hand, we started off, taking only the chief's *shikarees* and our own gun-bearers. I always had a horror of native gentlemen when out shooting; their utter ignorance of sport in any shape, and their inordinate love of noise and large followings, made them most undesirable companions. There are now and then exceptions, but they are like angels' visits.

On approaching the preserved ground we were met by the *shikarees* leading a tall and sagacious stalking bullock. A string was passed through his nostrils, and he was guided to the right or left by the rein being thrown on either side of his hump. We had not gone far when we came on a herd of nylghae, browsing among some thick bushes. One of them raised its head, and stood watching us at a distance of seventy yards. Hunt told me to shoot; so, aiming at what I supposed was its shoulder, I fired. The ball struck timber, and when it cleared, I saw the white blaze of the shot on the trunk of the tree, which I had mistaken for the shoulder of the beast. Hunt had done better, for, as they went off, he dropped a good blue bull.

It was now settled that we should separate and meet again about 3 P.M., at a place about four miles off. We were each accompanied by a couple of the Rajah's men; and those who came with me brought with them the stalking bullock. After moving quietly through the jungle for half-an-hour, we came on another herd of nylghae; one large cow was standing, broadside on, about eighty yards off. I dropped her with one shot, and one of the men behind me was in the act of rushing forward to finish her, when I checked him, and at that instant a blue bull bolted out into an open glade in the wood, and stood looking at us intently. Again my rifle cracked, and the bull staggered wildly forward for about fifty yards and fell. Fearing to lose the meat, owing to the throats not being cut in the orthodox manner, the men now ran up, and in a few seconds the poor beasts were lawful beef.

The style of shooting was by no means to my taste, but my attendants seemed highly satisfied, and looked forward to a great feast for themselves and their families, though they cared little for sport. Having covered up the dead beasts with boughs of trees, we went on a mile or two, when we saw a large cow nylghae feeding among some scrub jungle. The bullock was now brought into play, and stooping down behind him with one of the men, we allowed the beast to graze quietly, at the same time edging him up towards the game. The bullock seemed thoroughly to understand his work, and moved at the slightest hint from right to left. We got up within easy shot, and the cow was dropped with one bullet. Satiated with this slaughter, I intimated to my companions that we should now push forward to rejoin Hunt, who I knew would be ready for his luncheon. A man was therefore sent for a cart on which to carry home the game, and we moved on. Before long, a huge blue bull crossed our front, and stood within a hundred yards, with his shoulder well exposed. I raised my rifle and covered him, but thinking my companions and their friends would find they had sufficient occupation for their time and teeth, with the game already slain, I lowered my weapon, and soon after the bull went off.

Farther on, we heard some wild hogs moving in a thicket of bushes and high grass. Though I had spared the bull I thought a pork-chop might be desirable, so I crept forward. The sounder, however, had got our wind, and we heard them scurry off. One pig was left behind, and, on missing his companions, he set up a peculiar cry. Presently he moved out of the thicket, and stood in some long grass. I could just see his head, and I dropped him dead with a shot between the eyes. My attendant, by this time, regarded me with great respect. Four beasts had fallen to four successive shots, and he had not been accustomed, when sporting with his royal master, to see so large a result from so small an expenditure of ammunition. We now emerged into an open country, and were joined by Hunt, who had been most unsuccessful, not having killed anything since the bull in the morning. He had not had one other chance.

An abundant luncheon was now produced, and to it we did ample justice. Another party of the chief's men met us here. They had with them tame antelopes for stalking, and as neither of us had seen this style of shooting, we directed them to come with us in the afternoon. The tame antelopes were three in number — one buck, and two does — and their human confederate carried on his arm a screen of leafy twigs, having a small aperture in the middle, from which to shoot.

The antelopes were held by their cords, five or six yards in length, and were so trained that a doe was always on each side, while the buck passed backwards and forwards between them.

A herd of wild antelopes was soon seen, and Hunt moved forward with the trained deer and their keeper. As soon as they were observed by the herd, the reigning buck came forward, shaking his head, and evidently bent on having a fight with the new comer, whose does he no doubt intended, in true Oriental fashion, to sweep into his own harem. He was followed, at a few yards' distance, by the rest of the herd, and they all advanced steadily till within fifty yards of the stalking-party. Hunt would have dropped the buck had he had a fair chance of shooting, but he was so persuaded that he must be seen if he moved, that he kept his eye steadily fixed through the opening in the screen, which was placed too low to enable him to shoot conveniently. At this moment a horseman, who had been sent out by the chief to inquire after our welfare, came up on a screaming horse, and the herd went off at speed. Neither of us being inclined to go farther, we mounted our horses, and returned to the camp.

We marched next morning, and the chief sent with us his hunting cheetahs, with orders to their attendants to accompany us for several days on our journey. The country was not, however, favourable, and antelope were not seen. We went out one afternoon, on the report of a man who said he had seen deer. We found they were chinkara; and the man in charge of the cheetahs informed us that these small deer were too active for this sort of work. We therefore left the leopard behind some bushes with our horses, and, taking his cart, I went forward with my rifle. The deer allowed us to approach within eighty yards, and I dropped the buck with the first barrel. The doe darted off, and then stood looking at us. She was at least 150 yards off, and looked very small, but I bagged her with the second shot, greatly to the astonishment of the cartman. We then returned to the cheetah. Farther on we came on some more chinkara, and, at my request, the cheetah was slipped. We moved on quietly with the cart, and had a splendid opportunity of observing the leopard approach his game. Crawling like a snake over bare ground, and taking advantage of the smallest shrubs and tufts of grass, he crept forward. But the deer were in the middle of a bare field, and when the cheetah did make his rush, they saw him at once, and fled with amazing swiftness. No capture was effected, and we returned to the tents.

Our journeying took us through Hameerpoor to Cawnpore and

Lucknow, and we rejoined our own camp in Bundelcund, passing through Oorae. Here we were entertained very hospitably by two officers, who were on detachment duty. Food was scarce, and they trusted a good deal to their guns for provision. It was then the cold season, and a large pot was kept constantly on the fire in the sitting-room, and into this all manner of eatables were thrust promiscuously, — hens, hares, venison, ducks, quails, potatoes, turnips, sauces of sorts, etc. etc. The mess was, however, excellent, and there was always a pleasing uncertainty as to the nature of the food which the spoon would fish up. We were a merry party of four, but a few months later I was the only one left to tell the tale. Two fell in the massacre at Cawnpore, and Hunt, with another officer, was shot by the mutineer cavalry of the Mehidpore Contingent at Mulharghur.

Our return march was via Agra and Gwalior to Indore. We moved too fast to allow of any chance of large game. At Kolarus we were taken out by some of the people of the place, but the jungles were green and very extensive, and we saw that the whole thing was absurd. Late in the afternoon, as we were returning home on our elephants, we saw several nylghae on a hill above us. They were moving among thick bushes, and more from a wish to empty my rifle than from any hope of killing, I fired. The elephant had been by no means steady, and the bull at which I aimed was moving, but I heard the shot strike with a loud crack, and I observed a commotion among the bushes on the hill-side. Some of our people called out that the bull was shot, so, dismounting from the elephants, we went up the hill, which was very rough and stony, and covered with thick corinda jungle. Forcing our way through this, we found the bull, who had been shot through both hind legs, just below the hocks. The poor brute floundered violently, and I would have finished him with another shot, but for my gun-bearer, who was anxious to secure the skin for a shield, so the poor bull was knocked on the head with an axe.

As we approached the staging bungalow at Dewas, we observed from the carriage two fine bustard feeding near the road. During our march I had made several unsuccessful attempts to obtain a shot at bustard, but these seemed tamer; so, leaving one of the grooms behind to watch them, we drove on to the bungalow, where I got my gun, and loading with BB, I mounted on a small pony and cantered back.

The birds were feeding, and took but little notice of me so long as I remained on the road, but as soon as they saw me move towards them, they rose and took a short flight. I followed slowly, and this time I managed to approach somewhat nearer; but as I was about to check my pony, they again rose. Quitting the reins, I fired at the largest, and he dropped his legs, but recovering himself, he flew on. I saw he was hard hit, and I kept my eye on him, and after going about a mile, I saw him fall. Riding up, I found him dead. He was a very fine bird, and weighed twenty-two pounds. Some of the feathers of the bustard are invaluable to the salmon-fisher.

A Close Shot with a Charge of Sixpence

Sir Samuel Baker

*Samuel Baker is probably best known for his exploration of the
Nile. As a young man he lived in Ceylon (now Sri Lanka) for
several years. Though Ceylon was never part of India, much of the
flora and fauna and conditions for* shikar *were similar to those
found in India. This excerpt from his book,* The Rifle and The
Hound in Ceylon, *tells the story of a* shikar *he took with his
brother in the hills of Ceylon around 1860. In those days the guns
and rifles used for hunting were not as sophisticated or dependable
as modern weapons. The muzzle loader with which Baker was
armed provided anxious moments when he had to face the charge
of a wounded buffalo, acknowledged by most hunters to be the
most dangerous animal in Asia. Baker also wrote* Eight Years in
Ceylon *as well as a number of other books about his African
experience. He eventually became 'Pacha and Major-General of
the Ottoman Empire.'*

(In any description, account or story of the hill sports of Ceylon
there is one animal) who surpasses all others in dogged ferocity
when once aroused. This is the 'buffalo'.

The haunts of this animal are in the hottest parts of Ceylon. In the
neighbourhood of lakes, swamps, and extensive plains, the buffalo
exists in large herds; wallowing in the soft mire, and passing two-
thirds of his time in the water itself, he may be almost termed
amphibious.

He is about the size of a large ox, of immense bone and strength,
very active, and his hide is almost free from hair, giving a disgusting

appearance to his India-rubber-like skin. He carries his head in a peculiar manner, the horns thrown back, and his nose projecting on a level with his forehead, thus securing himself from a front shot in a fatal part. This renders him a dangerous enemy, as he will receive any number of balls from a small gun in the throat and chest without evincing the least symptom of distress. The shoulder is the acknowledged point to aim at, but from his disposition to face the guns this is a difficult shot to obtain. Should he succeed in catching his antagonist, his fury knows no bounds, and he gores his victim to death, trampling and kneeling upon him till he is satisfied that life is extinct.

This sport would not be very dangerous in the forests, where the buffalo could be easily stalked, and where escape would also be rendered less difficult in case of accident; but as he is generally met with upon the open plains, free from a single tree, he must be killed when once brought to bay, or he will soon exhibit his qualifications for mischief. There is a degree of uncertainty in their character which much increases the danger of the pursuit. A buffalo may retreat at first sight with every symptom of cowardice, and thus induce a too eager pursuit, when he will suddenly become the assailant. I cannot explain their character better than by describing the first wild buffaloes that I ever saw.

I had not been long in Ceylon, but having arrived in the island for the sake of its wild sports, I had not been idle, and I had already made a considerable bag of large game. Like most novices, however, I was guilty of one great fault. I despised the game, and gave no heed to the many tales of danger and hairbreadth escapes which attended the pursuit of wild animals. This carelessness on my part arose from my first debut having been extremely lucky; most shots had told well, and the animal had been killed with such apparent ease that I had learnt to place an implicit reliance in the rifle. The real fact was that I was like many others; I had slaughtered a number of animals without understanding their habits, and I was perfectly ignorant of the sport. This is now many years ago, and it was then my first visit to the island. Some places that were good spots for shooting in those days have since that time been much disturbed, and are now no longer attractive to my eyes. One of these places is Minneria Lake.

I was on a shooting trip accompanied by my brother, whom I will designate as B. We had passed a toilsome day in pushing and dragging our ponies for twenty miles along a narrow path through thick jungle, which half-a-dozen natives in advance were opening before us with bill-hooks. This had at one time been a good path, but was then overgrown. It is now an acknowledged bridle road.

At four P.M., and eighty miles from Kandy, we emerged from the jungle, and the view of Minneria Lake burst upon us, fully repaying us for our day's march. It was a lovely afternoon. The waters of the lake, which is twenty miles in circumference, were burnished by the setting sun. The surrounding plains were as green as an English meadow, and beautiful forest trees bordered the extreme boundaries of the plains like giant warders of the adjoining jungle. Long promontories densely wooded stretched far into the waters of the lake, forming sheltered nooks and bays teeming with wild fowl. The deer browsed in herds on the wide extent of plain, or lay beneath the shade of the spreading branches. Every feature of lovely scenery was here presented. In some spots groves of trees grew to the very water's edge; in others the wide plains, free from a single stem or bush, stretched for miles along the edge of the lake; thickly wooded hills bordered the extreme end of its waters, and distant blue mountains mingled their dim summits with the clouds.

It was a lovely scene which we enjoyed in silence, while our ponies feasted upon the rich grass.

The village of Minneria was three miles farther on, and our coolies, servants, and baggage were all far behind us. We had, therefore, no rifles or guns at hand, except a couple of shot-guns, which were carried by our horsekeepers: for these we had a few balls.

For about half-an-hour we waited in the impatient expectation of the arrival of our servants with the rifles.

The afternoon was wearing away, and they did not appear. We could wait no longer, but determined to take a stroll and examine the country. We therefore left our horses and proceeded.

The grass was most verdant, about the height of a field fit for the scythe in England, but not so thick. From this the snipe arose at every twenty or thirty paces, although the ground was perfectly dry. Crossing a large meadow, and skirting the banks of the lake, from which the ducks and teal rose in large flocks, we entered a long neck of jungle which stretched far into the lake. This was not above two hundred paces in width, and we soon emerged upon an extensive plain bordered by fine forest, the waters of the lake stretching far away upon our left, like a sheet of gold. A few large rocks rose above the surface near the shore; these were covered with various kinds of wild fowl. The principal tenants of the plain were wild buffaloes.

38

A herd of about a hundred were lying in a swampy hollow about a quarter of a mile from us. Several single bulls were dotted about the green surface of the level plain, and on the opposite shores of the lake were many dark patches undistinguishable in the distance; these were in reality herds of buffaloes. There was not a sound in the wide expanse before us, except the harsh cry of the water-fowl that our presence had already disturbed — not a breath of air moved the leaves of the trees which shaded us — and the whole scene was that of undisturbed nature. The sun had now sunk low upon the horizon, and the air was comparatively cool. The multitude of buffaloes enchanted us, and with our two light double-barrels, we advanced to the attack of the herd before us.

We had not left the obscurity of the forest many seconds before we were observed. The herd started up from their muddy bed and gazed at us with astonishment. It was a fair open plain of some thousand acres, bounded by the forest which we had just quitted on the one side, and by the lake on the other; thus there was no cover for our advance, and all we could do was to push on.

As we approached the herd they ranged up in a compact body, presenting a very regular line in front. From this line seven large bulls stepped forth, and from their vicious appearance seemed disposed to show fight. In the meantime we were running up, and were soon within thirty paces of them. At this distance the main body of the herd suddenly wheeled round and thundered across the plain in full retreat. One of the bulls at the same moment charged straight at us, but when within twenty paces of the guns he turned to one side, and instantly received two balls in the shoulder, B. and I having fired at the same moment. As luck would have it, his blade-bone was thus broken, and he fell upon his knees, but recovering himself in an instant, he retreated on three legs to the water.

We now received assistance from an unexpected quarter. One of the large bulls, his companions, charged after him with great fury, and soon overtaking the wounded beast, he struck him full in the side, throwing him over with a great shock on the muddy border of the lake. Here the wounded animal lay unable to rise, and his conqueror commenced a slow retreat across the plain.

Leaving B. to extinguish the wounded buffalo, I gave chase to the retreating bull. At an easy canter he would gain a hundred paces, and then, turning, he would face me; throwing his nose up, and turning his head to one side with a short grunt, he would advance quickly for a few paces, and then again retreat as I continued to approach.

In this manner he led me a chase of about a mile along the bank of the lake, but he appeared determined not to bring the fight to an issue at close quarters. Cursing his cowardice, I fired a long shot at him, and reloading my last square ball I continued the chase, led on by ignorance and excitement.

The lake in one part stretched in a narrow creek into the plain, and the bull now directed his course into the angle formed by this turn. I thought that I had him in a corner, and, redoubling my exertions, I gained upon him considerably. He retreated slowly to the very edge of the creek, and I had gained so fast upon him that I was not thirty paces distant, when he plunged into the water and commenced swimming across the creek. This was not more than sixty yards in breadth, and I knew that I could now bring him to action.

Running round the borders of the creek as fast as I could, I arrived at the opposite side on his intended landing-place just as his black form reared from the deep water and gained the shallows, into which I had waded knee-deep to meet him. I now experienced that pleasure as he stood sullenly eyeing me within fifteen paces. Poor stupid fellow! I would willingly, in my ignorance, have betted ten to one upon the shot, so certain was I of his death in another instant.

I took a quick but steady aim at his chest, at the point of connection with the throat. The smoke on the barrel passed to one side; — there he stood — he had not flinched; he literally had not moved a muscle. The only change that had taken place was in his eye; this, which had hitherto been merely sullen, was now beaming with fury; but his form was as motionless as a statue. A stream of blood poured from a wound within an inch of the spot at which I had aimed; had it not been for this fact, I should not have believed him struck.

Annoyed at the failure of the shot, I tried him with the left-hand barrel at the same hole. The report of the gun echoed over the lake but there he stood as though he bore a charmed life; — an increased flow of blood from the wound and additional lustre in his eye were the only signs of his being struck.

I was unloaded, and had not a single ball remaining. It was now his turn. I dared not turn to retreat, as I knew he would immediately charge, and we stared each other out of countenance.

With a short grunt he suddenly sprang forward, but fortunately, as I did not move, he halted,; he had, however, decreased his distance and we now gazed at each other within ten paces. I began to think buffalo-shooting somewhat dangerous, and I would have given something to have been a mile away, but ten times as much to have had my four-ounce rifle in my hand. Oh, how I longed for that rifle in this movement of suspense! Unloaded, without the power of defence, with the absolute certainty of a charge from an overpowering brute, my hand instinctively found the handle of my hunting-knife, a useless weapon against such a foe.

Knowing that B. was not aware of my situation at the distance which separated us (about a mile), without taking my eyes from the figure before me, I raised my hand to my mouth and gave a long and loud whistle; this was a signal that I knew would be soon answered if heard.

With a stealthy step and another short grunt, the bull again advanced a couple of paces towards me. He seemed aware of my helplessness, and he was the picture of rage and fury, pawing the water and stamping violently with his fore-feet.

This was very pleasant! I gave myself up for lost, but putting as fierce an expression into my features as I could possibly assume, I stared hopelessly at my maddened antagonist.

Suddenly a bright thought flashed through my mind. Without taking my eyes off the animal before me, I put a double charge of powder down the righthand barrel, and tearing off a piece of my shirt, I took all the money from my pouch, three shillings in sixpenny pieces, and two *anna* pieces, which I luckily had with me in this small coin for paying coolies. Quickly making them into a rouleau with the piece of rag, I rammed them down the barrel, and they were hardly well home before the bull again sprang forward. So quick was it that I had no time to replace the ramrod, and I threw it in the water, bringing my gun on full cock in the same instant. However, he again halted, being now within about seven paces from me, and we again gazed fixedly at each other, but with altered feelings on my part. I had faced him hopelessly with an empty gun for more than a quarter-of-an-hour, which seemed a century. I now had a charge in my gun, which I knew if reserved till he was within a foot of the muzzle would certainly floor him, and I awaited his onset with comparative carelessness, still keeping my eyes opposed to his gaze.

At this time I heard a splashing in the water behind me, accompanied by the hard breathing of something evidently distressed. The next moment I heard B's voice. He could hardly speak for want of breath, having run the whole way to my rescue, but I could understand that he had only one barrel loaded, and no bullets left. I dared not turn my face from the buffalo, but I cautioned B. to reserve his fire till the bull should be close into me, and then to aim at the head.

The words were hardly uttered, when, with the concentrated rage of the last twenty minutes, he rushed straight at me! It was the work of an instant. B. fired without effect. The horns were lowered, their points were on either side of me, and the muzzle of the gun barely touched his forehead when I pulled the trigger, and three shillings' worth of small change rattled into his hard head. Down he went, and rolled over with the suddenly checked momentum of his charge. Away went B. and I as fast as our heels would carry us, through the water and over the plain, knowing that he was not dead but only stunned. There was a large fallen tree about half a mile from us, whose whitened branches, rising high above the ground, offered a tempting asylum. To this we directed our flying steps, and, after a run of a hundred yards, we turned and looked behind us. He had regained his feet and was following us slowly. We now experienced the difference of feeling between hunting and being hunted, and fine sport we must have afforded him.

On he came, but fortunately so stunned by the collision with Her Majesty's features upon the coin which he had dared to oppose that he could only reel forward at a slow canter. By degrees even this pace slackened, and he fell. We were only too glad to be able to reduce our speed likewise, but we had no sooner stopped to breathe, than he was again up and after us. At length, however, we gained the tree, and we beheld him with satisfaction stretched powerless upon the ground, but not dead, within two hundred yards of us.

We retreated under cover of the forest to the spot at which we had left the horses, fortunately meeting no opposition from wild quarters, animals, and we shortly arrived at the village at which we took up our vowing vengeance on the following morning for the defeat that we had sustained.

A man is a poor defenceless wretch if left to defend himself against wild animals with the simple natural weapons of arms, legs, and teeth. A tom-cat would almost be a match for him. He has legs which will neither serve him for pursuit or escape if he is forced to trust only in his speed. He has strength of limb which is useless without some artificial weapon. He is an animal who, without the power of reason, could not even exist in a wild state; his brain alone gives him the strength to support his title of lord of the creation.

Nevertheless, a lord of the creation does not appear in much majesty when running for his life from an infuriated buffalo; —the assumed title sits uneasily upon him when, with scarcely a breath left in his body, he struggles along till he is ready to drop with fatigue, expecting to be overtaken at every step. We must certainly have exhibited poor specimens of the boasted sway of man over the brute creation could a stranger have witnessed our flight on this occasion.

The next morning we were up at daybreak, and we returned to the battle-field of the previous evening in the full expectation of seeing our wounded antagonist lying dead where we had left him. In this we were disappointed — he was gone, and we never saw him again.

I now had my long two-ounce and my four-ounce rifles with me, and I was fully prepared for a deep revenge for the disgrace of yesterday.

The morning was clear but cloudy; a heavy thunderstorm during the night had cooled the air, and the whole plain was glistening with bright drops; the peacocks were shrieking from the tree-tops and spreading their gaudy plumage to the cool breeze; and the whole face of nature seemed refreshed. We felt the same invigorating spirit, and we took a long survey of the many herds of buffaloes upon the plain before we could determine which we should first attack.

A large single bull, who had been lying in a swampy hollow unobserved by us, suddenly sprang up at about three hundred yards' distance, and slowly cantered off. I tried the long two-ounce rifle at him, but taking too great an elevation, I fired over him. The report, however, had the effect of turning him, and, instead of retreating, he wheeled round and attempted to pass between the guns and the banks of the lake. We were about three hundred yards from the water's edge, and he was soon passing us at full gallop at right angles, about midway or a hundred and fifty yards distant.

I had twelve drachms of powder in the four-ounce rifle, and I took a flying shot at his shoulder. No visible effect was produced, and the ball ricochetted completely across the broad surface of the lake (which was no more than a mile wide at this part) in continuous splashes. The gun-bearers said I had fired behind him, but I had distinctly heard the peculiar 'fut' which a ball makes upon striking an animal, and although the passage of the ball across the lake appeared remarkable, nevertheless I felt positive that it had first passed through some portion of the animal.

Away the bull sped over the plain at unabated speed for about two hundred paces, when he suddenly turned and charged toward the guns. On he came for about a hundred yards, but evidently slackening his speed at every stride. At length he stopped altogether. His mouth was wide open, and I could now distinguish a mass of bloody foam upon his lips and nostrils — the ball had in reality passed through his lungs, and, making its exit from the opposite shoulder, it had even then flown across the lake. This was the proof of the effect of the twelve drachms of powder.

Having reloaded, I now advanced towards him, and soon arrived within fifty paces. He was the facsimile of the bull that had chased us on the previous day — the same picture of fury and determination; and crouching low, he advanced a few paces, keeping his eyes fixed upon us as though we were already his own.

A short cough, accompanied by a rush of blood from his mouth, seemed to cause him great uneasiness, and he halted.

Again we advanced till within twenty paces of him. I would not fire, as I saw that he already had enough, and I wished to see how long he could support a wound through the lungs, as my safety in buffalo-shooting might in future depend upon this knowledge.

The fury of his spirit seemed to war with death, and although reeling with weakness and suffocation, he again attempted to come on. It was his last effort; his eyes rolled convulsively, he gave a short grunt of impotent rage, and the next moment he fell upon his back with his heels in the air; he was stone dead, and game to the last moment.

I had thus commenced a revenge for the insult of yesterday; I had proved the wonderful power of the four-ounce rifle — a weapon destined to make great havoc amongst the heavy game of Ceylon.

Upon turning from the carcass before us, we observed to our surprise that a large herd of buffaloes, that were at a great distance when we had commenced the attack upon the bull, had now approached to within a few hundred yards, and were standing in a dense mass, attentively watching us. Without any delay we advanced towards them, and, upon arriving within about a hundred paces, we observed that the herd was headed by two large bulls, one of which was the largest that I had ever seen. The whole herd was bellowing and pawing the ground. They had winded the blood of the dead bull and appeared perfectly maddened.

We continued to advance, and we were within about ninety paces of them when suddenly the whole herd of about two hundred buffaloes, headed by the two bulls before noticed, dashed straight towards us at full gallop. So simultaneous was the onset that it resembled a sudden charge of cavalry, and the ground vibrated beneath their heavy hoofs. Their tails were thrown high above their backs, and the mad and overpowering phalanx of heads and horns came rushing forward as though to sweep us at once from the face of the earth.

There was not an instant to be lost; already a short space intervened between us and apparently certain destruction. Our gun-bearers were almost in the act of flight; but catching hold of the man who carried the long two-ounce rifle, and keeping him by my side, I awaited the irresistible onset with the four-ounce.

The largest of the bulls was some yards in advance, closely followed by his companion, and the herd in a compact mass came thundering down at their heels. Only fifty yards separated us; we literally felt among them, and already experienced a sense of being overrun. I did not look at the herd, but I kept my eye upon the big bull leader. On they flew, and were within thirty paces of us, when I took a steady shot with the four-ounce, and the leading bull plunged head-foremost in the turf, turning a complete somersault. Snatching the two-ounce from the petrified gun-bearer, I had just time for a shot as the second bull was within fifteen paces, and at the flash of the rifle his horns ploughed up the turf, and he lay almost at our feet. That lucky shot turned the whole herd. When certain destruction threatened us, they suddenly wheeled to their left when within twenty paces of the guns, and left us astonished victors of the field. We poured an ineffectual volley into the retreating herd from the light guns as they galloped off in full retreat, and reloaded as quickly as possible, as the two bulls, although floored, were still alive. They were, however completely powerless, and a double-barrelled gun gave each the *coup-de-grace* by a ball in the forehead. Both rifle shots had struck at the point of junction of the throat and chest, and the four-ounce ball had passed out of the hind-quarter. Our friend of yesterday, although hit in precisely the same spot, had laughed at the light guns.

Although I have since killed about two hundred wild buffaloes, I have never witnessed another charge by a herd. This was an extraordinary occurrence, and fortunately stands alone in buffalo-shooting. Were it not for the two heavy rifles our career might have terminated in an unpleasant manner. As I before mentioned, this part of the country was seldom or never disturbed at the time of which I write, and the buffaloes were immensely numerous and particularly savage, nearly always turning to bay and showing good sport when attacked.

Having cut out the tongues from the two bulls we turned homeward to breakfast. Skirting along the edge of the lake, which abounded with small creeks, occasioning us many circuits, we came suddenly upon a single bull, who, springing from his lair of mud and high grass, plunged into a dead shot as he landed on the opposite bank about a hundred paces from us. The four-ounce struck him in the hind-quarters and broke the hip joint, and, continuing its course along his body, it pierced his lungs and lodged in the skin of the throat. The bull immediately fell, but regaining his feet he took to the water, and swam to a small island of high grass about thirty yards from the shore. Upon gaining this he turned and faced us, but in a few seconds he fell unable to rise, and received a merciful shot in the head, which despatched him.

We were just leaving the border of the lake on our way to the village, when two cow buffaloes sprang up from one of the numerous inlets and retreated at full gallop towards the jungle, offering a splendid side shot at about a hundred paces. The leading cow plunged headforemost into the grass as the four-ounce struck her through both shoulders. She was a fine young cow, and we cut some steaks from her in case we should find a scarcity of provisions at Minneria and, quitting the shores of the lake, we started for breakfast.

It was only eight A.M. when we arrived. I had bagged five buffaloes, four of which were fine bulls. Our revenge was complete, and I had proved that the four-ounce was perfectly irresistible if held straight with the heavy charge of twelve drachms of powder. Since that time I have frequently used sixteen drachms (one ounce) of powder to the charge, but the recoil is then very severe, although the effect upon an animal with a four-ounce steel-tipped conical ball is tremendous.

On our return to the village of Minneria we found a famous breakfast, for which a bath in the neighbouring brook increased an appetite already sharpened by the morning exercise. The buffalo steaks were coarse and bad, as tough as leather, and certainly should never be eaten if better food can be obtained. The tongues are very rich, but require salting.

In those days Minneria was not spoiled by visitors, and supplies were accordingly at a cheap rate — large fowls at one penny each, milk at any price that you chose to give for it. This is now much changed, and the only thing that is still ridiculously cheap is fish.

46

Give a man sixpence to catch you as many as he can in the morning and he forthwith starts on his piscatorial errand with a large basket, cone shaped, of two feet diameter at the bottom and about eight inches at the top. This basket is open at both ends, and is about two feet in length.

The fish that is most sought after is the 'lola.' He is a ravenous fellow, in appearance between a trout and a carp, having the habits of the former, but the clumsy shoulders of the latter. He averages about three pounds, although he is often caught of nice or ten pounds weight. Delighting in the shallows, he lies among the weeds at the bottom, to which he always retreats when disturbed. Aware of his habits, the fisherman walks knee-deep in the water, and at every step he plunges the broad end of the basket quickly to the bottom. He immediately feels the fish strike against the sides, and putting his hand down through the aperture in the top of the basket he captures him, and deposits him in a basket slung on his back.

These 'lola' are delicious eating, being very like an eel in flavour, and I have known one man catch forty in a morning with no other apparatus than this basket.

Minneria Lake, like all others in Ceylon, swarms with crocodiles of a very large size. Early in the morning and late in the evening they can be seen lying upon the banks like logs of trees. I have remarked that a buffalo, shot within a few yards of the lake, has invariably disappeared during the night, leaving an undoubted track where he has been dragged to the water by the crocodiles. These brutes frequently attack the natives when fishing or bathing, but I have never heard of their pursuing any person upon dry land.

I remember an accident having occurred at Madampi, on the west coast of Ceylon, about seven years ago, the day before I passed through the village. A number of women were employed in cutting rushes for mat-making, and were about mid-deep in the water. The horny tail of a large crocodile was suddenly seen above the water among the group of women, and in another instant one of them was seized by the thigh and dragged towards the deeper part of the stream. In vain the terrified creature shrieked for assistance; the horror-stricken group had rushed to the shore, and a crowd of spectators on the bank offered no aid beyond their cries. It was some distance before the water deepened, and the unfortunate woman was dragged for many yards, sometimes beneath the water, sometimes above the surface, rending the air with her screams, until at length the deep water hid her from their view. She was never again seen.

Some of these reptiles grow to a very large size, attaining the length of twenty feet, and eight feet in girth, but the common size is fourteen feet. They move slowly upon land, but are wonderfully fast and active in the water. They usually lie in wait for their prey under some hollow bank in a deep pool, and when the unsuspecting deer or even buffalo stoops his head to drink, he is suddenly seized by the nose and dragged beneath the water. Here he is speedily drowned and consumed at leisure.

The two lower and front teeth of a crocodile project through the upper jaw, and their white points attract immediate notice as they protrude through the brown scales on the upper lip. When the mouth is closed, the jaws are thus absolutely locked together.

It is a common opinion that the scales on the back of a crocodile will turn a ball; this is a vulgar error. The scales are very tough and hard, but a ball from a common fowling-piece will pass right through the body. I have even seen a hunting-knife driven at one blow deep into the hardest part of the back; and this was a crocodile of a large size, about fourteen feet long, that I shot at a place called Bolgodde, twenty-two miles from Colombo.

A man had been setting nets for fish, and was in the act of swimming to the shore, when he was seized and drowned by a crocodile. The next morning two buffaloes were dragged into the water close to the spot, and it was supposed that these murders were committed by the same crocodile. I was at Colombo at the time, and hearing of the accident, I rode off to Bolgodde to try my hand at catching him.

Bolgodde is a very large lake of many miles in circumference, abounding with crocodiles, widgeon, teal and ducks.

On arrival that evening, the *moodeliar* (headman) pointed out the spot where the man had been destroyed, and where the buffaloes had been dragged in by the crocodile. One buffalo had been entirely devoured, but the other had merely lost his head, and his carcass was floating in a horrible state of decomposition near the bank. It was nearly dark, so I engaged a small canoe to be in readiness by break of day.

Just as the light streaked the horizon, I stepped into the canoe. This required some caution, as it was the smallest thing that can be conceived to support two persons. It consisted of the hollow trunk of a tree, six feet in length and about one feet in   diameter.   A small outrigger prevented it from upsetting, but it was not an inch from the surface of the water when I took my narrow seat, and the native in the stern paddled carefully towards the carcass of the buffalo.

Upon approaching within a hundred yards of the floating carcass, I counted five forms within a few yards of the flesh. These objects were not above nine inches square, and appeared like detached pieces of rough bark. I knew them to be the foreheads of different crocodiles, and presently one moved towards the half-consumed buffalo. His long head and shoulders projected from the water as he attempted to fix his fore-claws into the putrid flesh; this however, rolled over towards him, and prevented him from getting a hold; but the gaping jaws nevertheless made a wide breach in the buffalo's flank. I was now within thirty yards of them, and being observed, they all dived immediately to the bottom.

The carcass was lying within a few yards of the bank, where the water was extremely deep and clear. Several large trees grew close to the edge and formed a good hiding-place; I therefore landed, and, sending the canoe to a distance, I watched the water.

I had not been five minutes in this position before I saw in the water at my feet, in a deep hole close to the bank, the immense form of a crocodile as he was slowly rising from his hiding-place to the surface. He appeared to be about eighteen feet long, and he projected his horny head from the surface, bubbled and then floated with only his forehead and large eyes above the water. He was a horrible looking monster, and from his size I hoped he was the villain that had committed the late depredations. He was within three yards of me; and, although I stood upon the bank, his great round eyes gazed at me without a symptom of fear. The next moment I put a two-ounce ball exactly between them, and killed him stone dead. He gave a convulsive slap with his tail, which made the water foam, and, turning upon his back, he gradually sank, till at length I could only distinguish the long line of his white belly twenty feet below me.

Not having any apparatus for bringing him to the surface, I again took to the canoe, as a light breeze that had sprung up was gradually moving the carcass of the buffalo away. This I slowly followed, until it at length rested in a wide belt of rushes which grew upon the shallows near the shore. I pushed the canoe into the rushes within four yards of the carcass, keeping to windward to avoid the sickening smell.

I had not been long in this position before the body suddenly rolled over as though attacked by something underneath the water, and the next moment the tall reeds brushed against the sides of the canoe, being violently agitated in a long line, evidently by a crocodile at the bottom.

The native in the stern grew as pale as a black can turn with fright, and instantly began to paddle the canoe away. This, however, I soon replaced in its former position, and then took his paddle away to prevent further accidents. There sat the captain of the fragile vessel in the most abject state of terror. We were close to the shore, and the water was not more than three feet deep, and yet he dared not jump out of the canoe, as the rushes were again brushing against its sides, being moved by the hidden beast at the bottom. There was no help for him, so after vainly imploring me to shove the canoe into deep water, he at length sat still.

In a few minutes the body of the buffalo again moved, and the head and shoulders of a crocodile appeared above water and took a bite of some pounds of flesh. I could not get a shot at the head from his peculiar position, but I put a ball through his shoulders, and immediately shoved the canoe astern. Had I not done this, we should most likely have been upset, as the wounded brute began to lash out with his tail in all directions, till he at length retired to the bottom among the rushes. Here I could easily track him, as he slowly moved along, by the movement of the reeds. Giving the native the paddle, I now by threats induced him to keep the canoe over the very spot where the rushes were moving, and slowly followed on the track, while I kept watch in the bow of the canoe with a rifle.

Suddenly the movement in the rushes ceased, and the canoe stopped accordingly. I leaned slightly over the side to look into the water, when up came a large air-bubble, and directly afterwards an apparition in the shape of some fifteen pounds of putrid flesh. The stench was frightful, but I knew my friend must be very bad down below to disgorge so sweet a morsel. I therefore took the paddle and poked for him; the water being shallow, I felt him immediately. Again the rushes moved; I felt the paddle twist as his scaly back glided under it, and a pair of gaping jaws appeared above the water, wide open and within two feet of the canoe. The next moment his head appeared, and the two-ounce ball shattered his brain. He sank to the bottom, the rushes moved slightly and were then still.

I now put the canoe ashore, and cutting a strong stick, with a crook at one end, I again put out to the spot and dragged for him. He was quite dead; and catching him under the fore-leg, I soon brought him gently to the surface of the water. I now made fast a line to his fore-leg, and we towed him slowly to the village, the canoe being level with the water's edge.

His weight in the water was a mere trifle, but on arrival at the village on the banks of the lake, the villagers turned out with great glee, and fastened ropes to different parts of his body to drag him out. This operation employed about twenty men. The beast was about fourteen feet long; and he was no sooner on shore than the natives cut him to pieces with axes, and threw the sections into the lake to be devoured by his own species. This was a savage kind of revenge, which appeared to afford them great satisfaction.

Taking a large canoe, I paddled along the shores of the lake with a shot-gun, and made a good bag of ducks and teal, and returned to breakfast. The fatness and flavour of the wild ducks in Ceylon are quite equal to the best in England.

A Good Bag Before Breakfast

G.P. Sanderson

G.P. Sanderson is best known for having introduced the Kheddah system of capturing elephants in South India. He was 'Officer In Charge of The Government Elephant Catching Establishment' in Mysore and also spent quite a bit of time in Assam. He was an avid naturalist and hunter and his book, Thirteen Years Among The Wild Beasts of India, *is a classic account of the Indian forests from the 19th century. Sanderson obviously hunted at a time when game was abundant and he had no compunction about shooting three leopards before breakfast. A confusing part of the story is the distinction he makes between leopards and panthers, which he considered to be two different species. Many of the hunters from this time and even later refer to not only the distinction between the 'black panther' and the 'spotted leopard' but also between the larger, 'true leopard' and the smaller 'village leopard.'* The Book of Indian Mammals *by S.H. Prater suggests that there may be as many as six different 'races' of panthers in India but they are all the same species,* Panthera pardus.

One of my most fortunate days with panthers and leopards occurred in May 1872, when I had the luck to bag three before breakfast. I happened to be stationed at the time at a place called Nursipoor, in a part of Mysore where, as there were no jungles near, there was very little game, so I had no better amusement for my spare hours than shooting the few antelope that were to be found, and crocodiles in the Hemavati river. I was therefore gratified at the intelligence brought to me one morning by a man named Subba, a local *shikarie*, that he had heard that some panthers had been long established near a village called Maderhully, thirty miles from Nursipoor, and he proposed that we should take an early opportunity of looking them up. Native report is not always reliable,however, so I sent Jaffer with Subba to make more careful inquiries. They returned in a few days with a satisfactory report; but as my duties did not admit of my beating up the panthers' quarters just at that time, I sent Subba to live at Maderhully till I could take a holiday, and to learn all he could the while about the panthers' goings and comings. Subba was one of the few natives one meets with who have the English love of roving, and unconcern for home ties. To the ordinary Hindoo, house and family are all in all. Even when pressed by such exigency as starvation he prefers to die in his own village rather than go to a distance to obtain relief. I have met some natives, however, of sporting tastes, who would roll up their blanket, tie up their simple cooking utensils, and start upon any service, perhaps to be absent for a month or more, at a moment's notice, merely asking that something should be sent to their wives, a point which the Hindoo never forgets. Subba was one of these rovers, and in consequence was looked upon as somewhat of a vagabond by his stay-at-home neighbours. As a tracker he had the great recommendation of being a taciturn man, never speaking till he was sure, and never substituting imagination for facts.

It so happened that before I went to Maderhully I made a more distant excursion after certain bears with a friend, and whilst four fell to my rifle he shot none. I was moved with compassion at his disappointment, and sent him to Maderhully after my preserved panthers, which Subba had been reporting for some time were to him as 'the dogs of his own house' — i.e., that he was as certain of being able to lay hands on them. I ordered him to show my friend every attention, as some consolation for his ill luck with the bears; but the same cause which had led to want of success in the one case — viz., lack of knowledge of his game —again operated in his panther-hunt; and though Subba and the beaters did their best, my friend rendered their efforts futile by leaving the place where he had been posted for one he himself deemed better, and by committing other blunders, and he finally crowned the whole by missing the panthers when he did get a chance at them! He tried again the following day; but Subba made no apology when relating the circumstances to me afterwards for having, with the villagers, purposely misled the *'Doray'* (gentleman), as, though they knew well where the panthers were on the second day, they feared they might only be frightened away, not secured; and it is not unnatural that men, whose hopes of reward rest on the death of the animals they may have spent much time in watching and marking, should not like to see them lost, and with them their hoped-for guerdon, by an unskillful sportsman.

The panthers — or two leopards and one panther, as they turned out to be — lived in a large, partly abandoned, and jungle-overgrown garden beneath the embankment of a lake or tank, the water of which had formerly been used for irrigating it. The proximity of this stronghold to Maderhully and other villages, in the environs of which dogs, goats, and stray cattle might frequently be pounced upon, rendered it a suitable retreat for the panther and leopards, and here they had lived unmolested for a long time as none of the villagers had firearms. Having allowed them a few days to recover from any alarm they might feel at the late hunt, I appointed the 25th of May as an auspicious day for further operations against them; and as it is always desirable for the sportsman to learn all he possibly can of the locality where he intends to shoot, I sent my tents to Maderhully and arrived there myself on the morning of the 24th. After a cup of coffee I proceeded with Subba and his chief auxiliaries amongst the villagers to inspect the ground.

The garden was about a mile long and a quarter of a mile broad. The middle part, throughout its entire length, was thinly planted with cocoa-nut and plantain-trees; whilst, from the state of decay into which it had fallen, the hedges had become overgrown patches of aloe-bushes, creepers, and thorny thickets. The length of the garden lay north and south. The best covers for the panthers and leopards were respectively the northern half of the east boundary hedge, and the southern half of the west one. Subba said that the leopards were generally to be found in the former, and the panther in the latter place; and we therefore decided that on the morrow the men should begin to beat the east hedge from the north corner, and that I should be stationed at a point about half-way down it, where a thin fringe of bushes ran across the garden and formed a line of communication between the thickets on each side. Of this connecting fringe we knew any animal retiring before the beaters would take advantage, to cross the otherwise open ground to the thickets in the south-west corner. There were no covers outside, and disconnected with, the garden itself, except one small patch of dense aloe-bushes, about a hundred yards away from the south boundary hedge. Having noted the places where markers should be stationed, and having pointed out their posts to the men with us, to be occupied by them next day, I returned to camp to breakfast. In the afternoon sixty stout fellows — all *Holoyas*, or low-caste Hindoos — were enrolled as beaters, and each had a gun-wad given him as a voucher, as after a beat many who only help latterly, or not at all, will appear at the time of paying, and either the sportsman is put to double expense, or the amount is divided amongst so many as to make no one much the better. With tickets, the black sheep have no opportunity of obtaining money under false pretences.

The *Holoya* caste is one of the few amongst Hindoos to which the use of intoxicants is permitted; and every afternoon those *Holoyas* who had leisure, and who are lucky enough to have the necessary coppers, betake themselves to the nearest beer-shop. This is a cleanly-swept spot under a shady tree, and is screened from the gaze of passers-by with plaited cocoa-nut leaves. It is always situated at a little distance from the village, in deference to the prejudices of the more numerous abstaining inhabitants. The liquor supplied in the booth is the fermented sap of the wild date-tree (*Phoenix sylvestris*), largely diluted with water. It stands in large froth-covered earthen jars, each containing several gallons, and is served out into the customers' own drinking-vessels, usually gourds or lengths of the giant-bamboo, at about a farthing a quart. *Henda*, as this liquor is called, is to the low-caste Hindoo what beer is to us; and it appears to be a whole-some beverage if not abused. It is not highly intoxicating when used fresh, as is customarily done; whilst it contains a large amount of nutritious saccharin matter. The contract for the sale of this product throughout Mysore is leased out by Government, and brings in a large revenue. The consumption of spirits (arrack) is comparatively trifling, and is chiefly confined to large towns. Many of the drinkers of *henda* never taste spirits, which are more difficult to procure, and almost prohibitory in price. The supply of *henda* to the people is effected by pet contractors who rent one or more of the numerous groves of the wild date that are scattered throughout the country. The trees require no attention or culture. The sap is drawn from them by an incision made just below the leafy crown of their otherwise bare stems, and then earthen vessels into which it drains are emptied daily into skin-bags borne by donkeys or ponies (the sacred bovine tribe is never used for this somewhat discreditable work), and is despatched direct to the places where it is consumed.

I had just made arrangements with my *Holoya* beaters when I saw a string of donkeys and ponies laden with the wobbling bullock-skins of fermented liquor dear to their hearts, and I immediately despatched Subba to purchase a load as a present for them. He returned shortly, accompanied by the contractor, and driving a donkey whose hocks rubbed painfully against each other, and whose hind-legs had the appearance of almost crossing each other as it walked, from its being systematically overloaded, and having been used when too young. Such is the condition of most of the *henda* contractors'cattle. Subba had arranged for the transfer of the load for a small sum, and he represented that he had further negotiated the purchase of the donkey for one rupee and three-quarters (three and sixpence) if approved, and advised its being taken as a bait for the panthers. I agreed to this, as it was advisable to give the animals a feed overnight to make them less inclined for exertion on the morrow. It may seem cruel to tie up a living animal as a lure for the carnivora, but this is often a necessary measure towards compassing their destruction, and by the sacrifice of one the salvation of many scores may be effected. So the donkey and its load were driven off by the delighted *Holoyas* to a shady tree at a distance, and when relieved of its burden, the wretched creature was led away to the garden to be tied up as a last-repast for the leopards and panther. As I sat outside my tent after dinner that evening, I could not help pitying the poor donkey left to its fate. The night was starlit and quiet. Fireflies glancing near the border of the lake, and in and out amongst the dark foliage of the garden, were the only signs of life in that direction, but I knew that a dark deed was being done, or would be done there before morning.

As soon as it was light the men collected at the tent. I sent Subba and two others to see what had become of the donkey, and as we were starting we saw them running excitedly towards us. They had seen the two leopards enter the thicket in the north-east corner where the donkey had been tied. They had killed and dragged it some distance, and had eaten more than half of it. The beaters formed line near this spot, whilst I took the markers with me and saw each one safely up his tree in different parts of the boundary-hedges, and in the middle of the garden. They were cautioned on no account to come down, nor shout to us whatever they saw, but merely to keep their eyes open, and be able to let us know when we wanted information. Knowing how cunning panthers often are, I thought it possible that, if hotly pressed in the garden, one or other of them might betake itself to the detached clump of aloe-bushes which I have already mentioned as being situated a hundred yards beyond the south boundary-hedge. There was a large tree growing in the centre of the clump, so I ordered an old fellow to climb into it on the remote chance of his being useful there. The men were so disposed in the trees along each boundary hedge that it was impossible for any animal once afoot to hide itself where it would not be under the silent observation of one or other of them.

I mounted my tree in the narrow belt of jungle that, as aforesaid, crossed the garden and linked the two chief thickets together, whilst a man was posted in the open ground outside the garden who could see me and also the advancing beaters. I arranged a code of signals with him for guiding the beaters. Accidents or failure frequently ensue in driving dangerous game from want of communication with the beaters. Either a wounded animal turns back and meets the advancing men, who imagine it has been killed or has gone forward, and continue the beat; or if they take the precautionary measure of leaving the cover upon hearing shots, when the beast may in reality have been missed, or have gone forward, his mate or others of his kind in the drive may take the opportunity of slipping back and escaping.

I sat alone. I have too often found that an attendant moves or coughs at the critical moment to desire company. I occupied myself until the beat began by settling myself comfortably. My seat was a blanket rolled round a thick bough. With my knife and a saw-blade I lopped off such surrounding twigs as obstructed the view. I fastened my spare gun to a branch with my handkerchief, ready to hand, and planted my large pewter tankard, full of cold clear water, in a fork above me. It was refreshing even to look up through its glass bottom and the limpid fluid, the sportsman's safest tipple. One is sometimes kept a long time in a tree if the beaters experience difficulty with the game, and this in a hot Indian May day is unpleasant without water. The tree I was in was shady and comfortable, but the heat in the air makes the sportsman thirsty. Underneath me was a dry sandy watercourse, with a narrow border of bushes on each side. The crisp leaves of deciduous trees lay thickly in its bed, and I knew that even the stealthy tread of a leopard upon them would not be unheard by me, even before it came in sight. My view extended for about fifty yards up the bed of the water-course.

The distant yells of the beaters soon warned me that the sport had commenced. Some little time passed when I saw my signalman raise both arms, a sign from the beaters that the two leopards were afoot. I was expecting their speedy appearance when an extra storm of yells, and an interchange of abuse amongst the men, followed by a sudden silence, told me that the leopards had broken back, I only hoped without accident. The men ran back to head them, and they recommenced at the original place and beat up merrily. Presently I heard a rustling in the dry leaves, and saw one leopard sneaking down the sandy ravine. It came on very cautiously and hesitatingly, and I amused myself by watching it. Though full grown it was a small animal (few if any leopards exceed five and a half feet in length), and I felt rather ashamed of being in a tree to shoot such a creature. I would have met it on foot with pleasure. It looked as if half inclined to turn back, but each yell of the men appeared to call to its mind some act of spoilation for which it feared retribution, and to make it dread a return more than an advance. On it came, and when directly under me I dropped it dead with a bullet through the neck. It never moved, but lay prone as it fell, with one paw before it in the attitude of advancing. I telegraphed 'dead,' and the beaters came on with redoubled cries.

Soon the male leopard approached with slow and stealthy step down the bed of the ravine. He looked very pretty to a sportsman's eye, grinning with mingled fear and anger at being disturbed in his early sleep. His belly almost touched the ground as he crept along. Fortunately the wind was from him to me, so he did not scent his dead spouse, nor did he even observe her as she lay. He seemed to have thoughts of leaving the bed of the ravine before he reached me, and drawing his head level with the bank he peered cautiously through the garden to see if the coast were clear in the line of his meditated departure. He gave me a rather difficult shot, but I rolled him over. He got up and rushed up the bank, but I tumbled him over again into the ravine. He now cantered back, but I caught my empty rifle between my knees and seized the spare one, and just as he was getting out of sight I killed him with a lucky shot in the ear.

Having laid out our game in the shade, I sent Subba to inquire of the markers along the other boundary-hedge of the garden if they had seen anything. After some time he came back to say that every man along the line reported that one panther, some said two, had passed him, and that the old fellow in the tree in the aloe-clump signalled that there was something hiding near its foot. I plumed myself greatly on my foresight in having stationed this marker in his present post. The panther (for such it was) had, with   cunning,   left the garden at the disturbance we made over the leopards, and had secreted itself in this unpretentious spot, hoping, no doubt, that we should confine our search to its regular haunts. The idea was a good one, but unfortunately for it, not quite novel; I had been played the trick before, successfully on that occasion, and had not forgotten the circumstance. The day was getting hot, but Subba's information was as refreshing as ice! I sent the men to the tank to get a drink of water, and we then set out without a word, as the place where the panther lay hidden was so small that the slightest alarm might have made it leave it. The old fellow in the tree had taken the precaution of climbing to the topmost branch (panthers have been known to pull sportsmen out of trees; a friend of mine shot one when in a tree which it had ascended to a height of thirty feet from the ground on being mobbed in a garden by some villagers), and he now directed us by silently pointing to the exact spot in the thicket where the hiding beast lay. The men formed up on the far side of the thicket without a sound, whilst I took post on foot close to the south hedge of the garden. I placed my spare rifle on full-cock against a tree ready to hand. Between the aloe-thicket and my post was a stretch of the greenest turf, as, though it was then the end of the hot weather in Mysore, the ground here was damp and marshy. The panther would have to cross this open space, close past me and in full view, in returning to the garden.

The men awaited my signal with upraised clubs, and a fiendish howl ready, no doubt, on each tongue. A little in advance of them stood Subba, with a lighted stick in one hand and a rocket in the other, waiting for orders to eject the animal. I raised my hand. The lighted stick was applied to the rocket, which fizzed slowly; when properly agoing it was thrown into the very spot where the beast lay, and its terrors supplemented by the said pent-up yells of the beaters. The panther came out like a jack-in-the-box! It had the air of having been blown out by the explosion of the rocket, so sudden was its appearance. The startling character of the demonstration against it was certainly sufficient to terrify any wild animal out of its ordinary demeanour; and with a series of springs and continued roars, the beast made straight for the garden. I stood almost in its path. I had set out in the morning with the usual resolves to be cautious, but it is more easy to make such vows at home than to keep them in the field. Prudent resolutions often vanish under excitement. Whilst awaiting the turning out of the panther I was anxious enough, and pondered within myself whether I should not be safer in a tree; but when it came bounding towards me I only thought of bagging it by a neat shot. It never saw me, its attention being centered on diving into the garden to escape the awful racket it had just listened to. Its rich, tawny, spotted skin glanced like a race-horse's coat, and contrasted beautifully with the green turf as it flew towards me. The instant it started the beaters stopped their yells, and looked on at the impending event with breathless interest. The panther's roars were the only sound which now broke the stillness. It would, in the course it was taking, pass about fifteen yards to my right. I kept it covered with my rifle from the moment it started; and when it was just passing me, and about twelve yards distant, I fired. My shot was rather too far forward, however, and merely grazed its chest; but the left barrel smashed both its shoulder-blades, and the beast alighted heavily on its chest, rolling over with the impetus of its spring. The beaters ran up, and we stood round the beautiful but fierce creature as it lay, biting at the turf and even its own paws in its impotent rage at being unable to rise. We watched it for a few seconds, when I put an end to its sufferings.

We now went to look for the reported fourth panther, and having found the point in the thicket where it had been last seen, I once more took up my position on foot, in the absence of a suitable tree, and the beat began. No panther, no trace of one, was to be found, however. but a very large wild cat made its appearance. This was evidently what the markers, seeing it indistinctly in the thicket, had mistaken for a panther. I killed it with a bullet.

I now returned to breakfast with a complacent mind. We had had a capital morning's sport. The arrangements had been perfect; the shooting had been — ahem! I will leave my readers to judge; nothing, even to the cat, had escaped us; and all this before ten o'clock!

People came from adjacent villages to see the three animals, which lay in a row under a tree near my tent. The sight afforded them evident satisfaction, as there was scarcely one of them whose flocks or dogs had not suffered from their depredations. The first two were a pair, and were the true leopards or *kerkals* of Mysore, having all the characteristics given by Elliot, and quoted by Dr Jerdon in his *Mammals*. The measurements of the animals from nose to tip of tail were: Panther (female), six feet ten inches. Leopards — male, five feet four inches — female, five feet two inches, both full grown.

The Government reward in Mysore for killing a panther or leopard is twenty-five rupees. I gave forty rupees of the amount due for the three to Subba, who had taken great trouble in their pursuit. As a native can live well on five rupees-a-month, this would suffice to make him happy for some time, especially in the matter of drink, to which he was much devoted. The remaining thirty-five rupees gave the beaters great satisfaction.

I have before mentioned the panther and leopard's habit of living in rocky hills near villages, and of preying upon domestic animals. Such depredators keep chiefly to deep and intricate caves, from which they cannot be dislodged even with fireworks; and almost the only plan of getting a shot at them is to watch, either before or after nightfall, over a live goat tied as a bait. Some cunning panthers, however, will not approach such a lure, as their suspicions are at once aroused by the sight of a solitary goat stationed near their retreats. With such sly animals I have found the most effective plan to be, to hide early in the afternoon amongst the rocks at the foot of the hill on the side where the panther will most probably be on the look-out about sunset, and, having an accomplice in the goat-herd, to have a goat quickly tethered and left behind as the flocks are driven villagewards in the evening. The sight of this apparent straggler, which bleats loudly for its fellows, will often deceive the most wary panther or leopard. It descends from its elevated post of observation with marvellous rapidity, and if the sportsman has chosen his post well, so that he may neither be seen nor winded by the animal, he will have a fair chance at it when it is seizing the goat.

I remember an absurd occurrence in connection with these hill-panthers. A pair was said to frequent an isolated pile of rocks in open country, so I proceeded one morning with some villagers of the neighbourhood to inspect their retreat with a view to devising plans against them. We separated amongst the rocks to look for recent marks. One villager accompanied me. Seeing an entrance to a likely-looking cave under a shelving sheet of rock, I stooped down and peered in, when I immediately heard a low, tremulous sound in the deep recesses which I took to be the growl of the objects of our search. I drew back, and the sound ceased. I was under no apprehension, as my experience of panthers and leopards is that they never charge out of the darkness to attack a person outside their retreats. I have even known a leopard in a cave to be poked with bamboos for a length of time. It could not be shot, and it refused to come out, though the titillation amongst its ribs must have been, one would think, not less hurting to its dignity than distressing to its bodily feelings.

On the present occasion, to make sure I peered in again. There could be no mistake; it was evidently a suppressed growl. The villager with me said it could not be the panthers, as the cave was not so extensive as others in the hill, and was never frequented by them. He walked up to the entrance and looked boldly in. His mien changed, however, in a moment. He evidently heard what I had heard, and he drew back with a gesture of astonishment and apprehension. I laughed at his change of countenance, and sent him to call the others, and when they came we proceeded to examine the vicinity of the cave, but could find no footprints. We approached the entrance, when the same sound was again audible. One of the men, after listening intently, laughed, and saying, 'I'll show you the panthers that made that noise,' crept into the cave, from which large numbers of bats began to issue. It was the tremulous sound produced by the movements of these creatures within, which, resounding in the hollow cavern, closely resembled a low growl. When the entrance had been darkened by our looking in the bats were disturbed, and fluttered their wings as they hung from the roof, and some of them flew about.

I have related at the commencement of the last chapter how the panther was the first wild animal of the audacious class that I made the acquaintance of in India. It strangely enough happened that it was also the last I encountered before leaving India. I am obliged to say I did not acquit myself in the leave-taking interview with as much address as I ought to have displayed. To have failed with my first panther through inexperience was natural enough; but the same excuse cannot be made for the loss of the last by a combination of indifferent shooting, and what was worse, want of strategy. The occurrence happened as follows: —

I was to leave Morlay, so long my jungle-home, for Madras next day, *en route* to England, so, wishful for a last evening stroll I took a rifle and drove in my pony-trap along the jungle-road which I had had cleared so as to be feasible for driving from Morlay Hall to the Koombappan Goody temple. Shooting was not my object so much as a quiet saunter through the scenes to which I had become so much attached, so leaving my trap at the temple, Murga (a tracker) and I wandered silently along the river-bank. The jungle was unusually thin and leafless even for the season of the year (the hot weather), owing to the lack of proper rain for many months, which had affected vegetation in the wilds as well as crops and pasturage. The ordinary water supplies of the country having dried up, spotted-deer, monkeys, jungle-fowl, and smaller creatures, were collected in unusual numbers in the neighbourhood of the Honhollay river. Such was the drought that no water had flowed in its bed for months, and the supply was now confined to a few pools.

It would have been inexcusable butchery to have shot many of the deer thus forced to the locality by the most pressing of creature wants, thirst; so contenting myself with one fat stag, to afford my men a parting feast, I wandered on, watching the different animals and scenes till sunset, and then mounted my trap and drove homewards. I was allowing the pony to jog along at his own pace, and thinking of the months that must elapse before I should again set foot in these free and beautiful wilds, when Murga, who was sitting behind me, touched my shoulder and said 'Panther.' I looked, and at a bend in the narrow track, about forty yards ahead, I caught sight of a large panther just disappearing into the jungle. We knew him instantly as an old brute that had defied all the arts of the trackers and myself to bring to book since I settled at Morlay. There were only two panthers in our jungles; the second was a female, and smaller than the male. This cunning old fellow would never kill our 'ties,' nor lie up in thickets where we could find him during the day. He procured his prey (dogs and stray cattle) in villages far in the open country, and was thus independent of the picketed animals with which we strove to tempt him, in the hope of tracing him, when gorged, to his lair. He was never to be found in any of the larger thickets, but resorted to straggling, undefined country, where it was impossible to arrange any sure plans for driving him. He had become so cunning, through being subjected to several unsuccessful hunts, that we latterly gave up making special search for him, and trusted to some accident to throw him into our hands at last. Here was such a chance.

Oh that I had only seen him a moment sooner! thought I. My rifle was at hand, and I could hardly have failed to bag him. Murga was of the opinion that he might show himself again. He said, 'You know, sir, he invariably keeps along paths. If you ran quietly to the bend you may see him.' Seizing my double express I reached the place where the panther had disappeared, leaving Murga with the trap. I noticed that his footprints led along this part of the road, and he must therefore have been visible from the trap, had we but been looking ahead, some time before we saw him. I peered into the jungle. All was quiet. I went a few paces forward and looked round the bend. There was the brute, walking along in the silent manner peculiar to panthers, neither looking to right nor left, and appearing as if he had never been disturbed in his life! He was seventy yards away, and end on, presenting a difficult shot; but I knelt, and taking a steady aim, fired. The brute only gave a start, and without looking behind him galloped heavily forward for a few yards, and then subsided into the same unconcerned pace! I was determined to make a better shot now, so waiting until the panther turned a bend in the path I ran quickly and silently after him, as I knew another bend, which the path almost immediately made, would give me a broadside view further on. Peeping eagerly ahead I saw the panther going round the second bend with an air of the most perfect abstraction. Here goes an awakener — to his doom — thought I, as I pressed the trigger. He was then only fifty yards away, but the light was failing, and though I certainly ought to have bagged him, I made one of those distressing misses which every sportsman does now and again. The panther sprang forward with a gruff growl, and as my rifle was empty, and the spare cartridges were in the trap, I ran back for them.

I found there were only two. It was fast growing dark, so we left the pony standing, and Murga ran back with me to where I had last fired, to where — as we did not then know I had missed — we expected to find the panther dead, or at least wounded. To our astonishment there was no blood, whilst his tracks kept on in the path, and at his former deliberate gait. 'He's a devil,' said my superstitious companion as we ran on round the next two bends. Still the track led forward. At the third turn we came suddenly on the brute, looking inquiringly over his shoulder in the direction in which he heard our footsteps. Almost before I could bring up my rifle he bounded into the cover, and I missed him again, though there was some excuse this time in his rapid movements. The chief strategic mistake we made occurred at this point. Instead of going back to the pony as we did, imagining that as the panther had now seen his enemies clearly, and had been deliberately fired at from the distance of a few yards, he would not show himself again, I ought to have hidden myself in the thicket bordering the path, and I should certainly have obtained a shot at him, at a few yards distance, almost immediately.

We met the pony coming slowly along with the trap, cocking his ears and stepping like a startled deer, as he well knew from a lengthy jungle experience that the shots and smell of the panther meant something serious. Jumping in I gave him his head, and as he was anxious to get home — all domestic animals in India evince the greatest disinclination to remain in the jungles after sunset, their instinct warning them of the danger they incur in so doing — we rattled rapidly forward, when, as we rounded the corner where I had last fired, we nearly drove over the brute of a panther, seated coolly on his haunches in the middle of the road! He bounded quietly into the jungle again. I had the presence of mind not to pull up, as we should probably have alarmed him by so doing — if anything would have done so! — so continuing less quickly I handed Murga the reins, and jumping out of the trap hid myself by the side of the path about forty yards further on, whilst he drove away. This ruse succeeded, and the panther, thinking the coast clear, stalked out and sat down again, looking after the receding trap. I tried to sight him, but it was now so dusk that though he could be seen plainly enough when my head was raised, with one eye closed and the other directed along a rifle-barrel, with a dark background, he was invisible. I tried repeatedly but could not get a sight, when he rose and came a few yards down the path, and then turned into one at right angles to it, and which led past me, but through bushes on my right. I had only one barrel loaded, but was determined to have the panther unless it were positively predestined that such was not to be my luck. I therefore slipped quietly through the bushes to cut him off in the small path he had now taken. I however made the mistake of stepping into it instead of waiting until he came level with me. I met him face to face at about five yards' distance, but a bush which overhung the narrow path obscured him; and whilst I delayed an instant to make certain of him — as in the dangerous position in which I stood it would not have done merely to wound him — he drew back with great quickness and vanished in the failing light.

This was the last I saw of him. I can only account for his extreme contumacy throughout by supposing he never saw clearly what we were, being confused by the presence of the trap, and also from the fact that many wild animals, even the most timid, are often very bold at night, as they are not accustomed to meet man abroad at that time. Deer may be approached much more easily late at night, or just as it grows light in the morning, than at other times, as they are not accustomed to being disturbed by people moving about at those hours.

At Close Quarters with a Tiger

The Hon. James Inglis (Maori)

James Inglis was an indigo planter in the terai region along the foothills of the Himalayas. He wrote the well known book Tent Life in Tigerland *as well as many other books including* Sport and Work on the Nepaul Frontier. *Inglis was obviously an eccentric character and the frontispiece of* Tent Life in Tigerland *shows him wearing a flamboyant turban. The illustrations in this book are some of the most beautiful in any* shikar *book, coloured lithographs taken from original photographs. Inglis worked for the government during the famine of 1874 after which failing health sent him to Australia where he became an active politician. As a member of the legislative assembly in Sydney, he became Minister for Public Instruction. His story of a tiger hunt is told in a lively, conversational tone which makes light of the dangerous situations he confronted.*

'I Fancy, Mac,' said Butty, 'that was about the narrowest *butch'* you ever had in your life.' (*'butch'* is from *'butchana'*, to escape.)

'Never a closer,' said Mac; 'I thought it was all up with me once or twice.'

'How did you feel?' I asked.

'Well, I can hardly tell you. Whenever I recognized that the brute was on me, I felt at once my only chance of safety was to lie perfectly still. Once or twice the oppression on my face from the pressure of the heavy canvas was almost suffocating, and when the huge tusk buried itself in the earth close to my side, I could scarcely refrain from calling out.'

'It must have grazed your ribs?'

'It did. After that, I seemed to turn quite unconcerned. All sorts of funny ideas came trooping across my brain. I couldn't for the life of me, help feeling cautiously about for my pipe, which had dropped somewhere near, when I tripped on the ropes. I seemed, too, to have a quick review of all the actions I had ever done, and was just dropping off into a dreamy unconsciousness, after pulling a desperate race against Oxford with my old crew, when your voices roused me to sensation once more.'

Said Joe, 'Well, do you know, I have had the same sensations exactly, during one very narrow squeak I once had.'

'Which one was that?' said George.

'Can't you remember the *buchao* (escape) I had in the Ryseree *mundir* (temple)?'

'Ah, yes! Tell them that. By Jove, that was a squeak, and no mistake!'

By this time our curiosity was all aflame, and there was a general cry of, 'Come on, Joe, let's have the yarn.'

'*Tamaco lao!*' shouted Mac, that being equivalent in English to 'Bring the tobacco!' and the white-robed old bearer appeared at the bidding; entering noiselessly from the outside gloom, as if a spectre, summoned by a cabalistic spell from the shadowy realms of spirit-land, had entered on the scene.

Another boy followed him, bearing the *Ag dan*, that is, a small brass or silver salver, containing pieces of glowing charcoal. Along with this fire-dish (they are often beautifully carved, and form a handsome ornament), the boy presented to each smoker a pair of '*chimtas*', or small silver tongs, with which the ruddy charcoal is lifted, and put into the bowl of the pipe; and while Mac was nearly burning his rubicund proboscis, in the attempt to ignite his strong moist tobacco, I may as well describe the *locale* of Joe's exciting adventure.

I knew Ryseree well. It was a straggling village, on the right bank of the main stream of the Koosee, and had been a place of considerable importance. The encroachments of the stream had laid waste many of its once fertile rice fields. The magnificent tanks, which had been excavated with such patient care, and at such a vast expenditure of labour by the villagers of some far-away remote time — so remote that even tradition failed to crystallize a single fact concerning them — were many of them now choked up with sand and matted growth of water-plants. Very few houses in the once populous and thriving town were now occupied. Tumble-down frameworks of rotting bamboos and mouldering thatch, festooned by rank luxuriant trailing creepers and wild gourds, lay scattered all round the open area, like an aggregation of big green ant-hills.

Round the environs of the dismantled village, white gnarled mango trees, denuded of bark and leaves, stretched out their gaunt arms, as if beseeching pity for their forsaken greenery and stripped condition. The soil all around was dank and clammy and moist. Here and there a huge embankment of sand, with a mound of brushwood and matted *debris*, showed where the annual floods tore down from the 'terai,' sweeping everything before them in their devastating rush. A few foundations of solid plastered brickwork, with rudely fashioned posts, standing up alone, battered, charred, and slowly rotting, evidenced the forsaken site of some wealthy grain merchant's *'dukan'*, or granary; but the only inhabitants now left in the village were a few humble cultivators of the cowherd and gardening castes, with two to three Brahmin and Rajpoot families; indigent, listless, fever-stricken, and subsisting entirely on the produce of their reduced herds, or the crops raised from a few patches of vetches, or rice, scattered at intervals among the tall encroaching jungle grass, which everywhere waved its rustling tops, and surrounded the ruined hamlet as with a belt of impenetrable, sapless, dun-coloured growth.

Such villages are common enough in these *'Dyaras'* or riverine plains, all over India. Many of the rivers that come thundering down into the plains from the Himalaya, to join the Ganges, shape for themselves a regular channel of gradual indentation parallel to their course. If any of my readers will take the trouble to look at the map, they will see that, like the ribs of a fern leaf, rivers come running into the Ganges from both sides. Those on the north-east side, while their current takes a southerly course, yet eat into the plain from east to west; and in this way many of their tracks, if we may use that term, are often many miles in width. As the river gradually works its way along, it eats into the settled cultivated country on the one side, leaving behind it, on the other, a wasted wilderness of sand-banks, patches of black mould on which grows a luxuriant vegetation, deep creeks, shallow sand-bars and stagnant lagoons; in fact, the very intricate country which I have described is the haunt of the tiger, rhinoceros, and buffalo, the most worthless country for culture of settlement, but the finest country in the world for game and sport.

The once thriving village and fertile rice-fields of Ryseree had reached just about the culminating stage of this gradual destructive process. The rich oil and seed merchants, the sleek Brahmins, the gallant Rajpoots with their free tread, manly forms, and independent bearing, had grown tired of warring against continued floods and annual irruptions of the predatory Koosee, and had sought a settlement further away from the turbulent stream. The cattle-folds and granaries had crumbled down, and lapsed into jungle. The bamboo *topes* had tangled and twisted themselves into a dense matted impenetrable brake. The orchards of mangoes no longer bore a single leaf. The temples were mouldering to dust. One shrine, sacred to Khristna, was still occasionally visited by some very aged and infirm devotee, from some faroff village, whence he had come in his old age, to offer up a prayer and deposit a few flowers once more before he died; at the shrine where he had worshipped in his vigorous early manhood, ere yet the terrible Koosee had swept away the glory of the village.

It was a dreary place. The village 'collections' were always in arrear. The chief item in the annual revenue was the fee charged at so much per head, on the foreign cattle that were driven every year after the subsidence of the floods, to graze on the fat pasture that then sprung up on the deserted clearings, now almost unrecognizable from the original jungle. Great herds of these cattle were driven to this part of the *Dyara*, as a favourite feeding ground, and, as a direct consequence, tigers were plentiful, and a 'drive' through the Ryseree *ilaka*, or jurisdiction, was always regarded as a sure 'find.'

And now to let Joe tell his story.

We were all attention. Our pipes were 'drawing' beautifully. The night was but young. There was little danger of 'Shumsher' again putting in an appearance, and while the *'noker chakur'* (servants) cleared up the wreck of the *'shamiana'* outside, and put things generally to rights, Joe, with a loud a-hem, commenced.

'Ye know, boys, I'm no hand at spinning a yarn, and I would much rather George pitched it to ye. He could do it better than I can, and he was with me at the time.'

'I remember the incident well,' said George, 'but I never poach.'

'Blaze away, Joe, and you'll soon come to the end of it!'

'Well,' said Joe, 'It was a good many years ago now, when my old father was alive; and he would seldom allow us to have any of the factory elephants to go out after a tiger, unless he went with us himself. On this occasion, George and I had got the loan of a few 'beater' elephants, from the *dehaat* (surrounding country). It was the

69

first time we had gone out by ourselves, and we were full of ardour and inexperience.

'We had beaten all over the *Basmattea tuppra* (*tuppra* is 'an island') round by Shikargunje and Burgamma, and had put up nothing but a few pig and hog-deer. It was an intensely hot day. We kept firing the jungle as we went along, and about two in the afternoon we stopped near Pokureea *Ghat* (ferry) to have some *tiffin* (lunch)

'While munching out *dalpattees* (a kind of cake) and drinking some milk, which a polite *Bataneea* (cowherd) had presented to us, a man came over in the boat and told us that there was a *man-eating tiger* over at Ryseree. We sent over one of our own *peons* to fossick out more information, and he soon came back with a confirmation of the report, and in a very short time we had swum our elephants across, and were making for the supposed lair of the tiger as fast as we could go; and you know, Maori, what sort of a *dehaat* it is?' said Joe, turning to me.

'Awful bad travelling,' I assented; 'I know the place.'

'There was not much jungle about the village then,' Joe continued, 'and we beat every possible patch we could think of as a likely sport, but coming on no 'sign,' we began to think we had been hoaxed, and we inclined to give up further attempts for that day at least, in no very amiable mood.

'Close by one of the tanks — a small tank, with its surface so covered by a dense carpeting of weeds that an incautious elephant might even have been deceived, and have plunged in, thinking it was dry land — there grew a solitary *semul*, or cotton tree. All round it was a dense, matted, inextricably tangled, wild growth of bamboos, laced together with creepers and climbing plants, and through the close-clustered, clinging maze we could discern the grey, weather-stained, domed roof of a temple, with great cracks gaping in the masonry, and the iron trident on the top, twisted, bent, and rust-eaten, hanging down over part of the roof. Amid the clefts of the masonry a few sinuous creepers had effected a lodgment, especially one broad-leaved, shady *peepul* tree (the *ficus indicus*). The shade below was dark as the mouth of a cave, and the ground was moist and yielding, while the elephants sank foot deep into it every time we went near it. It was so matted and wet, the creepers clung and intertwined so closely and tenaciously together, that I never imagined it would hide a tiger, and, indeed, we would not have thought of beating through it, had not the *mahout* on George's elephant directed our attention to a few scratches on the bark of the tree, which, very excitedly, he affirmed to be the marks of a tiger's claws.

'We both laughed at the idea, for the marks were fully eleven feet off the ground, and we never imagined a tiger could reach up that height.'

'I've seen marks higher up a tree than that,' said Mac.

'So have I since,' said Joe, 'but at that time we were rather incredulous. However, I was determined to be satisfied, and, getting down, I commenced to crawl through the brake in order to get to the trunk of the tree. Very fortunately for me, as you will see in a minute, I took my pistol with me. It was that identical pistol,' said the narrator, pointing to a handsome ivory-handled Thomas's patent lying on the table. 'You know it, all of you. It carries a heavy bullet, with a good charge, and is no toy at close quarters, as my story will prove anon.'

'Why did you get off the elephant?' said Butty. 'That was surely a foolish thing to do.'

'Ye don't catch this child doin' such griff-like tricks,' said Pat.

'Well, I have learned more caution since,' said Joe; 'but the fact is, both George and I were afraid there might have been an *eenar* (well) about the place, with perhaps blocks of masonry, and, to tell the truth, I don't think any elephant could have forced his way through such a tangled clump.'

'I remember, too,' put in George, 'that the edge of the tank was rotten, and the ground *panky* (stiff moist clay), and we were afraid of getting the elephants bogged, let alone tumbling them down a well. Besides, we never for a moment dreamed we would come upon 'old stripes' there after having been all over the place, and got never a sign. Go on, Joe.'

Joe continued:

'I got through to the tree with some difficulty, and there, sure enough, were the footprints of a large tiger, as distinct as any one might wish to see. The ground showed marks all over a space of several yards in circumference. The tiger had evidently been stretching itself up against the tree, and cleaning its nails on the bark. The scratchings on the bark were quite plain, and seemed of very recent date, as the white milky juice had scarcely yet dried on the tree.

'I narrowly scrutinized the whole surroundings. I could see at one portion where the huge brute must have slipped a little on the edge of the tank while drinking. The water was yet muddy where it had flowed into the track of the claws. It was hot, sultry, and still. The perspiration streamed from me. I called out to George that there were signs of tiger sure enough, and very fresh signs, too, but did not think the brute was now in the covert.

'Are there any signs of a *kill*?' cried George.

'I can't see any, but I'll have a look,' I answered; and then creeping on hands and knees, cutting away a twig here and a creeper there, I slowly made my way inwards, knife in hand, and my pistol ready in my belt. I penetrated yet farther and farther into the dark, noisome, gloomy tangle of matted undergrowth.'

'But hang it all, man alive! Was there a tiger inside?' burst forth Butty.

'Wait a bit, and you'll hear! said Joe.

'Dry up, Wheels! Go on, Joe,' said Pat.

Joe resumed his yarn.

'As I advanced farther and farther through the tortuous, intricate path I was forcing for myself, the sounds of the elephants and talking of the men grew fainter and fainter. The shade, too, deepened, and grew gloomier; and full of bounding health and spirits as I was, I could not repress a sort of shudder as I crept deeper and deeper into the heart of the *banswarree* (bamboo brake).

'I could hear George crying out occasionally, and I answered as well as I could. After one response, I could have almost sworn I heard a rustling and stealthy creaking, as if some animal were forcing a way through the thicket in front of me. A cold, creepy sensation came over me, and for a moment I could hear my heart beat audibly. Still, I never for a moment thought there could be a tiger. Neither of us ever imagined a tiger could have gone into such a close place, without leaving plain traces of his presence. Besides, I had often heard strange stories of the *Ryseree ka mundir* (the Ryseree Temple). The natives said it was haunted; that there was immense treasure hidden in it, and that all sorts of *'bhoots'* (ghosts) and spirits guarded the sacred deposit.'

George chimed in, 'Joe had often expressed a wish to explore this old temple, and it was that, I think, as much as anything, that led him to be so foolhardy.'

'Well, but the tiger!' said Butty.

'Hold on, man,' says Pat, 'hurry no man's cattle, you might have a donkey of your own some day.'

'Faith an' I'd never buy *you*, Pat, at any rate.'

'Oh, shut up, you fellows!' growled old Mac. 'Let's have the yarn.'

'Well,' continued Joe, 'by this time I was in a pretty mess with sweat and mud and muck of all sorts; but I was now well through the encircling brake, and close up to the mouldering wall of the old temple. Heaps of broken sculptured masonry lay scattered about. The wooden framework of a door in the wall, hung ajar, dropping noiselessly into dust. The shade and shelter were so complete, that not even a breath of wind could penetrate inside, to cause the trembling moth-eaten timber to stir. A ruined low wall, its coping all displaced, and great ugly chasms in its continuity, surrounded a circumscribed courtyard, literally choked with rank vegetation. Bushes started from every crevice and every crack in the mossy flag-stones. A greenish fungus-like growth covered all the masonry, and the smell was sickly, oppressive, and suggestive of rottenness. Everything spoke of ruin and decay and desolation — but desolate and dreary as the spot appeared, it wanted not inhabitants. As I shook from myself the dank leaves and withered twigs, and once more stood erect, a skulking jackal slouched over the crumbling wall, on the other side of the enclosure; an odious, repulsive-looking *Sap go* (a species of iguana) slithered noiselessly through a gap among the ruins; and numerous large-eared bats came flapping swiftly round me, and with an eerie, uncanny swoop and ghost-like swish, disappeared in the gloom.'

'Ugh,' said Butty, with a shudder, 'it must have been a lively sort of a place? Eh, Joe?'

'Lively?' said Joe. 'I tell you I never felt so uncomfortable in my life. I don't think I'm much of a *funk stick* either; but I'll never forget how I felt just then, nor how earnestly I wished I was well out of the infernal hole I had got into.

'A few cracked and crumbling steps, slippery with slimy mould and festooned across with spiders' webs, led up the low frowning archway. I could yet see the little chiselled gutter, with a stone spout, that carried away the milk, poured as a libation to the grim idol — perhaps the blood of human sacrifices, who knows? — formerly offered to the deity whose ruined shrine I was now surveying. Having come so far, I determined I would complete my exploration thoroughly. The temple was one of those ordinary triple-domed affairs you see so constantly in all these ruined Koosee villages. There is first a sort of antechamber, access to which is got through a low-browed door. Inside is a central square chamber, right under the biggest dome, with a black stone, placed in an oval on the floor, and a gutter round it, to let the blood, or oil, or milk, which are used as offerings, run away from this sacrificial stone or altar, and in the further recess, on a sort of pedestal, in an alcove, generally stood the idol.

'I peered into the temple. A few straggling fitful gleams of subdued light struggled through here and there a fissure in the rugged, massive walls; but they only served as a foil to the Cimmerian gloom which enshrouded the whole interior. The roof was high, vaulted, and reverberating. I could hear the swish of the horrid bats as they circled round and round the interior of the dome. The air seemed alive with whisperings. It was only the noise of the bat wings, but it sounded very ghost-like and fearsome. One would occasionally swoop almost in my face, causing me to start back involuntarily. As my eyes became a little more accustomed to the gloom, I could see the sinuous roots of the fig-tree that was silently but surely piercing every crevice, insinuating itself into every crack and cranny, and more certainly and swiftly than the destroying hand of time itself, was hastening onward the inevitable dissolution of the strong, massive, mysterious structure, that had been built perhaps when the Druids chanted their wild songs round the weird circle of Stonehenge.'

'Bravo, Joe! You're getting quite poetical!' This from Butty, who was quietly replenishing his pipe.

'Oh, do shut up!' snorted Mac. 'Let him finish his yarn. He's coming to the pith of the story now.'

'These roots, in some places,' continued Joe, who was evidently warming to his tale as the vivid recollection of the scene came back to him, 'looked like huge coiling snakes as they twisted about the fractured walls and roof. But the gloom and shade were so intense, I could not discern anything clearly inside the temple. At the far end, beyond the indistinctly shaped arches and buttressed projections, I could see something shining like a jewel through the gloom. It sparkled and shone just like a brilliant in a setting of jet; and not doubting but that it might be some tinsel round the mouldering fane in the hidden recess, or perhaps might even be a real jewel, for such a thing was not at all unlikely, I withdrew my head, and shouted out as loud as I could to George, to send a fellow in with matches, that I might thoroughly explore the gloomy interior of the murky ruin.

'I fancied then again, as the echo of my own shout lingered round the run, that a sharp sibilant sound came from the dark interior. It sounded like the 'fuff-fuff' of an angry cat; but imagining it to be only the hiss of a snake, or perhaps some sound made by the bats, I took no further notice of it.

'From George's responsive shout, I made out that he was hastening to join me himself; and I could, after a short pause, hear him forcing his elephant into the bamboos; but after a struggle, he seemed to find the task an impossibility, and retired.

'Again I called to him, and again I thought I heard the puffing, hissing sort of a sound inside.

'By-and-by, I could hear George laboriously making his way through the brake, following the track I had made, and swearing awfully at the prickly, spiky barrier of twigs and creepers that impeded his progress.

'He took such a time that I got impatient. I turned again, and peered into the dim chamber. I was startled. Far back in the cavern-like gloomy arch, glittered two lustrous orbs of a baleful greenish hue. Their intensity seemed to wax and wane, as does the sparkle of a diamond as the light strikes on its facets. I was struck dumb with astonishment for the minute. I could hear George rustling noisily through the last opposing barrier of twigs that separated him from me; my curiosity was now quite aflame. Strange, I felt no compunctious visitings of fear. The presence of my brother seemed to nerve me. The oppressive feeling of solitariness and sense of some impending danger seemed to have left me.

'The glittering light of the two blazing jewels seemed to expand and scintillate, and emit a yet more intense lustre. With a cry to George, 'Come on, George!' I stooped down and entered the close, stifling atmosphere — the darkness seemed to swallow me up. I strode forth; the bats surged round my head, brushing me with their wings in wild affright. I was directly under the dome. My hands were extended in front of me like a blind man groping in an unknown place, when — with a roar that seemed to shake the very walls and reverberated through the vaulted apartment, the jewels blazed like a lurid gleam of fire; a quick convulsive spasm seized my heart as if a giant hand had clutched it and squeezed it like a sponge, and I knew at once that I was face to face, cooped up in this loathsome kennel, caught in a deadly trap, Alone With a Man-Eating Tiger!

'At such a time, one does not take long to think,' Twas then the vista of my life appeared before my mental vision.' Twas then a similar experience as Mac's, when he was like to be crushed by that brute of an elephant, flashed across my brain. Every incident of my life came trooping back to memory, quick and distinct as the lightning flash lights up every leaf and dripping twig and falling rain-drop in a thunderstorm on a summer's night.

'My next act was purely instinctive. I realized, rather than thought or felt, that the brute had been crouching back in the chamber expecting to remain undiscovered. I had an instinctive perception that it was a cur, that it would have rather remained hidden than fought. It was probably gorged after a heavy repast. It must have been a coward, but my bold unceremonious entry must have been construed into an attack. It had no escape, and, rendered fierce by desperation, it was now springing upon me. As I say, all this flashed swift as thought over my intelligence. It took not an instant of time. But in that instant I grasped all the circumstances of the case. I realized my danger, and quick as thought I threw myself flat on my face. The echoing reverberations of that terrible roar yet deafened me. I knew there was a ringing sound in my ears. A huge body swept over me with a terrific rush. In the confused jumble of sound and conflicting emotions, I heard George's shout of dismay and terror. I seemed to dart forward, and for a minute I breathed again. In my mechanical instinct I *had* darted forward. I was now behind the pillar which supported the arch of the inner shrine. The man-eater was rushing round the central chamber, lashing his sides with his tail, and growling and roaring, but evidently in as great a funk as either George or myself.

'George was shouting like the devil outside, not knowing really what to do, and the tigress, for such she proved to be, was such an arrant cur that she was afraid to face him.

'Here, however, was your humble servant in as pretty a mess as you can well imagine.'

'Sweet Father! I think so,' said Mac.

'By Jove,' was all I could think of saying, while we all hung breathless on Joe's every sentence.

'Well, boys, to make a long story short,' said Joe, 'I got off safe and sound, and we killed the tiger between us.'

'How was that?' we all queried.

'This is what I did,' continued our captain. 'As you remember, I had my pistol. I was in a dreadful funk as you may imagine, but desperation gave me a certain nerve; and I knew that a movement or a whisper would probably bring down the fierce brute on me; and cooped up as I was in a mere den, what chance could I have against a real live tiger? By stretching out my hand, I could at any moment have touched the brute. She seemed to have forgot my existence quite, and after a few fierce boundings round the central chamber, she was now lying crouched down, peering eagerly out at the portal where George was yelling like a fiend to the *mahouts* and *peons* to come to him. Her head was between me and what little light there was. Slowly I raised the pistol. At the click of the hammer, faint as it was, she gave an ominous growl and turned her head.

'Now or never was the time.

'A flash that lighted up the gloom!!

'Again!!

'Yet again!!

'The arched temple once more resounded with reverberating echoes; but no roar this time from the tigress.

'She was stone dead.

'The first bullet had gone clean into the brain.

'And now, boys,' said Joe, as he reached out his hand for the soda water and brandy bottle, 'that's my yarn, and I don't want ever again to meet a *janwar* of that sort, under anything like similar circumstances' — (*janwar* means an animal).

Of course then the conversation turned on the feelings of both Joe and George during the quick but exciting succession of incidents. Various comments were made. We congratulated Joe on his good aim and lucky escape; and George told us of how they had taken home the tigress, having had to literally cut a passage out into the open, to let them remove the body.

The tigress killed by Joe under such memorable circumstances was an old mangy brute, almost toothless, lank, lean, and almost without a shred of hair. She measured eight feet four inches, and must have been a cowardly, timorous brute. Still it was a most foolhardy thing of any one to venture on foot into a thick jungle of the description above stated, when there were signs of tiger about.

Joe told me afterwards that he must have been several times quite close to the tigress as forced his way through the jungle. At any moment she could have killed him with one blow of her powerful paw, and in his after career, during his residence in the Koosee jungles, during which time he witnessed the death of over three hundred tigers, scores of them falling to his own gun, Joe was never known to move far from his line of elephants on foot, if tiger's foot-prints were to be seen in the vicinity.

The moon was now declining red and threatening through the rising mists, so finishing each his 'peg,' we called to our 'bearers,' retired to our camp beds, and were soon dreaming the dreams of the ardent Indian sportsman, while silence hovered over the snowy whiteness of our tents.

'Peer Bux', the Terror of Hunsur

A. Mervyn Smith

Many of Mervyn Smith's chapters from his book, Sport and Adventure in the Indian Jungle, *were originally published in the* Statesman *around the turn of the century. He contributed regularly to the Calcutta newspapers which carried a number of shikar stories. Unlike many shikar writers, Mervyn Smith did not only describe his own adventures but also recounted those of others. The Terror of Hunsur is one of his most dramatic stories. It is about 'Peer Bux', a government elephant owned by the Madras Commissariat Department. At certain periods of the year, male elephants go into* must. *They become violent and sometimes attack their own mahouts. A* must *elephant, however, is very different from a rogue. This was always a point of contention amongst British shikaris for they were reluctant to kill a very valuable and generally docile animal which occasionally went into fits of uncontrollable anger. Whether 'Peer Bux' was just in* must *or whether he had become a rogue it was hard to tell but he caused havoc in Hunsur, destroying entire villages. The hero of this story is Gordon Cumming who is finally called in to kill the rampaging elephant.*

Peer Bux was the largest elephant in the Madras Government Commissariat Department. He stood nine feet six inches at the shoulder and more than ten feet at the highest point of the convexity of the backbone. His tusks protruded three-and-a-half feet and were massive and solid, with a slight curve upwards and outwards. His trunk was large and massive, while the skin was soft as velvet and mottled red and white, as high-class elephants' should be. His pillar-like forelegs were as straight as a bee line from shoulder to foot, and showed

79

muscle enough for half-a-dozen elephants. Physically Peer Bux was the beau ideal of elephantine beauty, a brute that should have fetched fifteen thousand rupees in the market and be cheap at that price, for was he not a grander elephant to look at than many a beast that had cost its princely owner double that sum? He was quiet too and docile, and could generally be driven by a child. Yet with all his good qualities, with all his majestic proportions, Peer Bux was tabooed by the natives. No Hindoo would have him for a gift. He was a marked beast; *his tail was bifurcated at the extremity*. This signified, said those natives learned in elephant lore, that he would one day take human life.

When captured in the *kheddahs* in Michael's Valley, Coimbatore district, the European official in charge of the *kheddah* operations imagined the animal would bring a fancy price; but at the public sale of the captured herd no one would give a bid for him, although his tusks alone would have fetched over a thousand rupees for their ivory. The fatal blemish — the divided tail — was soon known to intending purchasers, and there being no bidders he had to be retained for Government use.

The Commissariat Department was justly proud of Peer Bux. He had done good service for six years. Did the heavy guns stick in the mud when the artillery was on its way to Bellary, Peer Bux was sent to assist, and with a push of his massive head he would lift the great cannon, however deep its wheels might be imbedded in the unctuous black cotton soil. Were heavy stores required at Mercara, Peer Bux would mount the steep ghaut road, and think nothing of a ton-and-a-half load on his back. The Forest Department too found him invaluable in drawing heavy logs from the heart of the reserves. His register of conduct was blameless, and beyond occasional fits of temper during the *must* season once a year he was one of the most even-tempered as well as one of the most useful beasts in the Transport establishment.

The Commissariat sergeant at Hunsur, who had known Peer Bux for two years, would smile when allusion was made to his bifurcated tail and the native superstition regarding that malformation. 'Look up his register,' he would say; 'no man-killing there. Why I would rather trust him than any other elephant, male or female, in the lines. Just you see that little beggar, no higher than this' (showing his walking cane), 'the *mahout's* son, take him out to the jungles and bring him back loaded with fodder, and lambaste him too, if he won't obey the little imp. He kill a man! Why he wouldn't kill a fly. The (natives) know nothing; they are a superstitious lot.'

But a little while, and quite another story had to be told of Peer Bux. This pattern animal had gone *must*. Fazul, his usual *mahout* (keeper), was not there to manage him (he had gone with Sanderson to Assam), and the new keeper had struck Peer Bux when he showed temper, and had been torn limb from limb by the irritated brute. Peer Bux had broken his chains; had stampeded the Amrutmahal cattle at Hunsur; had broken into the Government harness and boot factory and done incredible damage; had gone off on the rampage, on the Manantoddy road; had overturned coffee carts and scattered their contents on the road; had killed several cart-men; had looted several villages and torn down the huts. In fact a homicidal mania seemed to have come over him, as he would steal into the *cholum* (sorghum millet) fields and pull down the *machans* (bamboo platforms) on which the cultivator sat watching his corn by night, and tear the poor wretch to pieces or trample him out of all shape, and it was even said that in his blind rage he would eat portions of his human victims. I may here mention that natives firmly believe that elephants will occasionally take to man-eating. It is a common practice when a tiger is killed for the *mahouts* to dip balls of *jaggery* (coarse sugar) in the tiger's blood and feed the elephants that took part in the drive with this mess. They say the taste of the tiger's blood gives the elephant courage to face these fierce brutes. The taste for blood thus acquired sticks to the elephant, and when he goes mad or *must* and takes to killing human beings, some of their blood gets into his mouth and reminds him of the sugar and blood given him at the tiger-hunts, and he occasionally indulges in a mouthful of raw flesh.

Was Peer Bux *must*, or was he really mad? The *mahouts* at Hunsur, who knew him well, said he was only *must*. Europeans frequently speak of *must* elephants as 'mad' elephants, as though the two terms were synonymous. *Must*, I may state, is a periodical functional derangement common to all bull elephants, and corresponds to the rutting season with deer and other animals. It generally occurs in the male once a year (usually in March or April), and lasts about two or three months. During this period a dark-coloured mucous discharge oozes from the temples. If this discharge is carefully washed off twice a day, and the elephant given a certain amount of opium with his food and made to stand up to his middle in water for an hour every day, beyond a little uneasiness and irritability in temper no evil consequences ensue; but should these precautions be neglected, the animal becomes savage and even furious for a time, so that it is never safe to approach him during these periods. When an elephant shows signs of *must* — the dark discharge at the temples is an infallible sign — he should always be securely hobbled and chained. A *must* elephant, even when he breaks loose and does a lot of damage, can if recaptured be broken to discipline and will become as docile as ever, after the *must* period is passed.

It is wholly different with a mad elephant. These brutes should be destroyed at once, as they never recover their senses, the derangement in their case being cerebral and permanent, and not merely functional. This madness is frequently due to sunstroke, as elephants are by nature fitted to live under the deep shade of primeval forests. In the wild state they feed only at night, when they come out into the open. They retire at dawn into the depths of the forests, so that they are never exposed to the full heat of the noon-day sun.

Peer Bux being the property of the Madras Government, permission was asked to destroy him, as he had done much damage to life and property in that portion of the Mysore territory lying between Hunsur and the frontier of Coorg and North Wynaad. The Commissariat Department however regarded him as too valuable an animal to be shot, and advised that some attempt should be made to recapture him with the aid of tame elephants. Several trained elephants were sent up from Coimbatore, some more were obtained from the Mysore State, and several hunts were organized; but all attempts at his recapture entirely failed. The great length of his fore-legs gave Peer Bux an enormous stretch, so that he could easily outpace the fleetest *shikar* elephants; and when he showed fight, none of the tuskers, not even the famous Jung Bahadoor, the fighting elephant of the Maharaja of M could withstand his charge. Meanwhile the terror he inspired stopped nearly all the traffic between Hunsur and Coorg, and Mysore and Manantoddy. He had been at large now for nearly two months, and in that time was known to have killed fourteen persons, wrecked two villages, and done an incredible amount of damage to traffic and crops. In an evil moment for himself he took it into his head to stampede the Collector's camp on the Wynaad frontier. The Collector was away at Manantoddy, but his tents and belongings were destroyed, and one camp follower killed. Permission was now obtained to destroy him by any means, and a Government reward was offered to any one who would kill the brute.

Several parties went out from Bangalore in the hope of bagging him, but never got sight of him. He was here today, and twenty miles off next day. He was never known to attack Europeans. He would lie in wait in some unfrequented part of the road and allow any suspicious-looking object to pass; but when he saw a line of native carts, or a small company of native travellers, he would rush out with a scream and a trumpet and overturn carts and kick them to pieces, and woe betide the unfortunate human being that fell into his clutches! He would smash them to a pulp beneath his huge feet, or tear them limb from limb.

Much of the above information regarding Peer Bux was gleaned at the Dak Bungalow (travellers' rest-house) at Hunsur, where a party of four, including myself, were staying while engaged in a shooting trip along that belt of forest which forms the boundary between Mysore and British territory to the south-west. Our shoot thus far had been very unsuccessful. Beyond a few spotted deer and some game birds we had bagged nothing. The Government notification of a reward for the destruction of the rogue -elephant stared us in the face at every turn we took in the long, cool verandah of the bungalow. We had not come out prepared for elephant-shooting, yet there was a sufficiency of heavy metal in our armoury, we thought, to try conclusions with even so formidable an antagonist as Peer Bux, should we meet with him. Disgust at the want of success hitherto of our *shikar* expedition, and the tantalizing effects of the Government notice showing that there was game very much in evidence if we cared to go after it, soon determined our movements. The native *shikaris* were summoned, and after much consultation we shifted camp to Karkankotee, a smaller village in the State forest of that name, and on the high road to Manantoddy. The travellers' bungalow there, a second-class one, was deserted by its usual native attendants, as the rogue-elephant had paid two visits to that place and had pulled down a portion of the out-offices in his attempts to get at the servants. In the village we found only a family of Kurambas left in charge by the *Potail* (village magis-trate) when the inhabitants deserted it. These people, we found, had erected for themselves a *machan* (platform) on the trees, to which they retired at night to be out of the reach of the elephant, should he come that way. From them we learned that the rogue had not been seen for a week, but that it was about his time to come that way, as he had a practice of making a complete circuit of the country lying between the frontier and the Manantoddy-Mysore and Hunsur-

Mercara roads. This was good news, so we set to work at once, getting ammunition ready for this the largest of all game. Nothing less than eight drams of powder and a hardened solid ball would content most of us. K — , poor fellow, had been reading up 'Smooth-bore' or some other authority on Indian game, and pinned his faith to a twelve-bore duck gun, 'for' he argued, 'at twenty paces' — and that was the maximum distance from which to shoot at an elephant —'the smooth-bore will shoot as straight as the rifle and hit quite as hard.'

Our horses and pack-bullocks were picketed within one of the out-offices, and all the native servants took shelter inside the other. Great fires were kindled before the out-offices as a precautionary measure — not that we expected the elephant that night. We were in bed betimes, as we meant to be up at daybreak and have a good hunt all round, under the guidance of the Kurambas, who promised to take us to the rogue's favourite haunts when in that neighbourhood. The Dak bungalow had but two rooms. That in which O — and myself slept had a window overlooking the out-offices. In the adjacent room slept F — and K — . Towards the small hours of the morning I was awakened by a loud discharge of fire-arms from F —'s room, followed by the unmistakable fierce trumpeting of an enraged elephant. There is no mistaking that sound when once heard. Catching up our rifles we rushed into the next room and found F — , gun in hand, peering out through the broken window frame, and K — trying to strike a light. When F — had recovered sufficiently from his excitement, he explained that he had been awakened by something trying to encircle his feet through the thick folds of the rug he had wrapped round them. On looking up he thought he could make out the trunk of an elephant thrust through the opening where a pane of glass had been broken in the window. His loaded gun was in the corner by his side, and, aiming at what he thought would be the direction of the head, he fired both barrels at once. With a loud scream the elephant withdrew its trunk, smashing the whole window at the same time. He had reloaded and was looking out for the elephant, in case it should return to the attack, but could see nothing, as it was too dark. F —'s was a narrow escape, for had the elephant succeeded in getting his trunk around one of his legs nothing could have saved him. With one jerk he would have been pulled through the window and quickly done to death beneath the huge feet of the brute. The thick folds of the blanket alone saved him, and even that would have been pulled aside in a little time if he had not awakened and had the presence of mind to fire at the beast.

No amount of shouting would bring any of the servants from their retreat in the out-office, although we could distinctly hear them talking to each other in low tones; and it was scarcely fair of us to ask them to come out, with the probability of an infuriated rogue elephant being about. However, we soon remembered this fact, and helping ourselves to whisky pegs, as the excitement had made us thirsty, we determined to sit out the darkness, as nothing could be done till morning.

At the first break of day, we sallied out to learn the effects of F — 's shots. We could distinctly trace the huge impressions of the elephant's feet to the forest skirting the bungalow, but could find no trace of blood. The Kuramba trackers were soon on the spot, and on matters being explained to them they said the elephant must be badly wounded about the face, otherwise he would have renewed the attack. The shots being fired at such close quarters must have scorched the opening of the wound and prevented the immediate flow of blood. They added that if wounded the elephant would not go far, but would make for the nearest water in search of mud with which to plaster the wound, as mud was a sovereign remedy for all elephant wounds, and all elephants used it. The brute would then lie up in some dense thicket for a day or two, as any exertion would tend to re-open the wound. The Kurambas appeared to be so thoroughly acquainted with the habits of these beasts, that we readily placed ourselves under their guidance, and swallowing a hasty breakfast we set off on the trail, taking with us one *shikari* to interpret and a gun-bearer, named Suliman, to carry a tiffin-basket.

The tracks ran parallel with the road for about a mile, and then crossed it and made south in the direction of the Kabbany river, an affluent of the Cauvery. Distinct traces of blood could now be seen, and presently we came to a spot covered with blood, where the elephant had evidently stood for some time. The country became more and more difficult as we approached the river. Dense clumps of bamboo and wait-a-bit thorns, with here and there a large teak or honne tree, made it difficult to see more than a few yards ahead. The Kuramba guides said that we must now advance more cautiously, as the river was within half-a-mile, and that we might come on the 'rogue' at any moment. Up to this moment, I don't know if any of us appreciated the full extent of the danger we were running. Following up a wounded *must* elephant on foot, in dense cover such as we were in, meant that if we did not drop the brute with the first shot, one or more of us would in all probability pay for our temerity with our lives. We had been on the tramp two hours and we were all of us more or less excited, so taking a sip of cold tea to steady our nerves, we settled on a plan of operations. F — and I, having the heaviest guns, were to lead, the Kuramba trackers being a pace or two in advance of us. O — and K — were to follow about five paces behind, and the *shikari* and Suliman were to bring up the rear at an interval of ten paces. If we came on the elephant, the advance party were to fire first and then move aside. If the brute survived our fire, the second battery would surely account for it. It never entered our minds that anything living could withstand a discharge at close quarters of eight such barrels as we carried. Having settled matters to our satisfaction, off we set on the trail, moving now very cautiously, the guides enjoining the strictest silence. Every bush was carefully examined, every thicket scanned before an advance was made; frequent stops were made, and the drops of blood carefully examined to see if they were clotted or not, as by this the Kurambas could tell how far off the wounded brute was. The excitement was intense. The rustle of a falling leaf would set our hearts pit-a-pat. The nervous strain was too great, and I began to feel quite sick. The trail now entered a cart-track through the forest, so that we could see twenty paces or so ahead. Now we were approaching the river, for we could hear the murmuring of the water some two or three hundred yards ahead. The bamboo clumps grew thicker on either side. The leading Kuramba was just indicating that the trail led off to the right, when a terrific trumpet directly behind us made us start round, and a ghastly sight met our view. The elephant had evidently scented us long before we appeared in view, and had left the cart-track and, making a slight detour to the right, had gone back a little way and concealed itself behind some bamboo clumps near the track. It had quietly allowed us to pass, and then, uttering a shrill scream, charged on the rear. Seizing Suliman in its trunk, it had lifted him aloft prior to dashing him to the ground, when we turned. K — was standing in the path, about ten paces from the elephant, with his gun levelled at the brute. 'Fire, K —, fire!' we shouted, but it was too late. Down came the trunk, and the body of poor Suliman, hurled with terrific force, was dashed on the ground with a sickening thud, which told us he was beyond help. As the trunk was coming down K — fired. In a moment the enraged brute was on him. We heard a second shot, and then saw poor K — and his gun flying

86

through the air from a kick from the animal's fore-foot. There was no time to aim. Indeed, there was nothing to aim at, as all we could see was a great black object coming down on us with incredible speed. Four shots in rapid succession, and the brute swerved to the left and went off screaming and crashing through the bamboos in its wild flight. Rapidly reloading we waited to see if the rogue would come back, but we heard the crashing of the underwood further off and knew it had gone for good. We had now time to look round. The body of K — we found on the top of a bamboo clump a good many yards away. We thought he was dead, as he did not reply to our calls, but on cutting down the bamboos and removing the body we found he had only swooned. A glass of whisky soon brought him round, but he was unable to move, as his spine was injured and several ribs broken. Rigging a hammock, we had him carried into Manantoddy, where he was on the doctor's hands for months before he was able to move, and finally he had to go back to England and, I believe, never thoroughly recovered his health. Suliman's corpse had to be taken into Antarasante, and after an inquest by the native Magistrate it was made over to the poor fellow's co-religionists for burial.

Our tragic adventure with Peer Bux, the rogue elephant, was soon noised abroad and served only to attract a greater number of British sportsmen, bent on trying conclusions with the 'Terror of Hunsur,' as this notorious brute came to be called by the inhabitants of the adjacent districts. A month had elapsed since our ill-fated expedition, and nothing had been heard of the rogue, although its known haunts had been scoured by some of the most noted *shikaris* of South India. We began to think that the wounds it had received in its encounter with us had proved fatal, and even contemplated claiming its tusks should its carcass be found, and presenting them to K — as a memento of his terrible experience with the monster, but it was a case of 'counting your chickens,' for evidence was soon forthcoming that its tusks were not to be had for the asking. The beast had evidently been lying low while its wounds healed, and had retreated for this purpose into some of the dense fastnesses of the Begur jungles. Among others who arrived on the scene at this time to do battle with the Terror were two young officers from Cannanore — one a subaltern in a native regiment, the other a naval officer on a visit to the station. They had come with letters of introduction to Colonel M — in charge of the Amrat Mahal at Hunsur, and that officer had done all in his power to dissuade the youngsters from going after the 'rogue,' as he saw plainly that they were green at *shikar* and did not fully comprehend the risks they would be running, nor had they experience enough to enable them to provide against possible contingencies. Finding however that dissuasion only strengthened their determination to brave all danger, he thought he would do the next best thing by giving them the best mount possible for such a task. Among the recent arrivals at the Commissariat lines was 'Dod Kempa' (the Great Red One), a famous tusker sent down all the way from Secunderabad to do battle with Peer Bux. Dod Kempa was known to be staunch, as he had been frequently used for tiger-shooting in the notorious Nirmul jungles and had unflinchingly stood the charge of a wounded tiger. His *mahout* declared that the Terror of Hunsur would run at the mere sight of Dod Kempa, for had not his reputation gone forth throughout the length and breadth of India, even among the elephant folk? Kempa was not as tall as Peer Bux, but was more sturdily built, with short, massive tusks. He was mottled all over his body with red spots: hence his name Kempa (red). He was a veritable bull-dog among elephants and was by no means a handsome brute, but he had repeatedly done good service in bringing to order recalcitrant pachyderms, and for this reason had been singled out to try conclusions with the Hunsur rogue. With such a mount Colonel M — thought the young fellows would be safe even should they meet the 'Terror,' so seeing them safely mounted on the pad he bid them not to fail to call on D — , the Forest officer on the Coorg frontier, who would put them up to the best means of finding the game they were after.

They had been gone about four days when one morning the Commissariat sergeant turned up at Colonel M —'s bungalow and with a salute informed him that Dod Kempa was in the lines, and that his *mahout* was drunk and incapable and he could get no information from him. The elephant and *mahout* had turned up some time during the night; the pad had been left behind, and the man could give no information about the two *sahibs* who had gone out with him. Fearing the worst, the Colonel sent for the *mahout*, but before the order could be carried out, a crowd of *mahouts* (elephant drivers) and other natives were seen approaching, shouting '*Pawgalee hogiya! Pawgalee hogiya!* (he has gone mad! he has gone mad!).' Yes, sure enough, there was Dod Kempa's *mahout* inanely grinning and shaking his hands. Now and again he would stop and look behind, and a look of terror would come into his eyes. He would crouch down and put his hands to his ears as if to shut out some dreadful sound. He would remain like this for a minute or two, glance furtively around, and then as if reassured would get up and smile and shake his hands. It was plainly not liquor that made him behave in this manner; the poor fellow had actually become an imbecile through fear. It was hopeless attempting to get any information from such an object, so handing him over to the care of the medical officer, a search party mounted on elephants was at once organized and sent off in the direction of Frazerpett, twenty-four miles distant, where D's —camp was. When they got about half-way they were met by a native forest ranger, who asked them to stop and come back with him to a country cart that followed, in which were the dead bodies of the two unfortunate officers of whom they were in search. On coming up with the cart and examining its contents a most gruesome sight met their eyes. There, rolled up in a native *kumbly* (blanket), was an indistinguishable mass of human flesh, mud, and clothing. Crushed out of all shape, the bodies were inextricably mixed together, puddled into one mass by the great feet of the *must* elephant. None dared touch the shapeless heap, where nought but the boot-covered feet were distinguishable to show that two human beings lay there. A deep gloom fell on all, natives and Europeans alike; none dared speak above a whisper, and in silence the search party turned back, taking with them what was once two gallant young officers, but now an object that made anyone shudder to look at. The forest ranger's story was soon told: he had been an eye-witness of the tragic occurrence. Here it is:-

'The officers arrived two days ago at Periyapatna, a large village half-way to Frazerpett, and while camped there, a native brought in information of a bullock having been killed at his village some four miles off. The *sahibs* determined to sit up in a *machan* over the kill, and go for the tiger when he returned to his meal. They left their camp-followers and baggage at Periyapatna, and accompanied only by himself (the ranger) and the native who brought the information, they rode out on Dod Kempa, took their places on the *machan*, and sent the *mahout* back with the elephant with orders for him to come back at dawn next day to take them back to camp. The tiger did not turn up that night, and the whole party were on their way back to Periyapatna in the early dawn when suddenly Dod Kempa stopped, and striking the ground with the end of his trunk, made that peculiar drumming noise which is the usual signal of alarm with these animals when they scent tiger or other danger. It was still early morning, so that they could barely see any object in the shadow of the forest trees.

The elephant now began to back, curl away his trunk, and sway his head from side to side. The *mahout* said he was about to charge, and that there must be another elephant in the path. We could barely keep our seats on the pad, so violent was the motion caused by the elephant backing and swaying from side to side. The officers had to hold on tight by the ropes, so that they could not use their guns, when there in the distance, only fifty yards off, we saw an enormous elephant coming towards us! There was no doubt that it was the rogue, from its great size. It had not seen us yet, as elephants see very badly; but Dod Kempa had scented him out as the wind was in our favour. The *sahibs* urged the *mahout* to keep his elephant quiet so that they might use their guns, but it was no use, for although he cruelly beat the beast about the head with his iron goad yet it continued to back and sway. The rogue had now got within thirty yards, when it perceived us and stopped. It backed a few paces and with ears thrown forward uttered trumpet after trumpet and then came full charge down on us. No sooner did Dod Kempa hear the trumpeting than he turned round and bolted off into the forest, crashing through the brushwood and under the branches of the large trees, the *must* elephant in hot pursuit. Suddenly an overhanging branch caught in the side of the pad, ripped it clean off the elephant's back, and threw the two officers on the ground. I managed to seize the branch and clambered up out of harm's way. When I recovered a little from my fright, I saw the rogue elephant crushing something up under its fore-feet. Now and again it would stoop and drive its tusks into the mass and begin stamping on it again. This it did for about a quarter-of-an-hour. It then went off in the direction that Dod Kempa had taken. I saw nothing of Dod Kempa after the pad fell off. I waited for two hours, and seeing the mad elephant did not come back, I got down and ran to Periyapatna and told the *sahib's* servants, and we went back with a lot of people, and found that the mass the elephant had been crushing under its feet was the bodies of the two officers! The brute must have caught them when they were thrown to the ground and killed them with a blow of its trunk or a crush of the foot, and it had then mangled the two bodies together. We got a cart and brought the bodies away.'

Simple in all its ghastly details, the tale was enough to make one's blood run cold, but heard as it was, said one present, 'within a few yards of what that bundle of native blankets contained, it steeled one's heart for revenge.' But let us leave this painful narrative and hasten on to the time when the monster met with his deserts at the hand of one of the finest sportsmen that ever lived, and that too in a manner which makes every Britisher feel a pride in his race that can produce such men.

Gordon Cumming was a noted *shikari*, almost as famous in his way as his brother, the celebrated lion-slayer of South Africa, and his equally famous sister, the talented artist and explorer of Maori fastnesses in New Zealand. Standing over six feet in his stockings and of proportionate breadth of shoulder, he was an athlete in every sense of the word. With his heavy double rifle over his shoulder, and with Yalloo, his native tracker and *shikari* at his heels, he would think nothing of a twenty-mile swelter after a wounded bison even in the hottest weather. An unerring shot, he was known to calmly await the furious onset of a tiger till the brute was within a few yards, and then lay it low with a ball crashing through its skull. It is even said that, having tracked a noted man-eater to its lair, he disdained to shoot at the sleeping brute, but roused it with a stone and then shot it as it was making at him open-mouthed. He was known to decline to take part in beats for game or to use an elephant to shoot from, but would always go alone save for his factotum Yalloo, and would follow up the most dangerous game on foot. He was a man of few words and it was with the greatest difficulty he could be got to talk of his adventures. When pressed to relate an incident in which it was known that he had done a deed of the utmost daring, he would dismiss the subject with half-a-dozen words, generally: 'Yes, the beast came at me, and I shot him.' Yalloo was as loquacious as his master was reticent, and it was through his glibness of tongue round the camp fire, that much of Gordon Cumming's *shikar* doings became known. Yalloo believed absolutely in his master and would follow him anywhere. 'He carries two deaths in his hand and can place them where he likes (alluding to his master's accuracy with the rifle); therefore, why should I fear? Has a beast two lives that I should dread him? A single shot is enough, and even a *Rakshasha* (giant demon) would lie low.'

A Deputy Commissioner in the Mysore service, Cumming was posted at Shimoga, in the north-west of the province, when he heard of the doings of Peer Bux at Hunsur, and obtained permission to try and bag him. He soon heard all the *khubber* (news) as to the habits of the brute, and he determined to systematically stalk him down. For this purpose he established three or four small camps at various points in the districts ravaged by the brute, so that he might not be hampered with a camp following him about but could call in at any of the temporary shelters he had put up and get such refreshments he required. He knew it would be a work of days, perhaps weeks, following up the tracks of the rogue, who was here today and twenty miles off tomorrow; but he had confidence in his own staying powers, and he trusted to the chapter of lucky accidents to cut short a toilsome stalk.

Selecting the banks of the Kabbany as the most likely place to fall in with the tracks of Peer Bux, he made Karkankote his resting-place for the time, while a careful examination was made of the ground on the left bank of the river. Tracks were soon found, but these always led to the river, where they were lost, and no further trace of them was found on either bank. He learned from the Kurambas that the elephant was in the habit of entering the river and floating down for a mile or so before it made for the banks. As it travelled during the night and generally laid up in dense thicket during the day, there was some chance of coming up with it, if only the more recent tracks could be followed up uninterruptedly; but with the constant breaks in the scent whenever the animal took to the water he soon saw that tracking would be useless in such country, and that he must shift to where there were no large streams. A couple of weeks had been spent in the arduous work of following up the brute from Karkankote to Frazerpett and back again to the river near Hunsur and then on to Heggadavencotta. Even the tireless Yalloo now became wearied and began to doubt the good fortune of his master. Yet Gordon Cumming was as keen as ever, and would not give up his plan of following like a sleuth-hound on the tracks of the brute. On several occasions they had fallen in with other parties out on the same errand as themselves, but these contented themselves with lying in wait at certain points the brute was known to frequent. These parties had invariably asked Gordon Cumming to join them, as they pronounced his stern chase a wildgoose one and said he was as likely to come up with the Flying Dutchman as he was with the Terror of Hunsur.

It was getting well into the third week of this long chase, when the tracks led through some scrub jungle which would not give cover to anything larger than a spotted deer. They had come on to the ruins of an ancient village, the only signs of which were a small temple fast falling into decay, and an enormous banyan tree (*Ficus religiosa*). It was midday; the heat was intense, and they sat under the shade of the tree for a little rest. Cumming was munching a biscuit, while Yalloo was chewing a little *paan* (betel-leaf), when a savage scream was heard and there, not twenty paces off, was the Terror of Hunsur coming down on them in a terrific charge. From the position in which Cumming was sitting a fatal shot at the elephant was almost impossible, as it carried its head high and only its chest was exposed. A shot there might rake the body without touching lungs or heart, and then the brute would be on him. Without the least sign of haste and with the utmost unconcern Gordon Cumming still seated, flung his *sola topee* (sun hat) at the beast when it was about ten yards from him. The rogue stopped momentarily to examine this strange object, and lowered its head for the purpose. This was exactly what Cumming wanted, and quick as thought a bullet, planted in the centre of the prominence just above the trunk, crashed through its skull, and the Terror of Hunsur dropped like a stone, shot dead. 'Ah, comrade,' said Yalloo, when relating the story, 'I could have kissed the Bahadoor's (my lord's) feet when I saw him put the gun down, and go on eating his biscuit just as if he had only shot a bird of some kind, instead of that devil of an elephant. I was ready to die of fright; yet here was the *sahib* sitting down as if his life had not been in frightful jeopardy just a moment before. Truly, the *sahibs* are great!'

Seeall, the Wolf Boy

A. Mervyn Smith

Maneating wolves are a common image in folklore all over the world. Any number of accounts have been written about packs of wolves carrying off hapless travellers. Similarly, the popular myth of a wolf-child exists not only in India but in Europe as well. The Indian wolf, however, is an unlikely villain in this scenario. Quite a bit smaller than his North American and European cousins, he is far more timid and seldom seen. Nevertheless, the 'Bheria', as wolves are known in India, is considered by villagers to be a dangerous, bloodthirsty beast. A. Mervyn Smith seems to have shared this opinion, as he sets out to shoot a maneating wolf in Gaya district in Bihar. After successfully killing the wolf, he is told about a wolf child who is subsequently captured and brought to his tent. The horrific conclusion drawn in the story is that not only was Seeall a wolf-child but a maneating wolf-child as well. This is somewhat hard to believe but it does make a good story.

An engineer in the Public Works Department, India, who has had much experience of India lately told me that he thought none of the wild beasts of that country were equal to the wolf in savage ferocity, wanton destructiveness and wild daring. He has spent much of his life in the North-West Provinces and Oude, where wolves are very plentiful, and he has often had occasion to remember that there are other animals in India as dangerous as the man-eating tiger and even more destructive to human life.

On one occasion, while engaged on some bridge-work at Sheegottee, near Gya on the Grand Trunk Road, the native watchmen set to guard a brick-field were so frequently carried off by a pair of wolves that at last no one would remain after dark anywhere near the brick-kilns. One incident that my friend related well exemplifies the daring of these brutes. A watchman's hut had been erected near the brick-fields, and two men were appointed as care-takers. One moonlight night they were sleeping in the verandah of the hut, and, as natives of India generally do, they slept with their cloths drawn over their heads. One of the men was awakened by a gurgling noise and a sound of struggling. On looking up he saw that a large wolf had seized his brother-watchman by the throat, and was endeavouring to drag him off, while a second wolf was sitting on its haunches calmly watching the proceedings from outside. He at once got hold of his *lathie* (quarter-staff), and began belabouring the wolf, but it was only after repeated blows that it loosened its hold; and then it only went off a few yards and kept growling and showing its teeth. Fortunately the watchman was a brave fellow, and a man of resource. The fire had not yet gone out, and tearing a wisp of grass from the thatched roof, he lighted it and rushed at the wolves with the flaming firebrand, thus putting them to flight, as there is nothing the wolf dreads so much as flaming fire. He had now time to attend to his companion, who had fainted away. There were several slight wounds in the neck, but the thick cloth the man had drawn over him had prevented the wolf from seizing him by the throat, the spot for which these animals always make, and dragging him away.

Some years ago I was camped near the village of Sat-bowrie (Seven Wells) on the high-road from Nagpore to Jubbulpore. The village had an unenviable notoriety for thieves and was more frequently called Chor-bowrie (Thieves' Wells) than Sat-bowrie. The hill ranges to the north were inhabited by a wild race known as Bheels, the most expert thieves in the world, and a number of these Bheels had settled round Sat-bowrie, and were known to be concerned in the numerous robberies that had recently taken place in that neighbourhood. A special officer — Lieutenant Cumberledge, I think, of the Thuggi Department — had been sent down to investigate, as several persons had disappeared from the village of late and it was thought that the Thugs (professional stranglers) had had something to do with their disappearance, as the bodies were not recovered and these wretches were known to be particularly skilful in hiding away the corpses of their victims.

Cumberledge told me a strange story. His first search was for signs of Thugs, but no strangers were known to be about nor had parties of seemingly respectable Hindoo travellers (the usual disguise of Thugs) gone up or down the road. He then thought that the murderers might be Bheels; but Bheels were also among the missing persons, and a great fear had fallen on their people, as they ascribed the disappearance of their fellows to a malignant spirit. Robbery evidently was not an object, since most of those who had disappeared were poor people with few or no ornaments. The officer then imagined that the cause of all this mischief might be a man-eating tiger; but he soon had to dismiss that idea from his mind, as no tiger pugs had been seen, and the keenest trackers had been unable to find traces of one of these brutes anywhere in the neighbourhood. A man-eating wolf then suggested itself, as it was known that wolves frequently took to man-eating, and then became very daring. The circumstances attending the mysterious disappearances were very like the work of a man-eating wolf, as the victims — if victims they were — always vanished at night; they were taken from the verandah of their huts, and not a bone of the unfortunates was found. The Tiger will usually leave the larger bones of the creatures; not so wolves, as they love bones more than even dogs. But even this reasoning appeared to be at fault, for at first no trace of any creature's foot-marks could be found. Eventually, however, near to some of the houses from which people had disappeared, there was seen the trail of some animal which no one could recognize. It certainly was not the track of any known animal, and the Bheels and local *shikaris* regarded it as 'uncanny', and ascribed it to a wood-demon or *rakshasha*. Four rounded holes, with a brush-like mark before and behind, were all that could be seen, and these disappeared sometimes in places where distinct trail should have been found. Cumberledge was nonplussed, and told me his tale with much chagrin. He had been a fortnight on the spot and was no nearer the solution of the mystery than when he arrived. Indeed, he admitted to me that he was more puzzled now than when he first came, as the ideas he had formed on the subject had had to be abandoned one by one, and he was now further off than ever from scenting a trail. Two persons were missing since his arrival on the spot: one the wife of the village herdsman, taken from inside her hut; the other a youth of seventeen, last seen sleeping before the village shop in the heart of the hamlet. He asked me if I would join him in the endeavour to unearth this strange mystery, and as I expected to be in that neighbourhood for a month I readily consented.

About a week after this a child was taken from a Bheel's hut some distance from the village. The child was said to be sleeping in its mother's arms at the time. She heard a rustle during the night and, getting up, missed the child. Thinking that it had crawled away, she searched round the hut and, not finding it, gave the alarm. She found the bamboo door partly pushed aside, so knew that some animal had entered. Not a trace was to be seen on the hard-beaten clay in front of the hut, only a drop or two of blood showed that the poor infant had been carried away by some brute. We felt sure now that this night's work at least was done by a wolf, as both Cumberledge and I had heard of cases of wolves stealing into houses at night and taking sleeping children from their mother's arms without awakening the parent. We scouted the country for miles round, using several good dogs in the search, without any result. Two days afterwards the lieutenant's servant came to me early in the morning and said his master wished to see me, as the Demon had come to the village in the night and had carried off the *sonar* (goldsmith). He knew it was the Demon, as his marks were plainly to be seen in the roadway. When I got there I found a large crowd collected near the goldsmith's house, but they were carefully kept away from the vicinity of some well-marked signs in the dust before the house. They were similar to the marks seen near other houses from which inmates had been taken — four rounded holes, about fifteen inches apart and placed two and two together. The back holes were much wider than those in front, and from these latter a slight depression extended for about ten inches terminating in a knuckle mark. A similar knuckle mark was seen behind each of the near holes, but further away, and the longitudinal mark was wanting. My attention was drawn to these peculiarities by Cumberledge, whose training as a police officer qualified him for taking note of signs that others would have overlooked . The natives were loud in their expressions of opinion as to the machinations of a forest demon. One old man indeed declared that he had seen the evil thing. It first appeared as an old man, and then changed into a dog, and then vanished. His story, though laughed at by us, was firmly believed by the simple villagers, and after-events proved that there was some truth in it. Careful search showed the trail to lead to some stony ground outside the village, where all further trace of it was lost. Returning from an unsuccessful hunt all over the neighbourhood, we came back to the goldsmith's house, with the faint hope of finding some clue, when suddenly a thought struck me that I had seen a similar trail before, and I accordingly told one of the natives present to go down on all fours, knees and elbows on the ground, and crawl for a bit. His tracks gave a fairly good representation, with certain marked differences, of the mysterious track that had puzzled us. 'Wolf-boy?' I said to Cumberledge. He was sceptical. 'Surely, you don't think a wolf-boy has taken to man-eating? I have heard of such creatures, but I doubt all the stories I have been told of them,' he replied. 'I don't say we have a man-eating wolf-boy; I merely assert that the tracks have been made by such a creature. I have lately seen one at Seoni, and I noticed that he crawled on his knees and elbows. If you ask a native to go down on all fours, he will either go on his hands and feet or hands and knees; never on his elbows. I noticed this as a peculiarity of the wolf-boy I saw.'

On enquiring of the natives whether they had ever heard of or seen a wolf-boy in that neighbourhood, they all had stories to tell of boys being carried away by wolves and brought up by those creatures, but none could personally vouch for having seen one. Numbers of children had been carried off by wolves from their village, but they had been eaten by the beasts. Once, however, the mysterious marks had been cleared up by my explanation, the native *shikaris* appeared to regain all their astuteness. Now that all fear of demons and spirits had vanished, an old Bheel offered to lead us to a ruined temple near to which he had seen similar marks. We bade him lead the way, and we followed. The Bheel took us along some stony ground near to a rivulet about half-a-mile off. Going down the course about a mile-and-a-half we entered a dense jungle of thorn and brushwood among some hillocks, and at length in a thick clump we saw the ruins of a Sivaite temple. This was carefully surrounded, and guns and spear-men placed in position. The Bheel showed us tracks similar to those already noticed, near the margin of a water-hole in the rivulet, and along a path leading thence to the temple. In addition to these were the well-marked paws of a large wolf. The men were instructed on no account to injure the wolf-boy should he be found, but to capture him alive. The circle gradually narrowed round the old temple, and stones were now thrown among the brushwood to start the game, but with-out effect. Soon the stone plinth or platform on which these temples are always built was reached, yet no wolf or wolf-boy was to be seen. There was the little chamber in the temple, where the phallic emblem is displayed; the single entrance to this was almost concealed by ruins and brushwood, and was just the kind of place a wolf would select as a den. The *shikaris* were sure we should find the wolves within this lair. Several stones were thrown in, but nothing moved. Now a lighted firebrand was flung in, yet not a sound. Our Bheel guide at last ventured within, with a firebrand in hand, but the place was empty nor was there any sign of its having been frequented by animals of any kind. We turned away in disgust and were just leaving the precincts of the temple when an exclamation from one of the men caused us to return to the platform; and there, adhering to a stone, was a small splash of blood and a little human hair. The splash was recent and evidently made by a body being drawn over the stone. The search was redoubled, but all in vain; not a cranny or nook that would hide a hare was left unprobed.

Sivaite temples are built in the form of a square, for about eight feet of their height, and within this square is the altar or fane. Above the square a four-sided pyramid, highly ornamented, rises to a greater or less height, according to the size of the temple. Archways about eighteen inches high generally pierce the pyramid from side to side. One wall of the square had slightly fallen down at the top, and here also a splash of blood was observed. The men quickly surrounded the temple, and one or two who had mounted the terrace from which the pyramid starts, now announced that the wolf was within the low arch and that a dead body was there also! We were quickly drawn up on the terrace, and there sure enough was the wolf, crouched behind the dead body and snarling viciously. A well-directed shot from Cumberledge killed him on the spot, and one of the Bheels drew out the dead body of the goldsmith, and that of a large-sized female wolf. Not a trace of a wolf-boy was however to be seen anywhere about. The goldsmith's body was only partly eaten, the stomach being nearly gone. The tooth marks in the neck showed how he must have been seized by the wolf and all cry stifled, while death must have been almost instantaneous. The Bheels pointed to a portion of the arm that was eaten, and said that that had been done by the wolf-boy, as the teeth marks were human. This well might be, for it is well known that when wolf children have been captured and kept in captivity they evince great fondness for raw meat and bones. It was horrible to think of. A careful watch was now set for the wolf-boy.

Two days after the destruction of the man-eating wolf the Bheel guide and a crowd of followers turned up at our camp late in the evening, with an object swung on a pole and borne by two men. It proved to be the wolf-boy, with wrists and ankles firmly bound together and a pole thrust in between — just as one sees a pig carried about by the natives in country places. Marks of severe handling showed themselves all over his body, and bleeding wounds on several of his captors proved that his teeth and long talons had been freely used. We directed his captors to loose his hands and feet, but they declared he would make off at once if they did so. However, a dog-chain round the waist was all we would permit, and his hands and feet were soon free. Instead of taking to flight he cuddled up hands and feet together, just as children do when asleep. His hair was long, hanging down to his shoulders, and matted in places. It was of a blackish hue with ends of a sandy brown. His legs and arms were thin and sinewy and showed many a scar and bruise; the stomach large and protuberant, the shoulders rounded. His teeth were worn to stumps in front, but the canines and molars were well developed. On being given a piece of roast mutton he first smelt it, and then fell to greedily, tearing off pieces with the side of his mouth and swallowing them without mastication. The bone he kept crunching at and gnawing for hours; this explained the worn state of his front teeth. He emitted a strong foxy odour, so that at first even the dogs avoided him, but he appeared to take at once to a large Brinjaree dog of mine, that much resembled a wolf in appearance. When taken into the tent, he showed a great dread of the light, and no persuasion or threats would get him near it. He at once made for a corner, or under the camp stretcher, and coiled himself up. But he was not allowed to stay in the tent as it was found that his hair swarmed with large ticks, and the smell from his body was overpowering. He was therefore given a truss of straw and chained near to the dogs, and a watchman was told off to look after him.

Next morning we were able to examine our strange captive more closely. He was apparently about ten years old. With difficulty we got him to stand upright. He measured four feet one inch in height. His knees, toes, elbows, and the lower part of his palms were hard, and covered with a horny skin, showing that he habitually crawled on knees and elbows. He would occasionally get on to his feet, run a few paces, and then fall on to his palms and hurry along much as one sees a monkey do. When moving he was usually on his elbows and knees. This mode of progression was probably acquired from having to crouch low when entering and leaving the wolf's den. He would not tolerate clothing of any kind nor would he use straw. He preferred to scratch a hole in the sand and cuddle himself up in this. We had his hair close cropped and then took him to the river for a wash, but to

100

this he most strongly objected, and it required all the exertions of two *syces* (grooms) and the *mehter* (sweeper) to force him into the water. We could only get him quiet when Nandair, the Brinjaree dog, was washed beside him. He quite took to the big Brinjaree, but showed a strong aversion to a hairy terrier belonging to Cumberledge.

On being shown the skin of the large she-wolf he became quite excited, smelled at it several times, turned it over, and then uttered the most plaintive howls it has ever been my lot to listen to. They resembled somewhat the first cry of a jackal; hence the servants called him Seeall(jackal). After this he would never go near the skin, but showed evident marks of terror when taken near it. He would sleep all day, but became restless at nights, and would then try to escape to the woods. He would not touch dog-biscuits or rice stewed with meat, but would select all the meat and leave the rice. Raw meat he snatched at greedily. He appeared to be particularly partial to the offal of fowls. When on one occasion the cook threw away the entrails of a chicken in his presence, he instantly seized it and swallowed it before anyone could prevent him. He also showed a strong predilection for carrion. His sense of smell was so acute that he could scent a dead cow or buffalo a long distance off, and at once began tugging at his chain to get to it.

Unlike all the other 'wolf-boys' of whom we have any record, this creature soon showed he had a great deal of intelligence. He could not speak during the time I knew him, but I was afterwards told he had learnt the Gond language from his keeper and could converse fairly well. In a week's time he was far more intelligent than a dog, and many of his tricks showed that he thought and planned. He would sit by when the dogs were fed, and would remove pieces of meat from the dishes of the other dogs and give them to his particular friend, the great Brinjaree. After a few days we had his head close shaved, and turmeric and oil rubbed well into his skin, and he was then washed with hot water. This treatment soon removed the foxy smell, and the present of a raw chop every day if he kept on his loin-cloth soon induced him to take to clothing. He was an object of great curiosity among the natives, who came in from miles round to see him. All his hair and the parings of his nails, which were abnormally long, were bought by the natives from the *mehter* (sweeper) — in whose charge all private dogs in India are placed, and who therefore took over the care of 'Seeall'— and used by them as a remedy for hydrophobia. The women asked permission to worship him, and brought presents of milk and fowls. With the favour of the 'Lord of the Wolves,' as they called him, their flocks would, they said, be safe from the ravages of these fierce beasts. But Seeall disliked these offerings of the women, and his eyes would glare so savagely at the sight of the children that several attendants had to watch him at such times to see that he did no mischief. It required no stretch of imagination to believe that he had often shared in a meal, with his wolf companion, off a freshly-killed child, even if he did not himself help to carry off the little victim. The strange disappearance of his trail in the softer parts of the track, noticed in the account of the man-eating wolf, was accounted for by his rising on his feet in such places, and leaving marks undistinguishable from those of other human beings.

The natives declare that when a she-wolf has lost her whelps, from accident or otherwise, she experiences a soreness at the teats from the accumulation of milk, and she then generally steals a child. The sucking of the child relieves the wolf, and the infant is thenceforth regarded as a member of the family and shares the wolves' den and food. When young whelps have been noticed with a wolf-boy, they have always been of a subsequent litter.

When Lieutenant Cumberledge returned to Bhopal, Seeall went with him, and I learnt that he was afterwards sent to a missionary in the North-West. I have reason to believe that he was the original of Rudyard Kipling's *Mowgli*.

Tiger! Tiger!

Rudyard Kipling

*Mervyn Smith claims that Sceall, the wolf boy, was the inspiration
for Kipling's Mowgli. It would be difficult to substantiate this but
the comparison between the two characters is interesting. Most
people today associate* The Jungle Book *with Walt Disney's car-
toon adaptation and forget the original stories by Kipling which
often had a fierce and tragic edge to them. Kipling was not a gentle
writer despite his humour and sensitivity. In this story, one of the
later adventures of Mowgli, we are told of his fierce determination
to kill the tiger Shere Khan. The way he goes about it shows his
sense of ingenuity and his hunting instincts learned from the wolf
pack. For all his caricature and commentary on the British in
India, Kipling wrote very little about* shikar. The Jungle Book *is
not a collection of hunting stories but it does describe the sights
and sounds of the Indian forest in unforgettable detail.*

> *What of the hunting, hunter bold?*
> *Brother, the watch was long and cold.*
> *What of the quarry ye went to kill?*
> *Brother, he crops in the jungle still.*
> *Where is the power that made your pride?*
> *Brother, it ebbs from my flank and side.*
> *Where is the haste that ye hurry by?*
> *Brother, I go to my lair — to die!*

Now we must go back to the first tale. When Mowgli left the wolf's
cave after the fight with the Pack at the Council Rock, he went down
to the ploughed lands where the villagers lived, but he would not stop
there because it was too near to the Jungle, and he knew that he had

made at least one bad enemy at the Council. So he hurried on, keeping to the rough road that ran down the valley, and followed it at a steady jog-trot for nearly twenty miles, till he came to a country that he did not know. The valley opened out into a great plain dotted over with rocks and cut up by ravines. At one end stood a little village, and at the other the thick Jungle came down in a sweep to the grazing-grounds, and stopped there as though it had been cut off with a hoe. All over the plain, cattle and buffaloes were grazing, and when the little boys in charge of the herds saw Mowgli they shouted and ran away, and the yellow pariah dogs that hang about every Indian village barked. Mowgli walked on, for he was feeling hungry, and when he came to the village gate he saw the big thorn-bush that was drawn up before the gate at twilight, pushed to one side.

'Umph!' he said, for he had come across more than one such barricade in his night rambles after things to eat. 'So men are afraid of the People of the Jungle here also.' He sat down by the gate, and when a man came out he stood up, opened his mouth, and pointed down it to show that he wanted food. The man stared, and ran back up the one street of the village shouting for the priest, who was a big, fat man dressed in white, with a red and yellow mark on his forehead. The priest came to the gate, and with him at least a hundred people, who stared and talked and shouted and pointed at Mowgli.

'They have no manners, these Men Folk,' said Mowgli to himself. 'Only the gray ape would behave as they do.' So he threw back his long hair and frowned at the crowd.

'What is there to be afraid of?' said the priest. 'Look at the marks on his arms and legs. They are the bites of wolves. He is but a wolf-child run away from the Jungle.'

Of course, in playing together, the cubs had often nipped Mowgli harder than they intended, and there were white scars all over his arms and legs. But he would have been the last person in the world to call these bites, for he knew what real biting meant.

'*Arre! Arre!*' said two or three women together. 'To be bitten by wolves, poor child! He is a handsome boy. He has eyes like red fire. By my honour, Messua, he is not unlike thy boy that was taken by the tiger.'

'Let me look,' said a woman with heavy copper rings on her wrists and ankles, and she peered at Mowgli under the palm of her hand. 'Indeed he is not. He is thinner, but he has the very look of my boy.'

The priest was a clever man, and he knew that Messua was wife to the richest villager in the place. So he looked up at the sky for a minute, and said solemnly: 'What the Jungle has taken the Jungle has restored. Take the boy into thy house, my sister, and forget not to honour the priest who sees so far into the lives of men.'

'By the Bull that bought me,' said Mowgli to himself, 'but all this talking is like another looking-over by the Pack! Well, if I am a man, a man I must become.'

The crowd parted as the woman beckoned Mowgli to her hut, where there was a red lacquered bedstead, a great earthen grain-chest with curious raised patterns on it, half-a-dozen copper cooking-pots, an image of a Hindu god in a little alcove, and on the wall a real looking-glass, such as they sell at the country fairs.

She gave him a long drink of milk and some bread, and then she laid her hand on his head and looked into his eyes; for she thought that perhaps he might be her real son come back from the Jungle where the tiger had taken him. So she said: 'Nathoo, O Nathoo!' Mowgli did not show that he knew the name. 'Dost thou not remember the day when I gave thee thy new shoes?' She touched his foot, and it was almost as hard as horn. 'No,' she said, sorrowfully; 'those feet have never worn shoes, but thou are very like my Nathoo, and thou shalt be my son.'

Mowgli was uneasy, because he had never been under a roof before; but as he looked at the thatch, he saw that he could tear it out any time if he wanted to get away, and that the window had no fastenings. 'What is the good of a man,' he said to himself at last, 'if he does not understand man's talk? Now I am as silly and dumb as a man would be with us in the Jungle. I must learn their talk.'

It was not for fun that he had learned while he was with the wolves to imitate the challenge of bucks in the Jungle and the grunt of the little wild pig. So as soon as Messua pronounced a word Mowgli would imitate it almost perfectly, and before dark he had learned the names of many things in the hut.

There was a difficulty at bedtime, because Mowgli would not sleep under anything that looked so like a panther-trap as that hut, and when they shut the door he went through the window. 'Give him his will,' said Messua's husband. 'Remember he can never till now have slept on a bed. If he is indeed sent in the place of our son he will not run away.'

So Mowgli stretched himself in some long, clean grass at the edge of the field, but before he had closed his eyes a soft gray nose poked him under the chin.

'Phew!' said Gray Brother (he was the eldest of Mother Wolf's cubs). 'This is a poor reward for following thee twenty miles. Thou smellest of wood-smoke and cattle — altogether like a man already. Wake, Little Brother; I bring news.'

'Are all well in the Jungle?' said Mowgli, hugging him.

'All except the wolves that were burned with the Red Flower. Now, listen. Shere Khan has gone away to hunt far off till his coat grows again, for he is badly singed. When he returns he swears that he will lay thy bones in the Waingunga.'

'There are two words to that. I also have made a little promise. But news is always good. I am tired tonight, — very tired with new things, Gray Brother, — but bring me the news always.'

'Thou will not forget that thou art a wolf? Men will not make thee forget?' said Gray Brother anxiously.

'Never. I will always remember that I love thee and all in our cave; but also I will always remember that I have been cast out of the Pack.'

'And that thou mayest be cast out of another pack. Men are only men, Little Brother, and their talk is like the talk of frogs in a pond. When I come down here again, I will wait for thee in the bamboos at the edge of the grazing-ground.'

For three months after that night Mowgli hardly ever left the village gate, he was so busy learning the ways and customs of men. First he had to wear a cloth round him, which annoyed him horribly; and then he had to learn about money, which he did not in the least understand, and about ploughing, of which he did not see the use. Then the little children in the village made him very angry. Luckily, the Law of the Jungle had taught him to keep his temper, for in the Jungle life and food depend on keeping your temper; but when they made fun of him because he would not play games or fly kites, or because he mispronounced some word, only the knowledge that it was unsportsmanlike to kill little naked cubs kept him from picking them up and breaking them in two.

He did not know his own strength in the least. In the Jungle he knew he was weak compared with the beasts, but in the village people said that he was as strong as a bull.

And Mowgli had not the faintest idea of the difference that caste makes between man and man. When the potter's donkey slipped in the clay-pit, Mowgli hauled it out by the tail, and helped to stack the pots for their journey to the market at Khanhiwara. That was very shocking, too, for the potter is a low-caste man, and his donkey is worse. When the priest scolded him, Mowgli threatened to put him on the donkey, too, and the priest told Messua's husband that Mowgli had better be set to work as soon as possible; and the village head-man told Mowgli that he would have to go out with the buffaloes next day, and herd them while they grazed. No one was more pleased than Mowgli; and that night, because he had been appointed, as it were, a servant of the village, he went off to a circle that met every evening on a masonry platform under a great fig-tree. It was the village club, and the head-man and the watchman and the barber (who knew all the gossip of the village), and old Buldeo, the village hunter, who owned a Tower musket, met and smoked. The monkeys sat and talked in the upper branches, and there was a hole under the platform where a cobra lived, and he had his little platter of milk every night because he was sacred; and the old men sat around the tree and talked, and pulled at the big *huqas* (the water-pipes), till far into the night. They told wonderful tales of gods and men and ghosts; and Buldeo told even more wonderful ones of the ways of beasts in the Jungle, till the eyes of the children sitting outside the circle bulged out of their heads. Most of the tales were about animals, for the Jungle was always at their door. The deer and the wild pig grubbed up their crops, and now and again the tiger carried off a man at twilight, within sight of the village gates.

Mowgli, who, naturally, knew something about what they were talking of, had to cover his face not to show that he was laughing, while Buldeo, the Tower musket across his knees, climbed on from one wonderful story to another, and Mowgli's shoulders shook.

Buldeo was explaining how the tiger that had carried away Messua's son was a ghost-tiger, and his body was inhabited by the ghost of a wicked old money-lender, who had died some years ago. 'And I know that this is true,' he said, 'because Purun Dass always limped from the blow that he got in a riot when his account-books were burned, and the tiger that I speak of *he* limps, too, for the tracks of his pads are unequal.'

'True, true; that must be the truth,' said the graybeards, nodding together.

'Are all these tales such cobwebs and moon-talk?' said Mowgli. 'That tiger limps because he was born lame, as every one knows. To talk of the soul of a money-lender in a beast that never had the courage of a jackal is child's talk.'

Buldeo was speechless with surprise for a moment, and the head-man stared.

'Oho! It is the jungle brat, is it?' said Buldeo. 'If thou art so wise, better bring his hide to Khanhiwara, for the Government has set a hundred rupees on his life. Better still, do not talk when thy elders speak.'

Mowgli rose to go. 'All the evening I have lain here listening,' he called back over his shoulder, 'and, except once or twice, Buldeo has not said one word of truth concerning the Jungle, which is at his very doors. How, then, shall I believe the tales of ghosts and gods and goblins which he says he has seen? '

'It is full time that boy went to herding,' said the head-man, while Buldeo puffed and snorted at Mowgli's impertinence.

The custom of most Indian villages is for a few boys to take the cattle and buffaloes out to graze in the early morning, and bring them back at night; and the very cattle that would trample a white man to death allow themselves to be banged and bullied and shouted at by children that hardly come up to their noses. So long as the boys keep with the herds they are safe, for not even the tiger will charge a mob of cattle. But if they straggle to pick flowers or hunt lizards, they are sometimes carried off. Mowgli went through the village street in the dawn, sitting on the back of Rama, the great herd bull; and the slaty-blue buffaloes, with their long, backward-sweeping horns and savage eyes, rose out of their byres, one by one, and followed him, and Mowgli made it very clear to the children with him that he was the master. He beat the buffaloes with a long, polished bamboo, and told Kamya, one of the boys, to graze the cattle by themselves, while he went on with the buffaloes, and to be very careful not to stray away from the herd.

An Indian grazing-ground is all rocks and scrub and tussocks and little ravines, among which the herds scatter and disappear. The buffaloes generally keep to the pools and muddy places where they lie wallowing or basking in the warm mud for hours. Mowgli drove them on to the edge of the plain where the Waingunga River came out of the Jungle; then he dropped from Rama's neck, trotted off to a bamboo clump, and found Gray Brother. 'Ah,' said Gray Brother, 'I have waited here very many days. What is the meaning of this cattle-herding work?'

'It is an order,' said Mowgli. 'I am a village herd for a while. What news of Shere Khan?'

'He has come back to this country, and has waited here a long time for thee. Now he has gone off again, for the game is scarce. But he means to kill thee.'

'Very good,' said Mowgli. 'So long as he is away do thou or one of the four brothers sit on that rock, so that I can see thee as I come out of the village. When he comes back wait for me in the ravine by the *dhak* tree in the centre of the plain. We need not walk into Shere Khan's mouth.'

Then Mowgli picked out a shady place, and lay down and slept while the buffaloes grazed round him. Herding in India is one of the laziest things in the world. The cattle move and crunch, and lie down, and move on again, and they do not even low. They only grunt, and the buffaloes very seldom say anything, but get down into the muddy pools one after another, and work their way into the mud till only their noses and staring china-blue eyes show above the surface, and there they lie like logs. The sun makes the rocks dance in the heat, and the herd-children hear one kite (never any more) whistling almost out of sight overhead, and they know that if they died, or a cow died, that kite would sweep down, and the next kite miles away would see him drop and would follow, and the next, and the next, and almost before they were dead there would be a score of hungry kites come out of nowhere. Then they sleep and wake and sleep again, and weave little baskets of dried grass and put grasshoppers in them; or catch two praying-mantises and make them fight; or string a necklace of red and black jungle-nuts; or watch a lizard basking on a rock, or a snake hunting a frog near the wallows. Then they sing long, long songs with odd native quavers at the end of them, and the day seems longer than most people's whole lives, and perhaps they make a mud castle with mud figures of men and horses and buffaloes, and put reeds into the men's hands, and pretend that they are kings and the figures are their armies, or that they are gods to be worshipped. Then evening comes, and the children call, and the buffaloes lumber up out of the sticky mud with noises like gun-shots going off one after the other, and they all string across the gray plain back to the twinkling village lights.

Day after day Mowgli would lead the buffaloes out to their wallows, and day after day he would see Gray Brother's back a mile-and-a-half away across the plain (so he knew that Shere Khan had not come back), and day after day he could lie on the grass listening to the noises round him, and dreaming of old days in the Jungle. If Shere Khan had made a false step with his lame paw up in the jungles by the

Waingunga, Mowgli would have heard him in those long, still mornings.

At last a day came when he did not see Gray Brother at the signal-place, and he laughed and headed the buffaloes for the ravine by the *dhak*-tree, which was all covered with golden-red flowers. There sat Gray Brother, every bristle on his back lifted.

'He has hidden for a month to throw thee off thy guard. He crossed the ranges last night with Tabaqui, hot-foot on thy trail,' said the wolf, panting.

Mowgli frowned. 'I am not afraid of Shere Khan, but Tabaqui is very cunning.'

'Have no fear,' said Gray Brother, licking his lips a little. 'I met Tabaqui in the dawn. Now he is telling all his wisdom to the kites, but he told *me* everything before I broke his back. Shere Khan's plan is to wait for thee at the village gate this evening — for thee and for no one else. He is lying up now in the big dry ravine of the Waingunga.'

'Has he eaten today or does he hunt empty?' said Mowgli, for the answer meant life or death to him.

'He killed at dawn, — a pig, — and he has drunk too. Remember, Shere Khan could never fast, even for the sake of revenge.'

'Oh! Fool, fool! What a cub's cub it is! Eaten and drunk too, and he thinks that I shall wait till he has slept! Now, where does he lie up? If there were but ten of us we might pull him down as he lies. These buffaloes will not charge unless they wind him, and I cannot speak their language. Can we get behind his track so that they may smell it?'

'He swam far down the Waingunga to cut that off,' said Gray Brother.

'Tabaqui told him that, I know. He would never have thought of it alone.' Mowgli stood with his finger in his mouth, thinking. 'The big ravine of the Waingunga. That opens out on the plain not half a mile from here. I can take the herd round through the jungle to the head of the ravine and then sweep down — but he would slink out at the foot. We must block that end. Gray Brother, canst thou cut the herd in two for me?'

'Not I, perhaps — but I have brought a wise helper.' Gray Brother trotted off and dropped into a hole. Then there lifted up a huge gray head that Mowgli knew well, and the hot air was filled with the most desolate cry of all the Jungle — the hunting-howl of a wolf at mid-day.

'Akela! Akela!' said Mowgli, clapping his hands. 'I might have known that thou wouldst not forget me. We have a big work in hand. Cut the herd in two, Akela. Keep the cows and calves together, and the bulls and the plough-buffaloes by themselves.'

The two wolves ran, ladies'-chain fashion, in and out of the herd, which snorted and threw up its head, and separated into two clumps. In one the cow-buffaloes stood, with their calves in the centre, and glared and pawed, ready, if a wolf would only stay still, to charge down and trample the life out of him. In the other the bulls and the young bulls snorted and stamped; but, though they looked more imposing, they were much less dangerous, for they had no calves to protect. No six men could have divided the herd so neatly.

'What orders?' panted Akela. 'They are trying to join again.'

Mowgli slipped on to Rama's back. 'Drive the bulls away to the left, Akela. Gray Brother, when we are gone, hold the cows together, and drive them into the foot of the ravine.'

'How far?' said Gray Brother, panting and snapping.

'Till the sides are higher than Shere Khan can jump,' shouted Mowgli. 'Keep them there till we come down.' The bulls swept off as Akela bayed, and Gray Brother stopped in front of the cows. They charged down on him, and he ran just before them to the foot of the ravine, as Akela drove the bulls far to the left.

'Well done! Another charge and they are fairly started. Careful, now — careful, Akela. A snap too much, and the bulls will charge. *Huyah!*! This is wilder work than driving black-buck. Didst thou think these creatures could move so swiftly?' Mowgli called.

'I have — have hunted these too in my time,' gasped Akela in the dust. 'Shall I turn them into the Jungle?'

'Ay, turn! Swiftly turn them! Rama is mad with rage. Oh, if I could only tell him what I need of him today!'

The bulls were turned to the right this time, and crashed into the standing thicket. The other herd-children, watching with the cattle half-a-mile away, hurried to the village as fast as their legs could carry them, crying that the buffaloes had gone mad and run away.

But Mowgli's plan was simple enough. All he wanted to do was to make a big circle uphill and get at the head of the ravine, and then take the bulls down it and catch Shere Khan between the bulls and the cows; for he knew that after a meal and a full drink Shere Khan would not be in any condition to fight or to clamber up the sides of the ravine. He was soothing the buffaloes now by voice, and Akela had dropped far to the rear, only whimpering once or twice to hurry the rear-guard. It was a long, long circle, for they did not wish to get too near the ravine and give Shêre Khan warning. At last Mowgli rounded up the bewildered herd at the head of the ravine on a grassy patch that sloped steeply down to the ravine itself. From that height you could see across the tops of the trees down to the plain below; but what Mowgli looked at was the sides of the ravine, and he saw with a great deal of satisfaction that they ran nearly straight up and down, while the vines and creepers that hung over them would give no foothold to a tiger who wanted to get out.

'Let them breathe, Akela,' he said, holding up his hand. 'They have not winded him yet. Let them breathe. I must tell Shere Khan who comes. We have him in the trap.'

He put his hands to his mouth and shouted down the ravine, — it was almost like shouting down a tunnel, — and the echoes jumped from rock to rock.

After a long time there came back the drawling, sleepy snarl of a full-fed tiger just wakened.

'Who calls?' said Shere Khan, and a splendid peacock fluttered up out of the ravine screeching.

'I, Mowgli. Cattle thief, it is time to come to the Council Rock! Down — hurry them down, Akela! Down, Rama, down!'

The herd paused for an instant at the edge of the slope, but Akela gave tongue in the full hunting-yell, and they pitched over one after the other, just as steamers shoot rapids, the sand and stones spurting up round them. Once started, there was no chance of stopping, and before they were fairly in the bed of the ravine Rama winded Shere Khan and bellowed.

'Ha! Ha!' said Mowgli, on his back. 'Now thou knowest!' and the torrent of black horns, foaming muzzles, and staring eyes whirled down the ravine like boulders in flood-time; the weaker buffaloes being shouldered out to the sides of the ravine, where they tore through the creepers. They knew what the business was before them — the terrible charge of the buffalo-herd, against which no tiger can hope to stand. Shere Khan heard the thunder of their hoofs picked himself up, and lumbered down the ravine, looking from side to side for some way of escape; but the walls of the ravine were straight, and he had to keep on, heavy with his dinner and his drink, willing to do anything rather than fight. The herd splashed through the pool he had just left, bellowing till the narrow cut rang. Mowgli heard an answering bellow from the foot of the ravine, saw Shere Khan turn (the tiger knew if the worst came to the worst it was better to meet the bulls than the cows with their calves), and then Rama tripped, stumbled, and went on again over something soft, and, with the bulls at his heels, crashed full into the other herd, while the weaker buffaloes were lifted clean off their feet by the shock of the meeting. That charge carried both herds out into the plain, goring and stamping and snorting. Mowgli watched this time, and slipped off Rama's neck, laying about him right and left with his stick.

'Quick, Akela! Break them up. Scatter them, or they will be fighting one another. Drive them away, Akela. *Hai*, Rama! *Hai! Hai! Hai!* my children. Softly now, softly! It is all over.'

Akela and Gray Brother ran to and fro nipping the buffaloes' legs, and though the herd wheeled once to charge up the ravine again, Mowgli managed to turn Rama, and the others followed him to the wallows.

Shere Khan needed no more trampling. He was dead, and the kites were coming for him already.

'Brothers, that was a dog's death,' said Mowgli, feeling for the knife he always carried in a sheath round his neck now that he lived with men. 'But he would never have shown fight. His hide will look well on the Council Rock. We must get to work swiftly.'

A boy trained along men would never have dreamed of skinning a ten-foot tiger alone, but Mowgli knew better than any one else how an animal's skin is fitted on, and how it can be taken off. But it was hard work, and Mowgli slashed and tore and grunted for an hour, while the wolves lolled out their tongues, or came forward and tugged as he ordered them.

Presently a hand fell on his shoulder, and looking up he saw Buldeo with the Tower musket. The children had told the village about the buffalo stampede, and Buldeo went out angrily, only too anxious to correct Mowgli for not taking better care of the herd. The wolves dropped out of sight as soon as they saw the man coming.

'What is this folly?' said Buldeo angrily. 'To think that thou canst skin a tiger! Where did the buffaloes kill him? It is the Lame Tiger, too, and there is a hundred rupees on his head. Well, well, we will overlook thy letting the herd run off, and perhaps I will give thee one of the rupees of the reward when I have taken the skin to Khanhiwara.' He fumbled in his waist-cloth for flint and steel, and stooped down to singe Shere Khan's whiskers. Most native hunters singe a tiger's whiskers to prevent his ghost haunting them.

'Hum!' said Mowgli, half to himself as he ripped back the skin of a fore-paw. 'So thou wilt take the hide to Khanhiwara for the reward, and perhaps give me one rupee? Now it is in my mind that I need the skin for my own use. Heh! old man, take away that fire.'

'What talk is this to the chief hunter of the village? Thy luck and the stupidity of the buffaloes have helped thee to this kill. The tiger has just fed, or he would have gone twenty miles by this time. Thou canst not even skin him properly, little beggar-brat, and forsooth I, Buldeo, must be told not to singe his whiskers. Mowgli, I will not give thee one *anna* of the reward, but only a very big beating. Leave the carcass!'

'By the Bull that bought me,' said Mowgli, who was trying to get at the shoulder, 'must I stay babbling to an old ape all noon? Here, Akela, this man plagues me.'

Buldeo, who was still stooping over Shere Khan's head, found himself sprawling on the grass, with a gray wolf standing over him, while Mowgli went on skinning as though he were alone in all India.

'Ye-es,' he said, between his teeth. 'Thou art altogether right, Buldeo. Thou wilt never give me one *anna* of the reward. There is an old war between this lame tiger and myself — a very old war, and — I have won.'

To do Buldeo justice, if he had been ten years younger he would have taken his chance with Akela had he met the wolf in the woods; but a wolf who obeyed the orders of this boy who had private wars with man-eating tigers was not a common animal. It was sorcery, magic of the worst kind, thought Buldeo, and he wondered whether the amulet round his neck would protect him. He lay as still as still, expecting every minute to see Mowgli turn into a tiger, too.

'Maharaj! Great King,' he said at last, in a husky whisper.

'Yes,' said Mowgli, without turning his head, chuckling a little.

'I am an old man. I did not know that thou wast anything more than a herd-boy. May I rise up and go away, or will thy servant tear me to pieces?'

'Go, and peace go with thee. Only, another time do not meddle with my game. Let him go, Akela.'

Buldeo hobbled away to the village as fast as he could, looking back over his shoulder in case Mowgli should change into something terrible. When he got to the village he told a tale of magic and enchantment and sorcery that made the priest look very grave.

Mowgli went on with his work, but it was nearly twilight before he and the wolves had drawn the great gay skin clear of the body.

'Now we must hide this and take the buffaloes home! Help me to herd them, Akela.'

The herd rounded up in the misty twilight, and when they got near the village Mowgli saw lights, and heard the conches and bells in the temple blowing and banging. Half the village seemed to be waiting for him by the gate. 'That is because I have killed Shere Khan,' he said to himself; but a shower of stones whistled about his ears, and the villagers shouted: 'Sorcerer! Wolf's brat! Jungle-demon! Go away! Get hence quickly, or the priest will turn thee into a wolf again. Shoot, Buldeo, shoot!'

The old Tower musket went off with a bang, and a young buffalo bellowed in pain.

'More sorcery!' shouted the villagers. 'He can turn bullets. Buldeo, that was *thy* buffalo.'

'Now what is this?' said Mowgli, bewildered, as the stones flew thicker.

'They are not unlike the Pack, these brothers of thine,' said Akela, sitting down composedly. 'It is in my head that, if bullets mean anything, they would cast thee out.'

'Wolf! Wolf's cub! Go away!' shouted the priest, waving a sprig of the sacred *tulsi* plant.

'Again? Last time it was because I was a man. This time it is because I am a wolf. Let us go, Akela.'

A woman — it was Messua — ran across to the herd, and cried: 'Oh, my son, my son! They say thou art a sorcerer who can turn himself into a beast at will. I do not believe, but go away or they will kill thee. Buldeo says thou are a wizard, but I know thou hast avenged Nathoo's death.'

'Come back, Messua!' shouted the crowd. 'Come back, or we will stone thee.'

Mowgli laughed a little short ugly laugh, for a stone had hit him in the mouth. 'Run back, Messua. This is one of the foolish tales they tell under the big tree at dusk. I have at least paid for thy son's life. Farewell; and run quickly, for I shall send the herd in more swiftly than their brickbats. I am no wizard, Messua. Farewell!'

'Now, once more, Akela,' he cried. 'Bring the herd in.'

The buffaloes were anxious enough to get to the village. They hardly needed Akela's yell, but charged through the gate like a whirlwind, scattering the crowd right and left.

'Keep count!' shouted Mowgli scornfully. 'It may be that I have stolen one of them. Keep count, for I will do your herding no more. Fare you well, children of men, and thank Messua that I do not come in with my wolves and hunt you up and down your street.'

He turned on his heel and walked away with the Lone Wolf; and as he looked up at the stars he felt happy. 'No more sleeping in traps for me, Akela. Let us get Shere Khan's skin and go away. No; we will not hurt the village, for Messua was kind to me.'

When the moon rose over the plain, making it look all milky, the horrified villagers saw Mowgli, with two wolves at his heels and a bundle on his head, trotting across at the steady wolf's trot that eats up the long miles like fire. Then they banged the temple bells and blew the conches louder than ever; and Messua cried, and Buldeo embroidered the story of his adventures in the Jungle, till he ended by saying that Akela stood up on his hind legs and talked like a man.

The moon was just going down when Mowgli and the two wolves came to the hill of the Council Rock, and they stopped at Mother Wolf's cave.

'They have cast me out from the Man-Pack, Mother.' shouted Mowgli, 'but I come with the hide of Shere Khan to keep my word.' Mother Wolf walked stiffly from the cave with the cubs behind her, and her eyes glowed as she saw the skin.

'I told him on that day, when he crammed his head and shoulders into this cave, hunting for thy life, Little Frog — I told him that the hunter would be the hunted. It is well done.'

'Little Brother, it is well done,' said a deep voice in the thicket. 'We were lonely in the Jungle without thee,' and Bagheera came running to Mowgli's bare feet. They clambered up the Council Rock together, and Mowgli spread the skin out on the flat stone where Akela used to sit, and pegged it down with four slivers of bamboo, and Akela lay down upon it, and called the old call to the Council, 'Look — look well, O Wolves!' exactly as he had called when Mowgli was first brought there.

Ever since Akela had been deposed, the Pack had been without a leader, hunting and fighting at their own pleasure. But they answered the call from habit, and some of them were lame from the traps they had fallen into, and some limped from shot-wounds, and some were mangy from eating bad food, and many were missing; but they came to the Council Rock, all that were left of them, and saw Shere Khan's striped hide on the rock, and the huge claws dangling at the end of the empty, dangling feet. It was then that Mowgli made up a song without any rhymes, a song that came up into his throat all by itself, and he shouted it aloud, leaping up and down on the rattling skin, and beating time with his heels till he had no more breath left, while Gray Brother and Akela howled between the verses.

'Look well, O Wolves. Have I kept my word?' said Mowgli when he had finished; and the wolves bayed, 'Yes,' and one tattered wolf howled:

'Lead us again, O Akela. Lead us again, O Mancub, for we be sick of this lawlessness, and we would be the Free People once more.'

'Nay,' purred Bagheera, 'that may not be. When ye are full-fed, the madness may come upon ye again. Not for nothing are ye called the Free People. Ye fought for freedom, and it is yours. Eat it, O Wolves.'

'Man-Pack and Wolf-Pack have cast me out,' said Mowgli. 'Now I will hunt alone in the Jungle.'

'And we will hunt with thee,' said the four cubs.

So Mowgli went away and hunted with the four cubs in the Jungle from that day on. But he was not always alone, because years afterwards he became a man and married.

But that is a story for grown-ups.

A Small Shoot in the Lower Himalayas

A.G. Shuttleworth
(Silver Hackle)

Not all shikars *involved maneating tigers or rogue elephants. In most cases the quiet life under canvas, the hours of wandering through the forest and occasional shooting for the pot was enough reward for the average* shikari. *'Silver Hackle' was a well known writer of* shikar *stories. He was the author of* Indian Jungle Lore and the Rifle *and* Maneaters and Other Denizens of the Indian Jungle *from which this story is taken. His description of several weeks shooting in the hill districts around Mussoorie and Tehri in Uttar Pradesh is quite different from the plains'* shikars. *The terrain and forest are different and also the techniques of shooting. He hunts for bear and pheasant as well as the Serow, an unusual and rare goat-antelope which is found in the foothills of the Himalayas.*

It was from a comfortable hotel in the hill station of Mussoori in the United Provinces of India, that I began my preparations for a shoot and walking tour in the State of Tehri.

After a deal of trouble I managed to get my scanty allowance of baggage into thirty coolie loads, averaging only sixty pounds each, a few unwieldy loads being cut down to only one-third of that weight. I procured the services of a hillman by name of Roop Singh as *shikari* and general headman. He was quite a respectable and intelligent *pahari* (hillman), and carried a sheaf of certificates from his former employers, and was selected by me out of a crowd of other applicants, amongst whom he was the least exacting in demands for blankets, putties, and new coats. On the whole I was quite satisfied with the

118

service he gave me, finding him willing and hard working, and with eyesight rivalling that of a hawk. Often, later on, I found myself admiring his wonderful energy and cleverness in negotiating the precipitous hill-sides over which most of our game had to be sought.

It was fully a week before things were shipshape, and I started my coolie-borne luggage off one bright morning in May and followed up myself in the afternoon with Roop Singh. My small tent, only 8'x 8,' was ready pitched for me on a small flat just twelve miles out of the station; and my old and faithful butler Nur Khan had quite a palatable dinner ready for me by eight o'clock.

After dinner I tumbled into bed, which meant one of those narrow canvas contrivances called X pattern camp cots and which I had some trouble in settling on the uneven sloping ground, and, eventually succeeding after many efforts to get my feet on a lower level than my head, fell fast asleep, in spite of the noise and laughter amongst the coolies camped close by. The next day's march was only eight miles, but most of it was uphill along narrow paths, in many places positively dangerous for men with loads, and must have taken us at least fifteen hundred feet higher than the last camp. The scenery, to which my pen cannot do justice, was, I will content myself with describing by the single word, grand. The vast towering mountains all around were clothed chiefly with small moss and lichen-covered oak and occasional large clumps of beautiful pines.

The camp was pitched on the side of a steep slope and was comfortable enough, with a pretty view of a small village and its terraced cultivation, half-a-mile below us. I decided to stop here a few days as Roop Singh promised me some good gooral and barking deer shooting amongst the crags above camp, and possibly a chance at a black bear or two in the wooded valleys below us.

That evening I got some very pretty shooting close around camp at pheasants, of both the kalij and cheer varieties. I heard chikor calling on some bare slopes across the valley but decided to leave them alone for another morning. After my early morning cup of tea, I started with Roop Singh and a couple of coolies for some very precipitous slopes he had pointed out the evening before as a sure find for gooral. We came into some heavy mist near the top, and decided to sit down and let it clear off before proceeding any further. We were on good gooral ground by now but it was fully an hour before the mist lifted, and details on the hill-side more easily distinguished. I was now able with the help of a good pair of glasses to make out a small lot of gooral, about half-a-dozen in number, sitting and standing about amongst some large rocks; and though it was a long way round to get at them, we managed the tiring stalk very well and reached a spot we had marked above them, without being seen or alarming the animals. They were only two hundred yards below me when I picked out and fired at the biggest of the group. This animal was hit fair and went rolling down the hill while the remainder, not knowing where the shot came from, ran and came to a halt only a few yards further on, producing the strange sharp sneeze, peculiar to this animal when alarmed, and I easily knocked over another before they bounded down the side of the hill.

Leaving the two coolies to carry the game to camp, Roop Singh and I made for a thickly wooded valley a little further on. Here I picked up a very good specimen of the ribbed-faced or barking deer. He gave me an easy shot, as with his mate he grazed about among some thick bushes. He seemed to be identically the same animal as that found in the Central Provinces and Southern India. Having tied a white handkerchief to a bush to mark the spot where we left him lying, we turned our steps towards camp, on reaching which two fresh coolies were sent off to bring him in. That evening I gave up to shooting a few of the beautiful Koklass pheasants which were pretty plentiful on a particular slope not far from camp.

At dusk a couple of men of the village, half-a-mile below us, came to report that they had seen a bear in a ravine about a mile away from their village that very evening; so the chikor shooting which I had promised myself for the next morning, was again put off for another day. I sent Roop Singh back with the men to the village to prepare the villagers for a beat on the morrow, and that night tumbled into bed after a good dinner in which roast and stewed pheasants were the chief items in the menu.

Next day, on going to the village, I managed to collect about forty men, and with them started off to beat the ravine in which the bear had been seen the previous evening. Contrary to the usual custom prevailing in Central and Southern India, when beating for sloth bear, the beat in the Himalayas is always down a hill-side or ravine and never upwards or across, as the *pahari* beater always prefers to be above and never below Ursus Thibetanus. This bear invariably makes for the valleys which are generally more densely wooded than the hill-sides. We sent the beaters to the top of the hill with orders to beat down both sides of the ravine, whilst I took up a position right down at the bottom. The beat commenced and found Ursus at home. He was evidently very frightened at the noise made by the beaters and at the rocks which they rolled down from above, and it was astonishing with what rapidity he travelled down towards where I was standing. He covered the ground at a great pace, and was rushing past me at a distance of only ten yards before I got anything like a decent chance of firing. My bullet seemed only to thrust him along faster; anyhow it was only for a few yards, as he suddenly collapsed and was stone dead when I got to him. Standing over him, watching the beat coming on, I reloaded the Paradox I was using, with shot, and was in time to bowl over a couple of lovely Moonal pheasants which came soaring past overhead, giving out the peculiar whistle these birds make when flushed. The bear turned out to be a very fine specimen of Ursus Himalayensis with a beautiful soft coat of fur. Very different to the long coarse hair that clothes Ursus Labiatus.

Next day the chikor were again left alone, for at the request of the villagers, who after the previous day's successful beat had developed a great keenness for sport, I went across the valley to beat a couple of ravines, that from the thickness of the scrub jungle in them, looked very likely to hold bear. We started with the closest, and a bear was soon on foot, but just as I was on the point of firing at him I caught sight of another though different animal rushing down the side of the ravine. I recognized this at once to be a Serow, a rare animal and one which, up to then, I had never shot. I let the bear go, and as the Serow stopped for a few seconds in his downward rush, I brought him down with a .375 Mannlicher. He got to his feet, however, and disappeared round the spur of the hill, going towards the second ravine, I yet intended to beat. There was nothing else in the one we were beating, so we moved on and commenced operations in the next one.

When half way down the hill the beaters suddenly got extra noisy and excited, and I could distinguish the one word 'Reech' repeated over and over again, and I was quite surprised to see two bears, instead of only the one I had hoped for, coming leisurely down the ravine. I bowled one over with Mannlicher, and quickly exchanging this weapon for my Paradox, got in a lucky shot and bagged the other as it rushed at me with a loud 'wuh-wuh.' The beaters now shouted down to me that my wounded Serow was in the ravine, but that it was still able to elude all their attempts at seizing it. I accordingly climbed up the side of the ravine and gave the poor beast its *coup de grace*, as it was sitting under a bush too crippled to move far.

I was more pleased with my Serow than with the two bears I had bagged, though the latter were really good specimens. The Serow turned out to be an old male with a good pair of horns; but I must confess he smelt horribly; the strongest smelling old buck goat would have been a trifle alongside this, my first Serow. There was a great show of holding of noses and spitting on the ground by the beaters when they collected around him; but for all that, every atom of that poor Serow was greedily eaten that night by the same men.

The whole of the next day I was occupied with the skinning and pegging out of the trophies I had obtained the previous morning. I was determined, however, that on the day following nothing would keep me from the glorious shoot I expected after the chikor, which I heard daily calling to me, as it were, to give them a day. I was never more disappointed in my life; and though I brought home six-and-a-half brace of this beautiful Himalayan partridge, I thought they were not worth the trouble; I have never felt so tired and weary in my life as I did that evening on my return from my chikor shoot. It was a case of toiling up a big steep hill, having the birds flushed a little above you and getting in just the two barrels as they whizzed past on their way to another spur. You saw them alight and followed; this following often meant one mile of downhill and two miles of uphill. When you were in position the same procedure was followed, and you picked up the one or perhaps two birds your two barrels allowed you. Then you were off again to repeat the same old game, which the chikor and the untiring Roop Singh seemed to make harder each time. When I got to the bottom of a steep hill and looked at the spot on the opposite spur marked out by Roop Singh I felt sure my heart had moved from its usual place under my belt. Bison hunting, calling forth as it does every ounce of a man's endurance and stamina, is simply knocked into a cocked hat — it I may be allowed the expression — when compared with the shooting of the beautiful and alluring chikor. I made a vow on my return to camp never again to allow myself a whole day at these beautiful birds, but to confine myself to a simple right and left at any I came across. I am ashamed to confess, however, that this vow was broken. I have since had many a tiring but glorious day amongst them.

I spent the following day in camp quietly, allowing myself a rest, as I found I had staled a good bit after all the hill work I had done lately; and also as there was some packing to be done preparatory to my moving on to the next camp.

The tent was pulled down and a start made about 8 o'clock next morning. There was a good deal of uphill work again during this thirteen mile march, which terminated at a small village nestling at the foot of a very steep and rocky hill. It was nearly dusk before the tent and baggage came up, and the weather was very bleak and depressing with a nasty cutting wind all the afternoon and evening. There was also a little rain that night, quite enough to make things uncomfortable, especially for the coolies, obliged to take shelter wherever they could in the village and adjoining cowsheds.

There was a good deal of heavy mist hanging about, when, accompanied by Roop Singh and a couple of coolies, I started early in the morning to climb the steep hill overhanging our camp. The going was very bad; many nasty precipices had to be got over before we could reach some heights where Roop Singh expected to find Tahr (Capra Jharal). I scanned the surrounding hill-sides through my glasses for a sight of these animals as well as the shifting mists would allow. The glasses revealed nothing but a solitary musk deer standing on some rocks a long way off, but he was of no use to me, as his species are strictly preserved in the Tehri State where I was shooting. After an hour's fruitless search with the glasses for the game we were after, we decided to start on our way back to camp.

I was glad of the rest, and having got back my wind, which the steep climb had knocked out of me, started fully refreshed, on the climb down to camp. It was, however, more treacherous and nasty work than I had thought, and at one particularly bad place, where I was hanging on by my eyelids, so to say, and without my rifle which I had made over to a coolie, on turning a shoulder of a large rock, I came face to face with a shaggy old buck Tahr. He seemed as astonished as myself but the next second bounded down the precipitous hill-side Even now it turns me quite giddy when I picture dreadful places he negotiated with the greatest of ease; how he got a footing on those dreadful rocks, beats me. He was down the hill and up the opposite side in almost a flash, but quick as he was to cover the distance, I had ample time to snatch my .318 Mauser from the coolie carrying it, and have an uncomfortable shot at him, as he stood for a few seconds on the spur of the hill. It was fully four hundred yards, but I made a lucky shot and brought him down stone dead with a bullet in the neck. Success, when least expected, is, as other sportsmen must know, most appreciated. After recovering the game, I was highly satisfied with myself and the world in general, when I started homewards to camp.

I stayed here another two days, and though I tried hard for another Tahr, I never succeeded in spotting another buck, only seeing a small herd of four does, so had to content myself with the solitary old buck I had got. There seemed to be no gooral in the locality, in fact the hills here appeared to be dead, so far as game was concerned.

I picked up a good panther by sitting up over a calf, he had killed, one evening close to the village.

I was not sorry on the whole to leave this camp and start back on my return tramp to Mussoori. I did a double march the last day, leaving my camp and baggage to follow on more leisurely and got back to the station feeling quite satisfied with my little holiday in the Lower Himalayas.

Mrs. Packletide's Tiger

H.H. Munro
(Saki)

Saki was born in 1870 in Burma,but at an early age he was sent to England and raised by two maiden aunts in Devonshire. His writing is full of black humor and barbed satire, much of which is aimed at women like Mrs. Packletide and her arch rival Loona Bimberton. Most of Saki's stories take place in the idyllic English countryside though he often adds unusual and unbelievable animals to the landscape. Hardly anything Saki wrote, except for this story, had an Indian setting. Mrs. Packletide's Tiger *has less to do with* shikar *than it does with the 'idea' of shooting a tiger as perceived by an English spinster. What is particularly interesting about this story, besides its splendid humour, is that it does show that Saki and others of his period were familiar with* shikar *literature. Even though this story is a spoof, his description of the hunt is obviously based on other contemporary descriptions of sitting up in a machan.*

It was Mrs. Packletide's pleasure and intention that she should shoot a tiger. Not that the lust to kill had suddenly descended on her, or that she felt that she would leave India safer and more wholesome than she had found it, with one fraction less of wild beast per million of inhabitants. The compelling motive for her sudden deviation towards the footsteps of Nimrod was the fact that Loona Bimberton had recently been carried eleven miles in an aeroplane by an Algerian aviator, and talked of nothing else; only a personally procured tigers-kin and a heavy harvest of Press photographs could successfully counter that sort of thing. Mrs. Packletide had already arranged in her mind the lunch she would give at her house in Curzon Street, ostensibly in Loona Bimberton's honour, with a tiger-skin rug occupying most of the foreground and all the conversation. She had also already designed in her mind the tiger-claw brooch that she was going to give Loona Bimberton on her next birthday. In a world that is supposed to be chiefly swayed by hunger and by love Mrs. Packletide was an exception; her movements and motives were largely governed by dislike of Loona Bimberton.

Circumstances proved propitious. Mrs. Packletide had offered a thousand rupees for the opportunity of shooting a tiger without overmuch risk or exertion, and it so happened that a neighbouring village could boast of being the favoured rendezvous of an animal of respectable antecedents, which had been driven by the increasing infirmities of age to abandon gamekilling and confine its appetite to the smaller domestic animals. The prospect of earning the thousand rupees had stimulated the sporting and commercial instinct of the villagers; children were posted night and day on the outskirts of the local jungle to head the tiger back in the unlikely event of his attempting to roam away to fresh hunting-grounds, and the cheaper kinds of goats were left about with elaborate carelessness to keep him satisfied with his present quarters. The one great anxiety was lest he should die of old age before the date appointed for the memsahib's shoot. Mothers carrying their babies home through the jungle after the day's work in the fields hushed their singing lest they might curtail the restful sleep of the venerable herd-robber.

The great night duly arrived, moonlit and cloudless. A platform had been constructed in a comfortable and conveniently placed tree, and thereon crouched Mrs. Packletide and her paid companion, Miss Mebbin. A goat, gifted with a particularly persistent bleat, such as even a partially deaf tiger might be reasonably expected to hear on a still night, was tethered at the correct distance. With an accurately sighted rifle and a thumb-nail pack of patience cards the sportswoman awaited the coming of the quarry.

'I suppose we are in some danger?' said Miss Mebbin.

She was not actually nervous about the wild beast, but she had a morbid dread of performing an atom more service than she had been paid for.

'Nonsense,' said Mrs. Packletide; 'it's a very old tiger. It couldn't spring up here even if it wanted to.'

'If it's an old tiger I think you ought to get it cheaper. A thousand rupees is a lot of money.'

Louisa Mebbin adopted a protective elder-sister attitude towards money in general, irrespective of nationality or denomination. Her energetic intervention had saved many a rouble from dissipating itself in tips in some Moscow hotel, and francs and centimes clung to her instinctively under circumstances which would have driven them headlong from less sympathetic hands. Her speculations as to the market depreciation of tiger remnants were cut short by the appearance on the scene of the animal itself. As soon as it caught sight of the tethered goat it lay flat on the earth, seemingly less from a desire to take advantage of all available cover than for the purpose of snatching a short rest before commencing the grand attack.

'I believe it's ill,' said Louisa Mebbin, loudly in Hindustani, for the benefit of the village headman, who was in ambush in a neighbouring tree.

'Hush!' said Mrs. Packletide, and at that moment the tiger commenced ambling towards his victim.

'Now, now!' urged Miss Mebbin with some excitement, 'if he doesn't touch the goat we needn't pay for it.' (The bait was an extra).

The rifle flashed out with a loud report, and the great tawny beast sprang to one side and then rolled over in the stillness of death. In a moment a crowd of excited natives had swarmed on to the scene, and their shouting speedily carried the glad news to the village, where a thumping of tomtoms took up the chorus of triumph. And their triumph and rejoicing found a ready echo in the heart of Mrs. Packletide; already that luncheon-party in Curzon street seemed immeasurably nearer.

It was Louisa Mebbin who drew attention to the fact that the goat was in death-throes from a mortal bullet-wound, while no trace of the rifle's deadly work could be found on the tiger. Evidently the wrong animal had been hit, and the beast of prey had succumbed to heart-failure, caused by the sudden report of the rifle, accelerated by senile decay. Mrs. Packletide was pardonably annoyed at the discovery; but, at any rate, she was the possessor of a dead tiger, and the villagers, anxious for their thousand rupees, gladly connived at the fiction that she had shot the beast. And Miss Mebbin was a paid companion. Therefore did Mrs. Packletide face the cameras with a light heart, and her pictured fame reached from the pages of the *Texas Weekly Snapshot* to the illustrated Monday supplement of the *Novoe Vremya*. As for Loona Bimberton, she refused to look at an illustrated paper for weeks, and her letter of thanks for the gift of a tiger-claw brooch was a model of repressed emotions. The luncheon-party she declined; there are limits beyond which repressed emotions become dangerous.

From Curzon Street the tiger-skin rug travelled down to the Manor House, and was duly inspected and admired by the county, and it seemed a fitting and appropriate thing when Mrs. Packletide went to the County Costume Ball in the character of Diana. She refused to fall in, however, with Clovis' tempting suggestion of a primeval dance party, at which every one should wear the skins of beasts they had recently slain. 'I should be in rather a Baby Bunting condition,' confessed Clovis, 'with a miserable rabbit-skin or two to wrap up in, but then,' he added, with a rather malicious glance at Diana's proportions, 'my figure is quite as good as that Russian dancing boy's.'

'How amused every one would be if they knew what really happened,' said Louisa Mebbin a few days after the ball.

'What do you mean?' asked Mrs. Packletide quickly.

'How you shot the goat and frightened the tiger to death,' said Miss Mebbin, with her disagreeably pleasant laugh.

'No one would believe it,' said Mrs. Packletide, her face changing colour as rapidly as though it were going through a book of patterns before post-time.

'Loona Bimberton would,' said Miss Mebbin. Mrs. Packletide's face settled on an unbecoming shade of greenish white.

'You surely wouldn't give me away?' she asked.

'I've seen a week-end cottage near Dorking that I should rather like to buy,' said Miss Mebbin with seeming irrelevance. 'Six hundred and eighty, freehold. Quite a bargain, only I don't happen to have the money.'

Louisa Mebbin's pretty week-end cottage, christened by her 'Les Fauves,' and gay in summer-time with its garden borders of tiger-lilies, is the wonder and admiration of her friends.

'It is a marvel how Louisa manages to do it,' is the general verdict.

Mrs. Packletide indulges in no more big-game shooting.

'The incidental expenses are so heavy,' she confides to inquiring friends.

Gadarene Bears

Col. A.I.R. Glasfurd

The word 'gadarene,' according to the Oxford Dictionary, is defined as 'Of Gadara in ancient Palestine; involving or engaged in headlong rush or flight.' Colonel Glasfurd obviously uses the word to refer to the final tumultuous confrontation he had with a pair of sloth bears in which he fell down a steep hillside and saved himself by clutching onto a tiny bhiria *tree. But the 'headlong rush' could very easily apply to his style of writing. Throwing syntax and grammar to the wind, he writes as though he were speaking amongst his friends, recounting the incident in a volley of irrepressible anecdotes and descriptions. Colonel Glasfurd wrote* Rifle nd Romance in the Indian Jungle *and* Musings of an Old Shikari. *It is also interesting to note that he was born very close to the place where the bears and he became entangled. As did many of the other writers in this book, he also spent some time in Africa.*

When an old *shikari* is held at pistol's point on demand of an account of the 'greatest thrill' of his *shikar* experience he is likely to do some indecisive fumbling in the pockets of reminiscence.

If ever he had any 'thrills' of the kind desired, what caused them? And which will provide the reader with the better shudder? — actual misadventure; or mere might-or-might-not-have-been?

Mishaps with wild beasts have become rarer during the past fifty or sixty years of increasingly accurate and hard-hitting firearms; and although mistakes, foolhardiness, or sheer misfortune will always exact their toll, the likelihood of getting oneself or assistants into serious trouble has generally lessened. Nowadays, also, there is more risk in the unwary crossing of a street — and much more in meeting

Miss Lipstick or Master Anzora at the cross-roads — than in half a life-time-of the happiest-go-lucky pursuit of dangerous wild animals.

However, there seems to be more 'romance,' greater fun for the looker-on or listener-in in an encounter with fang or claw, horn or tusk, than in merely taking a radiator-cap in the neck or being flung through the windscreen. The viewpoint of chief actor and of bystander also differs, in that whereas the strong physical disturbance of a jungle catastrophe is liable to interfere with the former's 'thrill-perception,' the latter is never so enjoyably entertained as when the principal lad fails to extricate himself from trouble. This easily settles the choice of my own little try at the requisite thrill. And, since the business of the story-teller down the ages is to pander to this reprehensible interest in the affliction of others, I will refrain from Mr. Jabberjee Libelwala's — 'Sir! This is fault of Editor!'

*

Once only, in a 'lifetime of *shikar*,' has a wild beast succeeded in turning the tables of adversity on me. Let the reader decide for himself whether this was due to consummate skill in venery, to an exquisite marksmanship ('Yes, sir! Right through the heart every time, sir!'), to a fund of low cunning, or mere fleetness of foot. 'Once only,' I repeat; and she was a bear, a so-called 'sloth' bear, in the Central Provinces of India.

As soon as I was able after the occurrence — which took place on the first of May thirty-five years ago — a little song and dance, an opportunity not to be missed, was made for the dear-old-long-since-dead-and-gone *Asian*, once the premier sporting weekly of India and indeed of all the East. Into that now very old story, in which the writer figures as Queen of the May, every available drop of descriptive juice would seem to have been expressed, leaving nothing for today but a dusty desiccation of the Indian years. Yet it is possible that age, analytical and dispassionate, may get the picture in a different light, afford an aspect missed by younger eyes — or perhaps no longer obscured by the *mauvaise honte* of having been caught napping by a mere bear.

I have therefore purposely avoided the influence of a re-perusal of my youthful impressions; and, here in my cottage in an old English village, long past midnight, silent save for the occasional hoot of owls from the old church tower, I turn the ancient pages of 'Betul, 1902' to their last curt entry — 'Bear got me!' and try to set the retrospective scene.

*

Nineteen hundred and two was not one of my good years, in a *shikar* sense. Stationed at Ellichpur in Berar, I had turned up my nose at a shoot in the neighbouring Melghat, our 'home' jungles in that part of the Satpuras; and hypnotized by *ulterioris ripae amor*, had fancied the more distant tiger country of the Betul District — once of great fame — and trekked across the Tapti to the valley of the Machna. On the way I visited the headquarters Civil Station of Betul — which happened to be my birthplace — and was most hospitably received by the three *sahibs*, district officials, there at the time. Guided by a letter from my mother, I located the room in the Deputy Commissioner's house where I had been born; and was also visited by some of my father's old servants.

Drawing the Machna jungles a blank, I made a number of marches in the direction of the Pachmarhi Hills, attracted chiefly by a proscribed rogue elephant, actually once a tamed animal that had run amok, killed his *mahout*, escaped into the jungle, and ranged those regions, so far without yielding up the price that had been set on his head. But 1902 was not my year, and I was soon on my way back across the Tawa.

Halting at a small village, Sataldehi, and hearing of bears some five miles to the north, I rode out early next dawn and found my young sepoy orderlies awaiting me near some low hills known as Chitra-Katra. These lie about six miles due east of Dhar, a village 18 miles south of Itarsi railway junction and on the Itarsi-Betul high road. My local native *shikaris*, the brothers Sawat and Bharat, were reported to be marking down a bear on the hill. Well, the bear was there all right. And something quite surprising was about to occur.

Yet, although I believe that the onlookers obtained full value from the interesting entertainment that so soon followed, I can aver that it afforded me far less 'thrill' than any of the fair share of 'might-have-beens' that have fallen to my lot before — or since.

It was 'so sudden,' as the young lady used to say, and the trombone-cum-saxophone accompaniment so rowdy, that there was really no room for 'thrill-appeal'; and, as we know, the moral is to the physical as three to one.

To those who do not know him, the Indian 'sloth'- bear (Melursus) needs a word of introduction. Zoologically different from all other kinds of bear (Ursus), he lives almost entirely on jungle fruits, roots, honey, insects, etc; climbs tall and difficult trees, and seems almost to enjoy heavy falls. He is about six feet long, weighs from fifteen to twenty stone, is covered with long, harsh, black hair, has poor sight and hearing but a very acute sense of smell, and is an uncouth, uncertain, unlovable, but far from slothful creature, liable to fly into hysterical furies on slight provocation.

Sloth-bears have an evil reputation for meaningless attacks on anything that may rile or startle them, females of the species accompanied by cubs being particularly savage, and having an extraordinary habit of carrying one or even both of their young clinging to their shoulders on their forays abroad. Jungle natives seldom bother themselves about tigers; but are terrified of these bears.

The only other wild animal of my acquaintance that has a somewhat similar disposition is the African black rhinoceros, but he is a slow-witted fool when compared with the bawling lunatic of which I write.

A curious fact is that Melursus, if he has time, nearly always attacks the head of a man; and aboriginals have confided in me that this is due to his jealousy of man's upright carriage; that, regarding himself as one of the *Adam-zad* or sons of man (and the skinned corpse of this bear has a singularly human appearance) he bitterly resents the fact that God has made him plantigrade on all-fours.

There is, however, a funny side to this jungle maniac, and his crazy buffoonery, particularly, perhaps, his ludicrous death-song, an ululation laughably resembling an ill-executed Swiss yodel, introduces a ridiculous atmosphere, so that the pursuit of sloth-bears tends to a lack of seriousness, a facetious frame of mind that may lead to carelessness.

But let us cut the cackle and get down to business.

*

Briefly—and brevity lived up to its epigram that morning — I crept along a ledge on the southern face of a blazing hot sandstone cliff and shoved my head into a bear's cave, shouting (as I was told but certainly don't believe)*La-la-lahitu*! or words to that effect. My own recollections is that I arrived fortuitously in front of an unsuspected cave, saw fresh tracks of a bear leading in, and lingered a fraction too long in a hopelessly compromising situation.

Anyhow, the response to my 'darkening the front door' was startlingly prompt.

There was an instant thunderous rumbling in the dark bowels of the hill: a quickly-swelling 'Gurgle-Wurble-Burble!' as I leapt back from the cliff-edge, pushing my followers away and telling them to run for it.

And I had barely turned and flattened against the cliff-wall before a frenzied yelling burst from the cave-mouth fifteen or twenty feet away, and a mass of black hair flew straight at me.

Just time to thrust my rifle-muzzle into it — the shattering blast of cordite right in the middle of the hairiness — a glossy black forehead (with eyes shut) buried in my right thigh, seemingly for quite a long time — than my legs swept back from under me, and my face, chest, fists and wildly-gripping fingers all mixed up with coarse, musky-smelling hair and a horribly strong back.

Then upside down and downside up, a confused thumping rolling with hands scrabbling on stone — a hideous sensation of falling — a sickening bash in the ribs — a desperate wrapping of all my arms and legs round something that swung and swayed abominably — and the clatter of something far below . . .

*

That, not more and no less, undimmed by the lapse of all those years, is the nearest that I can get to the sensations of those few but crowded moments.

The rest is clearer, belonging to less a disturbed condition of mind and body.

*

Caught by a branch.

The sudden silence and peace that fell on that atrocious hurly-burly was the exact counterpart of an interrupted nightmare —blessed relief; and readjustment of values, mental and physical.

It is not the world, but I who am wrong side up, the hot sun burning my bare head and face . . . and it is a branch, a little bending tree, round which I am so tightly wound . . . and that hullabalooing devil has gone!

Though still useful on the 'horizontal bar,' one of my legs won't co-operate, and I can't get straight . . .

Then agitated voices, up above — '*Arre! Bhagwan! bach-gaya, bach-gaya!*' — (O Great God! he's escaped, he's saved!) — followed by a view of large naked toes and the dangling end of a loosened *puggri.* '*Shabash!* Well done!' It's Mallu and Kanhaya, my Jat orderlies. A double twist of *puggri* round hand and wrist, and up she comes. A bump. A scrambling knee-and-elbow struggle on the rounded cliff-verge. Eager, helping hands. And then, a bit 'winded,' the ledge once more, and the cave . . .

The *cave*, by Jingo! Blue Hell! *Any more of the swine in there?* Not likely now, after all that 'hoo-ha!' Here! . . . shot-gun, anyway . . . load up with slugs; and move to healthier spot.

Everybody talking at once. 'Where's the bally bear? Gone? Yes. Big one's gone. Big one! there was only one! Where did he go? He went slowly, slowly. There were two bears! Slowly into jungle at foot of hill. But only one bear came out. Yes, but two bears fell down with the sahib. Yes, yes. I saw! I too! Two bears? Don't talk nonsense. Oh, yes two bears. First one — then the shot — then there were two. Oh damn the bears — where's my waterbottle? Oh, Mallu! — the sahib's water! Here it is. Be pleased to sit in the shade and rest. Go, Sawat! search for the sahib's hat. Yes, two bears and the sahib all rolled together, but the sahib — ?

'*Arre Bap!* Oh, my father! *How much blood has come out of your honour! Look at the blood!*'

'Eh? . . . blood?' . . .

Great Scott! Am covered with blood all down right side, and front . . . breeches hanging in clotted strips . . . that's not all bear's blood . . . thought my leg felt funny . . . then he did get me . . . that head, with eyes shut, on my thigh!

Yes, dammit, he's got me all right . . . nasty hole a hands-breadth above knee . . . let's have breeches off . . . by gum! *more* holes . . . bitten clean through . . . torn about too — that's when we came apart . . . but bleeding nearly stopped now . . . good . . . no pain, and feel perfectly O.K . . . extraordinary!

H'm! What happens now? Back to camp, I suppose. Antiseptics. That perchloride, without too much delay. But better wash out wounds now. Boiled water from my bottle. Wonderful! flows right through leg; but only slight stinging at edges of skin. Bind up with handkerchief and strips of my cotton drawers, finishing off with ever-useful *puggri* cloth.

Munch some chocolate. Have some more water. Light up a large cheroot. Two more jungle men arrive. Mallu stages a little farce 'featuring' Gadarene Bears. His round eyes, ridiculous postures, and slow-mouthing Jat utterance move one to — *agh*! rather painful laughter. But Kanhaya, who has cut me a stout stick, shakes his head. 'No good sitting here!' — and he gives me his arm, pointing to the little tree, but for which, says he, my coconut would infallibly have been cracked.

'Wah!' he continues, 'the *sahib's* luck is very very good; his star potent indeed! Undoubtedly the *sahib* must have deserved this, earned great merit by some outstanding act of piety . . . in another life,' he adds, 'in another incarnation.'

For the moment, I miss his point, and hobbling to the edge, look down in thoughtful silence.

Quite solitary, sole excrescence in all that smooth face of rock, rooted in a cleft, it is barely six feet in length, about as thick as one's forearm, with soft, fluted, cork-like bark, and has a few straggling branchlets with acacia-type leaves. I know it by sight, a dwarfed, useless (useless!!) jungle growth of marvellous elasticity. Bharat says it is called *bhiria*.

'*Bhiria!* Shan't forget that! Can't touch my hat to you, *Bhiria*; as I'm wearing my folded coat instead. But *salam Bhiria! Salam!* Long live *Bhiria! Bhiria bahadur ke ja-a-a-e!*'

A long and bothersome one-legged descent to the foot of stony Chitra-Katra, meeting Sawat and another man with my poor old rifle, and — hullo! — the carcass of a bear cub! Nasty, hairy little replica of its horrid parent. Now I understand. Neither time nor mood for 'autopsies'; but can see that the little brute's head had been shattered by the soft-nosed bullet, which, with that high velocity at the very muzzle, must have flown into fragments, blowing him from his dam's shoulders and failing to arrest her rush at me. The evidence is out. The whole affair clear. An extraordinary mixture, my men argue, of *dhoka* (trickery, deception) and marvellous luck; a combination of evil influences on the one hand and supernatural intervention on the other. For who but the gods alone could have provided that *bhiria*, at that time, and in the exact place, the one and only conceivable means of simultaneously snatching me away from the bear and of safely arresting my certain and fatal fall — for any less yielding tree would have broken my back.

And with their simple faith who will greatly disagree? Not I, assuredly. For only nine months later, when returning with my regiment from the great Delhi Durbar of that year, I revisited the scene of disaster, with a brother officer, a coil of rope, and a camera; and I find it described in my diary as an appalling place, much worse than I had realised at the time, the position of the providential tree showing that when I struck it I was falling perpendicularly.

Should this meet the eye of somebody in a position to follow my description and sketch, and visit Chitra-Katra, it would be extraordinarily interesting to me to know whether my little patron *Bhiria* still grows there,

It was additional good fortune that the bear seized me in about the least vulnerable place, breaking no bone; for it might easily have been knee, groin, or abdomen — or (if the brute had had the time) face and head, according to Melursine practice.

I need not labour the lessons learnt; nor the leaky and almost empty bottle of perchloride solution that taught me to carry a proper medical outfit thereafter. The forty-mile journey to Betul on a native bedstead, with a leg like a balloon, a couple of cracked ribs, and the reaction to serious loss of blood, is not of any interest; and it is about time to draw to a close. I parted with a nice little cut of steak to the doctor, after I got to Betul; where, also, my superstitious retainers stood aghast at my being placed in my very birth-chamber. I also caused my wife a lot of bother. She underwent an arduous hot weather journey by jungle tracks, in order to nurse me; and we still smile when we remember how exceedingly firmly she intimated to me, on her arrival, that I was to consider my horrid *shikar*-ing ways definitely at an end.

Finally, on eventually returning to Chikalda, our little hill-station, it appeared that some of the she-bear's temperament must have been imparted to her victim; for, when the first of my old *shikar* cronies looked in, grinning, he had barely got out *La-la-lahi* — when I rose in livid and staggering wrath, and only his superior agility prevented my getting him good and proper with my crutch.

Shooting an Elephant

George Orwell

The events described in this essay took place in the Burma of the 1930s, when that country was still a part of British India (Burma was separated from India by the 1935 Government of India Act). In many ways, this essay is not a conventional shikar *story for Orwell's purpose was not so much to tell about his killing an elephant, as to present the dilemma of 'the white man' in his eastern empire. It is a remarkable commentary on the political and social situation which existed in Burma at that time. As an individual, Orwell had ambivalent feelings about his role as a police officer in an alien and hostile corner of the world. Forced to shoot an elephant which has gone into* 'must' *he describes his own reluctance to kill the animal and the overpowering force of a Burmese crowd, expecting from him the actions of a British sahib. On its own this essay, written in 1936, is arguably one of the finest pieces of English prose ever written. Read in the context of the other stories in this collection, it provides contrast as well as commentary on the role of the* shikari.

In Moulmein, in Lower Burma, I was hated by large numbers of people — the only time in my life that I have been important enough for this to happen to me. I was sub-divisional police officer of the town, and in an aimless, petty kind of way anti-European feeling was very bitter. No one had the guts to raise a riot, but if a European woman went through the bazaars alone somebody would probably spit betel juice over her dress. As a police officer I was an obvious target and was baited whenever it seemed safe to do so. When a nimble Burman tripped me up on the football field and the referee (another Burman) looked the other way, the crowd yelled with hideous laughter. This happened more than once. In the end the sneering yellow faces of young men that met me everywhere, the insults hooted after me when I was at a safe distance, got badly on my nerves. The young Buddhist priests were the worst of all. There were several thousands of them in the town and none of them seemed to have anything to do except stand on street corners and jeer at Europeans.

All this was perplexing and upsetting. For at that time I had already made up my mind that imperialism was an evil thing and the sooner I chucked up my job and got out of it the better. Theoretically — and secretly, of course — I was all for the Burmese and all against their oppressors, the British. As for the job I was doing, I hated it more bitterly than I can perhaps make clear. In a job like that you see the dirty work of Empire at close quarters. The wretched prisoners huddling in the stinking cages of the lock-ups, the gray, cowed faces of the long-term convicts, the scarred buttocks of the men who had been flogged with bamboos — all these oppressed me with an intolerable sense of guilt. But I could get nothing into perspective. I was young and ill-educated and I had had to think out my problems in the utter silence that is imposed on every Englishman in the East. I did not even know that the British Empire is dying, still less did I know that it is a great deal better than the younger empires that are going to supplant it. All I knew was that I was stuck between my hatred of the empire I served and my rage against the evil-spirited little beasts who tried to make my job impossible. With one part of my mind I thought of the British Raj as an unbreakable tyranny, as something clamped down, in *saecula saeculorum*, upon the will of prostrate peoples; with another part I thought that the greatest joy in the world would be to drive a bayonet into a Buddhist priest's guts. Feelings like these are the normal by-products of imperialism; ask any Anglo-Indian official, if you can catch him off duty.

One day something happened which in a roundabout way was enlightening. It was an incident in itself, but it gave me a better glimpse than I had had before of the real nature of imperialism — the real motives for which despotic governments act. Early one morning the sub-inspector at a police station the other end of the town rang me up on the phone and said that an elephant was ravaging the bazaar. Would I please come and do something about it? I did not know what I could do, but I wanted to see what was happening and I got on to a pony and started out. I took my rifle, an old .44 Winchester and much too small to kill an elephant, but I thought the noise might be useful in *terrorem*. Various Burmans stopped me on the way and told me about the elephant's doings. It was not, of course, a wild elephant, but a tame one which had gone *must*. It had been chained up, as tame elephants always are when their attack of *'must'* is due, but on the previous night it had broken its chain and escaped. Its *mahout*, the only person who could manage it when it was in that state, had set out in pursuit, but had taken the wrong direction and was now twelve hours' journey away, and in the morning the elephant had suddenly reappeared in the town. The Burmese population had no weapons and were quite helpless against it. It had already destroyed some-body's bamboo hut, killed a cow and raided some fruit-stalls and devoured the stock; also it had met the municipal rubbish van, and, when the driver jumped out and took to his heels, had turned the van over and inflicted violences upon it.

The Burmese sub-inspector and some Indian constables were wait-ing for me in the quarter where the elephant had been seen. It was a very poor quarter, a labyrinth of squalid bamboo huts, thatched with palm-leaf, winding all over a steep hillside. I remember that it was a cloudy, stuffy morning at the beginning of the rains. We began ques-tioning the people as to where the elephant had gone, and, as usual, failed to get any definite information. That is invariably the case in the East; a story always sounds clear enough at a distance, but the nearer you get to the scene of events the vaguer it becomes. Some of the people said that the elephant had gone in one direction, some said that he had gone in another, some professed not even to have heard of any elephant. I had almost made up my mind that the whole story was a pack of lies, when we heard yells a little distance away. There was a loud, scandalized cry of 'Go away, child! Go away this instant!' and an old woman with a switch in her hand came round the corner of a hut, violently shooing away a crowd of naked children. Some more women followed, clicking their tongues and exclaiming; evi-dently there was something that the children ought not to have seen. I rounded the hut and saw a man's dead body sprawling in the mud. He was an Indian, a black Dravidian coolie, almost naked, and he could not have been dead many minutes. The people said that the elephant had come suddenly upon him round the corner of the hut, caught him with its trunk, put its foot on his back and ground him into the earth. This was the rainy season and the ground was soft, and his face had scored a trench a foot deep and a couple of yards long. He was lying on his belly with arms crucified and head sharply twisted to one side. His face was coated with mud, the eyes wide open, the teeth bared and grinning with an expression of unendurable agony. (Never tell me, by the way, that the dead look peaceful. Most of the corpses I have seen looked devilish.) The friction of the great beast's foot had stripped the skin from his back as neatly as one skins a rabbit. As soon as I saw the dead man I sent an orderly to a friend's house nearby to borrow an elephant rifle. I had already sent back the pony, not wanting it to go mad with fright and throw me if it smelt the elephant.

The orderly came back in a few minutes with a rifle and five cartridges, and meanwhile some Burmans had arrived and told us that the elephant was in the paddy fields below, only a few hundred yards away. As I started forward practically the whole population of the quarter flocked out of the houses and followed me. They had seen the rifle and were all shouting excitedly that I was going to shoot the elephant. They had not shown much interest in the elephant when he was merely ravaging their homes, but it was different now that he was going to be shot. It was a bit of fun to them, as it would be to an English crowd; besides they wanted the meat. It made me vaguely uneasy. I had no intention of shooting the elephant — I had merely sent for the rifle to defend myself if necessary — and it is always unnerving to have a crowd following you. I marched down the hill, looking and feeling a fool, with the rifle over my shoulder and an ever-growing army of people jostling at my heels. At the bottom, when you got away from the huts, there was a metalled road and beyond that a miry waste of paddy fields a thousand yards across, not yet ploughed but soggy from the first rains and dotted with coarse grass. The elephant was standing eight yards from the road, his left side towards us. He took not the slightest notice of the crowd's approach. He was tearing up bunches of grass, beating them against his knees to clean them and stuffing them into his mouth.

I had halted on the road. As soon as I saw the elephant I knew with perfect certainty that I ought not to shoot him. It is a serious matter to shoot a working elephant — it is comparable to destroying a huge and costly piece of machinery — and obviously one ought not to do it if it can possibly be avoided. And at that distance, peacefully eating, the elephant looked no more dangerous than a cow. I thought then and I think now that his attack of *'must'* was already passing off; in which case he would merely wander harmlessly about until the *mahout* came back and caught him. Moreover, I did not in the least

140

want to shoot him. I decided that I would watch him for a little while to make sure that he did not turn savage again, and then go home.

But at that moment I glanced round at the crowd that had followed me. It was an immense crowd, two thousand at the least and growing every minute. It blocked the road for a long distance on either side. I looked at the sea of yellow faces above the garish clothes — faces all happy and excited over this bit of fun, all certain that the elephant was going to be shot. They were watching me as they would watch a conjurer about to perform a trick. They did not like me, but with the magical rifle in my hands I was momentarily worth watching. And suddenly I realized that I should have to shoot the elephant after all. The people expected it of me and I had got to do it; I could feel their two thousand wills pressing me forward, irresistibly. And it was at this moment, as I stood there with the rifle in my hands, that I first grasped the hollowness, the futility of the white man's dominion in the East. Here was I, the white man with his gun, standing in front of the unarmed native crowd — seemingly the leading actor of the piece; but in reality I was only an absurd puppet pushed to and fro by the will of those yellow faces behind. I perceived in this moment that when the white man turns tyrant it is his own freedom that he destroys. He becomes a sort of hollow, posing dummy, the conventionalized figure of a *sahib*. For it is the condition of his rule that he shall spend his life in trying to impress the 'natives,' and so in every crisis he has got to do what the 'natives' expect of him. He wears a mask, and his face grows to fit it. I had got to shoot the elephant. I had committed myself to doing it when I sent for the rifle. A *sahib* has got to act like a sahib; he has got to appear resolute, to know his own mind and do definite things. To come all that way, rifle in hand, with two thousand people marching at my heels, and then to trail feebly away, having done nothing — no, that was impossible. The crowd would laugh at me. And my whole life, every white man's life in the East, was one long struggle not to be laughed at.

But I did not want to shoot the elephant. I watched him beating his bunch of grass against his knees, with that preoccupied grandmotherly air that elephants have. It seemed to me that it would be murder to shoot him. At that age I was not squeamish about killing animals, but I had never shot an elephant and never wanted to. (Somehow it always seems worse to kill a *large* animal.) Besides, there was the beast's owner to be considered. Alive, the elephant was worth at least a hundred pounds; dead, he would only be worth the value of his tusks, five pounds, possibly. But I had got to act quickly. I turned to some experienced-looking Burmans who had been there when we arrived, and asked them how the elephant had been behaving. They all said the same thing: he took no notice of you if you left him alone, but he might charge if you went too close to him.

It was perfectly clear to me what I ought to do. I ought to walk up to within, say, twenty-five yards of the elephant and test his behaviour. If he charged I could shoot, if he took no notice of me it would be safe to leave him until the *mahout* came back. But also I knew that I was going to do no such thing. I was a poor shot with a rifle and the ground was soft mud into which one would sink at every step. If the elephant charged and I missed him, I should have about as much chance as a toad under a steam-roller. But even then I was not thinking particularly of my own skin, only of the watchful yellow faces behind. For at that moment, with the crowd watching me, I was not afraid in the ordinary sense, as I would have been if I had been alone. A white man mustn't be frightened in front of 'natives'; and so, in general, he isn't frightened. The sole thought in my mind was that if anything went wrong those two thousand Burmans would see me pursued, caught, trampled on and reduced to a grinning corpse like that Indian up the hill. And if that happened it was quite probable that some of them would laugh. That would never do. There was only one alternative. I shoved the cartridges into the magazine and lay down on the road to get a better aim.

The crowd grew very still, and a deep, low, happy sigh, as of people who see the theatre curtain go up at last, breathed from innumerable throats. They were going to have their bit of fun after all. The rifle was a beautiful German thing with cross-hair sights. I did not then know that in shooting an elephant one should shoot to cut an imaginary bar running from ear-hole to ear-hole. I ought, therefore, as the elephant was sideways on, to have aimed straight at his ear-hole; actually I aimed several inches in front of this, thinking the brain would be further forward.

When I pulled the trigger I did not hear the bang or feel the kick — one never does when a shot goes home — but I heard the devilish roar of glee that went up from the crowd.In that instant, in too short a time, one would have thought, even for the bullet to get there, a mysterious, terrible change had come over the elephant. He neither stirred nor fell, but every line of his body had altered. He looked suddenly stricken, shrunken, immensely old, as though the frightful impact of the bullet had paralyzed him without knocking him down. At last, after what seemed a long time — it might have been five seconds, I dare say — he sagged flabbily to his knees. His mouth slobbered. An enormous senility seemed to have settled upon him. One could have imagined him thousands of years old. I fired again into the same spot. At the second shot he did not collapse but climbed with desperate slowness to his feet and stood weakly upright, with legs sagging and head drooping. I fired a third time. That was the shot that did for him. You could see the agony of it jolt his whole body and knock the last remnant of strength from his legs. But in falling he seemed for a moment to rise, for as his hind legs collapsed beneath him he seemed to tower upwards like a huge rock toppling, his trunk reaching skywards like a tree. He trumpeted, for the first and only time. And then down he came, his belly towards me, with a crash that seemed to shake the ground even where I lay.

I got up. The Burmans were already racing past me across the mud. It was obvious that the elephant would never rise again, but he was not dead. He was breathing very rhythmically with long rattling gasps, his great mound of a side painfully rising and falling. His mouth was wide open — I could see far down into caverns of pale pink throat. I waited a long time for him to die, but his breathing did not weaken. Finally I fired my two remaining shots into the spot where I thought his heart must be. The thick blood welled out of him like red velvet, but still he did not die. His body did not even jerk when the shots hit him, the tortured breathing continued without a pause. He was dying, very slowly and in great agony, but in some world remote from me where not even a bullet could damage him further. I felt that I had got to put an end to that dreadful noise. It seemed dreadful to see the great beast lying there, powerless to move and yet powerless to die, and not even to be able to finish him. I sent back for my small rifle and poured shot after shot into his heart and down his throat. They seemed to make no impression. The tortured gasps continued as steadily as the ticking of a clock.

In the end I could not stand it any longer and went away. I heard later that it took him half-an-hour to die. Burmans were bringing dahs and baskets even before I left, and I was told they had stripped his body almost to the bones by the afternoon.

Afterwards, of course, there were endless discussions about the shooting of the elephant. The owner was furious, but he was only an Indian and could do nothing. Besides, legally I had done the right thing, for a mad elephant has to be killed, like a mad dog, if its owner fails to control it. Among the Europeans opinion was divided. The older men said I was right, the younger men said it was a damn shame to shoot an elephant for killing a coolie, because an elephant was worth more than any damn Coringhee coolie. And afterwards I was very glad that the coolie had been killed; it put me legally in the right and it gave me a sufficient pretext for shooting the elephant. I often wondered whether any of the others grasped that I had done it solely to avoid looking a fool.

A Maharaja's Shoot

Olive Smythies

*Olive Smythies lived for many years in India. Much of this time
was spent touring the forests of the terai with her husband, who
was Assistant Conservator of Forests in Kumaon. It is from this
experience that she took the title for her book,* One Thousand
Miles On Elephants. *A Maharaja's Shoot describes a shikar
organized by the Maharaja of Nepal for King George V, probably
one of the largest and most elaborate hunts ever undertaken. Olive
Smythies and her husband were working in Nepal at this time and
accompanied the royal party. The entire Smythies family seems to
have loved the Indian jungle. Olive Smythies' son, William, was
Conservator of Forests in Burma and she lived with him there in the
years following her husband's death.*

From the days of the Mogul Emperors, and earlier still, tiger hunting
has been a favourite sport of the rulers of India, and nowhere more so
than in Nepal, with the unparalleled opportunities that wild jungle
country provides.

Jung Bahadur, that amazing and almost mythical character who
started as a catcher of wild elephants and ended as the Prime Minister
and Supreme Ruler, the Founder of the Rana dynasty which ruled
Nepal for 100 years, was able to indulge in his passion for big game
hunting, and in thirty years is said to have killed 550 tigers! Contemporary paintings of tiger hunting in the Nepal Terai hundred years
ago give a vivid impression of the thrills of big game hunting by
comparatively primitive means and methods in those early days.
Sometimes the tiger was brought to bay by a posse of elephants,

161

occasionally he was attacked at close quarters on foot with sword and spear. Wherever Jung Bahadur camped, enquiries were made from the local villagers regarding recent kills or where tigers had been seen or heard, and on such uncertain information an area was beaten by elephants in the hope that the tiger might be inside. In those days the number of tame elephants in Nepal was enormous, and Jung Bahadur frequently had as many as 700 for his *shikar*. But the uncertain methods of locating tigers did not at first produce very good results. Later Jung Bahadur created a special service of 120 *shikaris*, whose duty it was to find fresh tiger tracks and other signs, to tie up baits (goats at first and later young buffalo calves), and quickly send in news of any kills. It was Jung Bahadur, who first evolved and developed the 'Ring' method, which was gradually elaborated and improved by later Maharajas into the supremely efficient system finally employed.

Before attempting to describe a Maharaja's shoot, it will help the reader to visualize the scene if a description is first given of the method almost invariably used in all big shoots in Nepal, the famous and unique 'Ring.' This method is used only in Nepal, where it has been brought to an art, the highest pitch of perfection, and a most deadly method of killing all big game. There is in fact no other country in the world where the necessary factors for the 'Ring' shoot exists, the enormous stud of *shikar* elephants, the trained experience and skill of their *mahouts* and the *shikaris*, the tremendous stretches of Terai forests, and the wonderful stock of tiger and rhino.

The natural home of tiger is the forest-clad foothills of of the Churia (Siwalik) range of the Himalayas, with the enclosed duns and valleys, and the adjoining forests of the flatter Terai. This great belt of tiger country stretches the whole length of Nepal, a distance of nearly 550 miles on the map, and for more than half the year it is deadly to man owing to the malignant Terai malaria. But from December to March it is a perfect paradise, with a glorious climate, wonderful scenery, and always to the north the incredible panorama of the eternal snows towering into the sky.

In this superb setting occur the big Nepal shoots to which many distinguished guests have been invited including King George V. A wonderful organization is employed to ensure success. For weeks before the shoot commences, rough but serviceable motor roads and temporary bridges are constructed radiating out from the various jungle camps. All the jungle paths and streams and sandy river beds

162

are examined to see where the tigers are, for in such places they leave their footmarks. A day or two before the shoot starts, young buffalo calves are tied up as bait, in scores or even hundreds, on every likely route a tiger may take. (The cow, being venerated, its progeny cannot be used for tiger bait.)

There are seven or eight groups of regularly appointed *shikaris*, each consisting of an officer (*subedar*), ten or twelve subordinates, and two mounted soldiers for taking messages. Every group of *shikaris* has ten to fifteen buffalo calves (*padahs*) for tying up at suitable places. They live in temporary sheds in the jungle, primitive huts of wooden poles, leaves and jungle grasses fastened with strands of creepers, which they quickly erect with their kukris from the abundant material all around. Between them the various groups cover the whole tract of forest for miles around the central camp.

At dawn the *shikaris* go out and examine the *padahs*, tied out the previous evening. If, or when, one has been killed, they carefully examine pugmarks (footprints) to see if it is a big tiger or small, or one or several. They examine the drag and the direction taken. They then quietly proceed on foot and make a large circle of a quarter to a half mile diameter, demarcating the circumference with chipped stems and grass knots as they go, and are very careful to see that the drag has not gone beyond the circle. If it has, they make another one, as they must have the circle enclosing the end of the drag. This is called 'cutting the circle' by the *shikaris*, and the final circle makes the future 'Ring.'

Meanwhile, as soon as it is seen that a *padah* has been killed and dragged, a special messenger mounts his horse, and gallops off to bring the news. Sometimes motor cars are parked at central spots to accelerate the delivery of the message, and sometimes even a telephone line has been prepared and operators engaged to flash news to the camp.

Within a very short time the news has reached the camp from all directions whether and where there are kills, and the day's plan of campaign is discussed and settled. Immediately a great string of 200 or 300 elephants moves off in single file to the first kill, a few with howdahs, the majority with pads. The shooting party follows at leisure in cars as far as possible, and then on pad elephants.

The tiger or tigers have been approximately located by the *shikaris* from the direction of the drag, the nature of the cover for lying up, and the process of cutting the circle as already described. When the elephants arrive, they divide into two parties, which proceed very quietly in single file right and left along the line of the cut circle — and it is astonishing how quietly an elephant or line of elephants can move through the jungle. The rear elephants gradually drop out to take their stations at regular intervals, and finally the two leading elephants meet and the word is passed down both sides that the circuit is completed.

The shooting party mount the howdah elephants and the whole circle now moves inwards, crushing the grass and shrubs, and the men on their backs shouting and whistling to drive the tiger towards the centre. The circumference of the circle of elephants gets smaller, until finally it is less than half-a-mile round, and the elephants get closer and closer until they are almost touching, and the tiger is surrounded by a solid wall of elephants. Then the order — stop the line — is shouted out and the ring is complete.

The stauncher elephants then move into the ring. Glimpses of one or more slinking forms are seen in the grass and undergrowth, when suddenly a tiger breaks cover and charges with a roar, to be met by shots from the rifle or shouts and missiles if he charges the ring. It is the moment of climax of a culminating excitement. Backwards and forwards he dashes striving to find an escape, to a pandemonium of men shouting and elephants trumpeting, grumbling and gurgling, thumping on the ground and, occasionally, when directly charged turning tail and bolting in terror.

It is necessary to emphasize that a tiger is not normally a dangerous animal and does not attack an elephant or a man, but once he feels cornered, he becomes a fighting mass of diabolical fury utterly fearless of man or elephant, whom he attacks in his mad rage without a moment's hesitation. He has been known to leap a height of fifteen or sixteen feet into a tall howdah, and more often than not a tiger will try to break through a ring by charging home on an elephant unless he is killed or crippled first by a well-directed shot.

It must also be realized that the Nepal Terai jungles with a fertile soil and rainfall of hundred inches are either gigantic grass growth, frequently the height of a howdah, or are a dense forest of trees, matted together with great climbers and a thick undergrowth of shrubs and shade-bearing plants in which, if an elephant bolts, it is almost inevitable that howdah and rider and *mahout* and everything on the elephant's back will be swept with a crash to the ground by a thick branch or the loop of a tough climber. In either case it is extremely difficult to see a tiger at all until the area has been well

164

trampled, by which time, naturally, the tiger or tigers are desperate and in a highly dangerous condition. "It is no sport for bad shots, hasty excitable people, or those with no stomach for danger. Even the most blase hunter is likely to experience for a second or two a sudden spasm of fear when he first hears the blood-curdling roar of an infuriated tiger, and sees the great striped body launched in its charge, a thunder-bolt of death and anger in mid-air.It is one of the most terrific sights in the world.' writes Wentworth Day in his book on *shikar*.

Imagine what it must be like when, as frequently happens in the rings in Nepal, not one, but four or five and, once or twice, six tigers have been trapped simultaneously in one ring! The danger and heart-bursting excitement may continue for hours, until a succession of well-placed shots finally brings the thrill and nerve-tension to an end.

This describes briefly a typical tiger shoot in the Nepal forests by the famous 'Ring' method. Personally I never thought that this was a very sporting way of shooting tigers as they did not seem to have much chance of escaping with their lives.

The whole marvellous organization is itself unrivalled; the elaborate arrangements for locating every tiger for miles around — by skilled parties of *shikaris*, the quick receipt of information, the great stud of well-trained elephants with their splendid and plucky Tharu *mahouts*, the methods to prevent the encircled tiger from breaking the ring and escaping, all this, with first-class shooting, make such a deadly combination that few tigers can escape. In fact, if repeated at too frequent intervals in any locality, there would be a considerable risk of tigers becoming exterminated in that locality. In Nepal, however, although the stock of tigers has no doubt been reduced appreciably (at the start their numbers were excessive, and they did much damage to village cattle), extermination was safeguarded by two factors. One was the expanse of broken hill forests, where the ring method cannot be used, which forms a natural sanctuary and breeding ground for tiger. The other was that with tiger country stretching along the foot of the hills for 550 miles, there was such a vast tract to visit that the Maharaja could have shoots with the ring method without frequent visits to any one locality.

A few concrete examples, selected from innumerable cases recorded in the official shooting diary of Maharaja Jodha Shumshere, will illustrate how the 'Ring' works. One year in January, three guests had been invited, the British Minister in Nepal, a distinguished American naturalist, and a film operator. They had indeed a day to remember!

The ring was eight miles from the camp and provided hours of excitement. This locality was characterized by very heavy grass taller than the elephants and undergrowth in which it was almost impossible to see the quarry. A tiger was first put up at which two shots were fired. The noise disturbed *four* more tigers, so there were five tigers in all enclosed (two tigers, two tigresses and a large cub, i.e. two families). It was a nerve-racking business to tackle so many tigers in that tremendous grass in which they could lie unseen within a few feet of the elephants. They were moving about, growling and slinking unseen, without offering a shot to the marksmen. Suddenly pandemonium broke out at one section of the line, elephants trumpeting, fidgeting and curling up their trunks, with the usual accompaniment of shouts and yells, clearly indicating that one or more tigers were trying to escape that way. At last after further beating, a tiger came out where the undergrowth had been trampled, and was killed.

The ring was beaten again, and a tiger leapt on to the rump of one of the beating elephants, and stayed on for several yards before dropping off. The American guest fired and killed it. Again the howdahs and beating elephants went through the heavy grass, and six shots were fired at intervals as one or another tiger showed itself for a moment. The next to fall was a tigress.

By this time the sun had set, but there were still two tigers in the ring, and the howdahs turned once more into the heavy grass. For a change, the next tiger charged the ring. A pad elephant, panic-stricken, whisked round and bolted, throwing off its *mahout* and passenger to the ground. They were however unscathed by the fall, or by the tiger, and were quickly mounted on another elephant. This tiger broke through and escaped.

It was now 6.45 p.m. on a winter night, and the light had completely gone. But still there was another tiger in the ring, a tigress as it happened, and by now a fury incarnate. It was a weird amazing scene, a nocturne of the jungle, where nothing could be seen except the crowns of the scattered trees against the glimmer of stars. Then the hunt took on a different aspect, as resinous torches blazed out all round, and by their light the tigress was at last spotted and shot. Four tigers in one ring, the last killed by torchlight! Was ever *shikar* like this before?

Occasionally, however, the proceedings did not go according to plan, and the sportsmen in the ring found themselves in considerable danger, as happened in the following episode. A tiger and tigress were put up and wounded; both wounded animals retired into thick cover in the middle of the ring. Nothing could be seen of them in the undergrowth, but suddenly, from a range of eight feet, the tiger leapt on to the Maharaja's elephant, Bhimgaj, catching hold high up on the trunk, and started savagely biting and clawing. The other elephants turned tail and commenced to bolt, but Bhimgaj vigorously counter-attacked, and tried to kill the tiger by crushing it on the ground. This meant that the elephant was almost standing on his head, and 'the howdah was tilted downwards almost to the ground. There seemed to be no possibility of the men in the howdah keeping their position. If they fell out, they would inevitably fall into the jaws of death.' (The second wounded tiger was circling around, near its mate.) In this critical situation, deafened by the mad roaring of the tigers and the trumpeting of the elephants, the Maharaja and his A.D.C. by some miracle successfully avoided being hurled out of the howdah. For minutes, which seemed like hours, this life and death struggle between elephant and tiger continued, while any attempt at shooting was out of the question. A superb painting of this dramatic moment by the photographer-artist, who was an eye-witness of it, hung for years in the great Durbar Hall in Kathmandu. Whether it is still there I do not know. Finally, the elephant drew back with its trunk severely mauled, and the tiger was finished off.

Tigers were not the only big game that was hunted in Nepal for the famous Chitawan sanctuary was the home of several hundred rhino, which were very strictly preserved. In this rhino preserve posts were stationed at various points, each post manned by five to seven guards. In all there were over hundred guards in Chitawan, whose main duty was to protect the rhino from poachers, and find out where they fed and wallowed. The fact that the rhino horn has a very high commer-cial value in India — a good horn is worth well over 100 pounds — makes it a valuable prize for the professional poacher, and the species was nearly exterminated in Assam by poachers until adequate steps were taken for its protection. (Rhino horn is supposed to be a power-ful aphrodisiac, hence its fantastic value.) We were told that in years gone by, the penalty for unlawfully killing a rhino was seventy-five *hereditary* years imprisonment!

When hunting rhino, the 'Ring' method frequently fails and for the following reason. Elephants, despite their great bulk and strength, are naturally timid animals, and even small animals like cats or porcu-pines in their vicinity make them nervous and restless. But of all things that elephants fear most, the rhino is *facile princeps*. Most elephants bolt at the mere sight of a rhino and very few are staunch. A rhino in a ring has only to charge the ring to break it in confusion and make his escape, and although rhino have been shot in rings, the more usual practice is to stalk them, or track them down with three or four of the staunchest elephants available.

Rhino shooting is sufficiently exciting of itself, but when wild bees take a part, they add painful variety and still more excitement. It may be mentioned in passing that there is nothing more dangerous in the Indian jungles and nothing more detestable, than to disturb a large swarm of the big venomous wild bees when engaged in trying to finish off a wounded tiger. They come down in their thousands and start stinging every living thing in sight; the elephants get wild and the tigers get wilder. Attempts to flee are futile, one might as well try to flee from a dive-bomber. However, the elephant and his driver very often do not appear to know this, and the possibility of one's elephant bolting through the forest adds further complications. In any case, whether the elephant flees or stays, it is quite certain that the *shikari* on its back will get stung, and may be badly stung, without the protection of a bee net — or a smoke screen.

This once occurred when a ring was being formed for a rhino hunt and, to quote from the official records: 'The bees scattered about creating panic, furiously stinging every man in the ring. There was no escape from them, clouds of bees were everywhere and their ceaseless threatening hum in our ears. Everyone pulled off his coat and covered his face but none was left unstung.' However, after a time the bees departed and when the ring was reformed, it seemed alive with rhino, ten or twelve becoming visible! One was shot, and the blood libation ceremony had to be performed, but the presence of numerous live rhino still in the ring made this very difficult. Elephants, as previously mentioned, hate the proximity of rhino and they refused to approach them close. They were goaded on a few steps forward with difficulty and then they retreated to their original positions, and 'for a whole hour the scene became one of rhinos and elephants moving forward and backward.' A minuet of the pachyderms! Finally when the rhinos had retired in good order, 'the dead rhino's entrails were laid aside, giving the dead animal the appearance of a big canoe. The blood libation was then performed.'

I must explain what the blood libation ceremony is; to Western ideas it is a most astounding ceremony. It is connected with the sacred

Shraddha ceremony of the Hindus, and it will be interesting to give a brief description. Every year the head of a Hindu family has to make this religious performance on the anniversary of his father's death, and again in some particular fortnight a similar ceremony in honour of all his departed ancestors. Part of the ceremony consists of pouring water out of a vessel. If the vessel used can be a hollowed rhino horn, the ceremony increases very greatly in value. If further, the libation can be rhino blood this again very greatly enhances the importance of the ceremony. This is called the *khadga-rudhir Tarpan* ceremony. Finally, if the offer of the rhino blood from a rhino horn can be made from inside the body of the rhino, it is of such high merit that the ancestors are freed from re-incarnations in their journey to Nirvana. Hence when a rhino is killed, the great mass of bowels and entrails are removed, leaving a vast cavity into which the man crawls to make the blood libation.

Wild elephants do not normally figure as the hunted in a Maharaja's shoot, but they sometimes create considerable diversion. A large herd of tame female elephants is a great attraction to a solitary wild tusker when they invade his domain, and he is liable to hang about a shooting camp.

The Maharaja had arranged a shoot for a Viceroy and the camp was being prepared. News was received that a tusker was in the forest to the east of the camps, and while a party of female elephants was reconnoitring along a broad stream, he suddenly appeared from the dense tree forest, and came towards the small female elephants who rapidly retired. Large reinforcements of tame elephants including some of the big fighting tuskers, were collected and advanced on the wild one who, as the official record puts it, 'did not care a fig.' More of the fighting elephants arrived and stood around the wild one, but were unwilling to attack. However, with the increased numbers and the yelling of the *mahouts*, the wild one turned round and ran away, to be followed hell-for-leather by the whole pack. That night the big tusker walked through the Nepalese camp, nearly upsetting the tent of one of the Generals, and next morning he was in evidence again. To quote the official diary: 'The band played at 10.15 a.m. before the Viceroy's camp. Sixty of them, while returning to their encampment, met the wild elephant, and were paralyzed in nervous fear. One fell upon the other, and the whole party became a solid entangled mass. However, when a party of orderlies arrived, they started up on their legs and departed to their lodgings.'

Some days later, after the Viceroy and his party had left, the wild tusker, an animal of phenomenal size, was seen in a stream near the camp. The Maharaja seized the opportunity to try a new form of sport, resulting in one of the most amazing incidents that has ever been reported. He gave instructions that, if possible, the wild elephant should be brought into the stream bed below a high bluff, fifty feet high, from where an elephant fight could be watched in safety.

At 3.31 p.m. the wild elephant was seen approaching the stream, and the Maharaja, the senior Maharani with her attendants, the Generals and Staff, went and sat down on benches and seats on top of the bluff, below which it was hoped to stage the elephant fight. But the wild elephant would not come out into the stream bed of his own accord, and showed an indication of going back into the forest. So a number of female elephants went across to entice him out, and he rose to the occasion and followed them into the open.

The big fighting tuskers Bikram Prasad and Bahadur Prasad were then brought out to attack him, but refused to advance and, in fact, the latter, despite his name (Bahadur means brave) turned tail and ran away. But a comparatively small *makna* (a tuskless male) called Ram Prasad, with his *mahout* and *pachwa* (the man who stands behind), with incredible pluck on the part of man and beast alike crashed forward, and began to fight. It must be realized that the wild elephant was of huge size and weight, and had powerful sharp-pointed tusks. What a wonderful setting for a primeval titanic fight, with the Maharaja, the ladies and high officials of the court looking down on the jungle stream bed, and the dense high forest behind, watching a scene that civilized men have seldom seen — the wild elephant fighting in his jungle haunts for his life and freedom! To quote from the diary:

'The tussle was a very thrilling one, and although his trunk was wounded by the tusk of the wild elephant, Ram Prasad knocked him about and the *mahout* wounded him with his lance. No other elephant would go forward to help against the wild one. For four or five minutes the fight continued and the spectacle was most exciting and dramatic. Then our elephants made an encircling movement round the wild elephant at close quarters, who turned and bolted away along the stream banks, and Ram Prasad pursued his rival, striking him with his trunk, pulling his tail, and trying to entangle his back legs, while the *mahout* too made thrusts with his lance in an admirable manner, and the whole pack of tame elephants followed closely behind. It was a very fine sight to see the wild one being pursued by the domestics like a hawk is sometimes pursued by a flock of crows.

' Then a surprising reverse took place, as the wild elephant suddenly turned back and charged his rival Ram Prasad violently from a vantage ground which placed the smaller elephant at a disadvantage. Ram Prasad retired, but the wild elephant turned him over and began to gore the prostrate body with his tusks at various points, sometimes on the head, sometimes on the limbs. For some time he placed his feet upon the body and tried to crush it with his mighty weight. The *pachwa* jumped off Ram Prasad's back at the first onset, but the *mahout* was seen going down with the falling *makna*, and all the beholders cried out in pity for the poor *mahout*, thinking it was all over with him. But God's will is wonderful, and the impossible sometimes turns out to be possible. Jaghan Dhari, the *mahout*, was in imminent danger of being crushed by the weight of his own elephant, but in some miraculous way he was jerked off and fell behind the hind legs of the wild elephant, and crawled away into safety.'

' The wild elephant was about to kill Ram Prasad, when a party went forward and resorted to blank firing. This did not drive off the infuriated elephant, but a bullet in the leg at last made it fly into the jungle.'

' Ram Prasad was prostrate, and a large number of men were employed in giving him some relief when the Maharaja went down to inspect the daring fighter, who had earned for himself immortal renown by his unexampled bravery. Ram Prasad could not be moved at that time, and orders were given that a number of men should keep guard over him with guns and torches during the night, as precaution against the almost certain return of the wild one to the scene of the fight.'

' Doctors were engaged in dressing the wounds, which were terrible, and men with explosives, crackers and guns were ready against accidents, when the wild elephant returned again in the night, and although it was scared away for a time by the report of guns, it returned again. The prostrate Ram Prasad got its wind and, with superb courage, staggered to his feet and advanced towards the jungle as if he wanted to have another bout. But a dozen female elephants were able to obstruct him, and he was taken to a more comfortable place about 300 yards away. The trunk, legs, neck, and thigh were injured very severely, he could not raise his trunk, which was much swollen.'

This plucky fighting elephant died a few days later from his wounds. His equally heroic *mahout* escaped unhurt.

Two days later, on 15 December, the wild tusker turned up again in the night and created some trouble, so orders were give to try and capture him! A party of ten or fifteen female elephants, eight or ten tuskers, and three or four men with guns, accordingly set out to tackle the wild elephant. One is lost in admiration of the pluck of these Nepalese, who, having seen for themselves two days before what this elephant could do when roused, set out again to try and capture him alive! The elephant was soon found, and this time Bahadur Prasad lived up to his name and reputation, and, assisted by other tuskers, soon put the wild tusker to flight. For mile after mile the great beasts went crashing through the forests, smashing down saplings and shrubbery, tearing down lianas and creepers. Whenever the wild elephant tried to turn or rest, Bahadur Prasad and Jaya Prasad, urged on by their *mahouts*, at once attacked with trunk and tusks. After three-and-a-half hours, the wild elephant was run to a standstill. Bahadur Prasad and Bikram Prasad, the two biggest tame tuskers, closed in, one on either flank, and pressed him firmly onward towards the bed of a nearby stream with flowing water. Here the elephants began to drink thirstily, and while the wild tusker was so engaged and prevented by side pressure from turning round, the other *mahouts* came up behind and quickly fastened nooses and strong ropes, tying the back legs together, and the great beast was captured! One admires the combination of pluck and skill of the Nepalese which brought this exciting *shikar* to a successful conclusion.

These true stories are no longer of our day and age, but belong to an epoch and regime that passed away a decade ago. The characteristics of present-day Nepal, such as air services, hotels, press correspondents, tourists, and mountaineers — if we can judge by the numerous books recently published — were still very strictly prohibited at that time. There is no Maharaja now with unlimited powers and resources to organize such shoots, and we were fortunate to live in Nepal while such spectacular shoots were still in fashion, which enables me to describe them.

An Exciting Week at Santha

Col. Kesri Singh

Many accounts have been written about pig-sticking but I have chosen to include only this one by Colonel Kesri Singh. Pig-sticking was very different to most other forms of shikar, *in that it involved riding down a wild boar on horseback and spearing it with a bamboo lance. This sport was particularly popular amongst the royalty of Rajasthan. Col. Kesri Singh is from Rajasthan and began his career as a hunter in the game department of the princely state of Gwalior. Later on he became both a Superintendent of Police and Conservator of Forests in Rajasthan. He accompanied George V, Lord Mountbatten, and the Maharajah of Jaipur on a number of* shikars *and was obviously skilled at organizing large beats for tiger.* Hunting With Horse *and Spear is the book in which this selection appears.* Col. Kesri Singh *wrote several other collections of* shikar *stories, the best known of which is* The Tiger of Rajasthan.

> *No game was ever worth a rap,*
> *For rational man to play,*
> *Into which no accident no mishap*
> *Could possibly find its way.*

My Cousin Bhojraj Singh, fifteen years my senior, often used to invite me to pig-sticking and to big game shooting parties at his village at Santha, and by his invitation I was there during Christmas week of 1916.

One morning we were looking for pigs in a grassy area. The party consisted of my cousin, Gulab Singh and myself. We had no beaters, but were finding the game ourselves by forming a line and riding

173

through the grass. I was riding my pet Arab 'Rustam,' my cousin was on his favourite waler 'Paris' and Gulab was on a country-bred pony. My cousin was a tall and stout person, but one of the advantages of pig-sticking for a heavy man is that weight is no handicap. It gives some balance and power to turn a horse and to stop a charging boar.

When we entered the grass we separated at a space of a few yards from each other and started to look for the game. We had not gone very far when I heard a whistle from Gulab. My cousin and I went up to him and asked him what it was. He quietly pointed out a small bush into which be said he had seen a panther go.

I had tried panther-sticking once in the company of the General, but on that occasion he took the whole credit. I, therefore, told my host that I would like very much to try it again. During my last experience I had learnt that it is not safe to play the fool with a panther. He should be speared and killed on the very first attempt. If he is only wounded or missed in the first round, he will soon be aware of your intention and he will jink aside, spring on your horse and pull you down.

An accident like this had happened the previous year when we were chasing a panther in a nearby place. I was leading on my Arab and when the panther jinked to the right and being a bit too far from me, I was only just able to prick him with my spear. I was immediately followed by Chawand Singh, and the panther after dodging sprang and pulled him down. My cousin and myself came to his rescue and the panther after mauling him entered a thick patch of bushes. We first attended Chawand, but since the claw wounds were not of a serious nature, we turned our attention to the panther again. As it refused to come out of the thicket, we decided to send Gulab to bring the hunting dogs and a rifle from the camp. The dogs after entering the thicket soon brought the panther to bay and I put a bullet into him to prevent any further damage.

Here I noticed the grass was girth high only and we had ample space between the two thickets for a good opportunity for a gallop. The height of the grass was of great advantage to the horse but just the reverse for the panther. We all three got round the bush into which the panther had entered and tried to beat him out towards the open bit knowing that he would make a bee-line for the next cover. It happened as I had anticipated and the panther slipped into the grass in the hope that he was hidden from our view, but it was not so. We spotted him at once and galloped after him. He found it difficult to move through the thick grass, so began to leap over it. Unlike pigs, panthers do not run a long distance, and when I rode forward I was lucky enough to get him from the side while he was in the act of leaping and my spear went clean through his body. I had to let go, and when I turned round my cousin gave him the *coup de grace* as the panther was trying to free himself from the spear.

It was over a panther-sticking incident my father once told me that Maharaja Sir Pratap became very much annoyed with him. They were both great friends and the best sportsmen of their time. News was brought to them of a panther hiding in the cellars of Rambagh. This was a building which stood on the site of the present Rambagh Palace, but in those days it was merely a country house and not lived in. There was ridable country all round with Moti Dungri Hill about a quarter of a mile to the east. The idea was to beat the panther out and stick him before he reached the hill, and both, as usual, were contending for the honour of the first spear. A great effort was made to dislodge the animal from the cellar but without success. No one volunteered to enter the building to push him out; so father proposed to do so. He entered with spear in hand but found it so dark that on reaching the far end the panther slipped out without his noticing. A pack of dogs were there in readiness and, when it came out, the dogs got away and started to bait it. Father, hearing all this commotion, rushed out and, seeing the panther mauling one of the pet dogs, he speared it through the heart and killed it. Old Sir Pratap, who was watching all this from his horseback was very cross at not having the opportunity of a chase. He cantered away to his house remarking that he would not speak to father until he stuck a panther alone. Luckily, two days after this incident, report was brought of a panther from Khatipura, and Sir Pratap went out alone with an orderly and stuck and killed it, after which he was happy again.

Our panther having given us practically no run, we started looking for pigs again. But owing to the panther there were no pigs in the area. So we proceeded towards the Ramgarh *roond* (preserve) for more game.

It did not take us long to find a good-sized boar who emerged out of a bush at a stilted trot but instead of running away charged in our midst. He missed us all but gave quite a shock to Gulab's country-bred pony. My Arab pricked his ears, his heart started hammering against his ribs more in excitement than in alarm. We followed the boar at a gentle trot, nursing him away from the thicket. He had not

175

yet realized that we were after him and so was loping gently along. When he was sufficiently far away from the thicket we spread out in a line and increased our pace. When the noise of our horses' hooves sounded nearer, the old boar grumbled his displeasure. He realized that we meant business and increased his own speed. We did not press him hard at first because of the fear that he might double back. For a moment he stopped short and looked round in our direction and then was off again at full speed. We kept on increasing our pace and the boar did the same. He was still full of running, but it was too fast to last much longer.

He was a clever animal and utilized every scrap of cover and every obstacle that came his way. Then suddenly he entered an irrigated area and started galloping along a footpath through ploughed fields which did not suit our horses. Coming out of these fields, he had gained a head on us and made straight for the long grass in the direction of Ganoli. I still pushed my horse at the best pace he could manage, and on coming nearer I could see the boar's open mouth, heaving flanks and faltering action, showing he was blown, and almost coming to a standstill. He had given us a good run, but now he showed signs of complete exhaustion. He now entered a grassy area in which he was lost for the moment. While we were looking for him we saw the boar running in front. We kept on riding after him, but on approaching I saw that it was not the same pig but a fresh one. What actually happened was that the old boar knew of a young boar's *basha* in the grass and when he was too tired he jumped in and turned out the fresh pig to take on the race. The second boar did not run very far but leaped over a dry nullah, and misjudging the distance he hit his snout against the opposite bank and broke his neck.

I was bent, however, on getting the first boar and, knowing from where he had put up the young boar, we went back to find him out and coming near the *basha* I caught his strong scent. Old boars in rutting time give out a very strong smell like that of a buckgoat and this was the rutting season. When I approached the nest, out he came and charged straight at my pony, but I got my spear near his ear which kept him off. In the meantime my cousin speared him through the heart and killed him. After this first morning's sport we returned to our camp.

The next morning I found that my faithful Arab had become slightly lame, so my cousin asked me to ride another horse, a waler. The previous day we had gone westward from our camp, but this morning being cloudy and the visibility being poor, we went eastward. As we were passing through a cultivated field, a farmer having seen us came hurriedly and informed us that a pig had just left his field and was going away towards the hills. We went in the direction he pointed out and soon saw it quietly going along picking *ber* from bush to bush. We followed him at a walk for a short time as he had not seen us, but on spotting us he trotted away and we galloped on and soon overtook him. We had not gone far when he turned to give battle. Seeing me coming too close, the boar charged with a savage grunt. My new mount, for whom it was the first experience of pig-sticking, took fright and bucked me off. The boar in his hurry had moved away and I, not hurt by the fall, having landed on my feet, with the reins still in my hand, mounted and joined the party at once.

It being a cloudy morning, we had caught the boar napping in open country. He now knew that he could not outpace us, so decided to fight. He made a couple of charges in which neither side had the advantage, and then entered some patches of thicket, taking advantage of every obstacle that came in his way. He started running along a low mud wall, and when the riders were on one side he crossed on the other. After he had performed this trick three times, I decided to remain on one side with my host on the other. On failing in this strategy he saw a farmer standing in his field and he charged straight into him, knocking him down with a nasty cut in the stomach. Being hard pressed had made him desperate, and under such circumstances a boar will often charge anything he sees, whether it be connected with the pursuit or not. Having vented his rage, he went on his way rejoicing.

When the farmer fell, his turban was knocked off and landed on the pig's head blinding him. The boar was slowed up by the cloth over his eyes and that gave me an opportunity to dash forward and spear. Being in the vicinity of the farmer's habitation, there were many obstacles in my way and I could not get my spear deep enough. The boar, seeing the farmer's hut ahead went straight into it. Fortunately, there was nobody inside but he refused to come out. We rode round the hut shouting all the time but with no effect. I now decided to meet him on foot and, throwing my reins to Gulab, I walked towards the door holding my spear ready as I advanced. The boar was watching my movements and, as I came nearer, he charged straight into me. I was afraid that if my spear hit his bony head and glanced off he would certainly knock me down just as he had done the farmer, but I took my chance and stood his charge. As he closed on me I stepped aside and jammed the spear right into his ribs. I had a broad blade which fortunately did not penetrate right through and thus prevented the brute working its way towards me. Although he kept on jerking all the time, the bamboo shaft was strong and did not give way.

He pressed furiously against the spear to reach me, at the same time struggling to get rid of it. He was champing and grinding his tushes and foaming from his mouth in rage while I hung on like grim death on the other end of the spear trying to keep myself away from him. In this I was successful, because the spear had struck a rib and refused to go through. Sometimes the shaft of the spear would bend in a highly unpleasant manner but actually did not break. My cousin seeing me in this fix came forward to help, but the brute, seeing him advancing from the side, turned towards him. As he did so out came my spear, giving me an opportunity to drive it again into a more vital part. After a short struggle the gallant boar rolled over on his side, still with a fierce look in his dead eyes.

We now turned our attention to the poor peasant who was knocked down by the boar and on going over to him we found that the cut inflicted by the boar on his stomach had brought his intestines out and he was lying in great agony. I applied first aid by pushing the bowels in and tied a bandage with his turban round his body. We hired a bullock-cart from the nearest village and took him to the hospital at Mahwa, six miles away, and left him there under the care of a qualified doctor. I was sorry to learn that the poor fellow died after three days.

The General arrived on short leave and joined our party next day when we went out for a bird shoot. And on the following day when my Arab had recovered from his lameness we again went out pig-sticking and had the pleasure of the General's company. While we were looking for pigs, I saw a blue bull standing in the open looking at us without fear. I suggested that we should try to run him down and kill him with spears. My brother and cousin having agreed, we gave him a chase. We all knew that if we allowed him to get his second wind he would never let us approach him. Therefore we pressed him hard from the very beginning. The General took the lead but when the bull jinked to his right he came towards me and I was able to thrust the spear into his side. The spear shaft was very strong and did not break but was wrenched out of my hand and left in the body of the running animal. The spear swinging with the action of the bull checked his speed but also made it difficult for anyone to approach him. The General, an expert at the jabbing of the spear, getting near the bull hurled his spear which lodged in the ribs of the animal, but he still kept on going at a loping gallop. The General's spear after swaying a bit fell out on the ground and was picked up. The bull now took to charging, attacking my cousin's horse, but was cleverly checked by him on spear-point. The ground over which we were riding was more or less open as the blue bull always prefers such country. So there was not sufficient thicket for the beast to hide in. He kept up this lolloping gallop for another mile or so and was now nearing the hills when the General, who had picked up his spear, rushed at the bull, and as the beast turned his face to charge, got his spear right through the neck and left it there. The bull after running a few paces staggered and fell on the ground. He could not get up again with the spear through his neck, and my cousin finished him quickly with a thrust through the heart. Our horses were very tired as the bull had given us at least a four-mile run, so we decided to return to the camp.

Resolved to stick one more pig for the pot before returning to Jaipur, we went out early the next morning. The day before, when we were delayed by the blue bull,we had not been able to go to the pig area. This morning our way was through the same place and, as we were approaching the dead bull, we saw a few jackals and one big hyena feeding on it. Seeing the hyena in the open, I decided to stick him first before going further. My brother and cousin having agreed we set off after him. I quickly closed on the animal as he had been gorging on the bull and his stomach was full. The moment I tried to spear, he jinked like a dog to one side and I missed him. The General and my cousin both tried also but the brute was so clever and quick that he avoided their spear. His trick lay in stopping suddenly and darting off in the opposite direction. Next time when I rushed at him I pulled up my Arab, and the moment he stopped and before he could dart off again, I had speared him through the lungs. He got up and ran for a short distance with blood coming through his mouth, and in a moment the General bowled him over. A hyena, if permitted to get his second wind, will keep on running forever.

After spearing the hyena which really did not give much of a run, we proceeded to where pigs were to be found. As we were nearing the place we saw a sounder of pigs consisting of a few females and two male pigs. As we galloped our horses after them they were off. We all should have gone after one boar, but this morning the temptation was

179

too great. When I saw my brother and cousin going after the one, I went after the other in order to kill it single-handed. I dashed off and soon overtook the boar. He proved to be a very cunning animal. Twice he made a wide deviation from his direct line to take advantage of some cover. Although the ground was good for riding, rocks, holes and pits had to be negotiated every now and then. A narrow nullah, full of water, now came into view, and into this the boar dashed without the slightest hesitation, vanishing for a few seconds and reappearing on the opposite bank. I knew the country well, and, finding the stream leapable, I pulled my horse together, got him well between my thighs and crammed him at it, and in a second we were on the other side.

He was a young boar and gave me a long run, but now seeing his tail drop I knew that he was blown and had to get his second wind. He suddenly dashed into a bush and squatted. Being all alone I found it very difficult to evict him out of the bushes and so prevent him from resting. Ultimately he came out of the bush and took a route to the left. I again caught him up and, before he could jink, speared him in the hind quarters. There was a small pool nearby and the boar plunged straight into it. He lay down in the shallow water resting and facing me. I did not like the idea of his getting refreshed, but he did not heed my shouting at all. There was a small ridge across the pool along which I rode towards him but, seeing me coming, he left the pool and resumed his journey.

My Arab, half way along the ridge, slipped and fell into the deep part of the pool, and with the weight of the horse and myself we were bogged. The more he struggled the worse it became. I jumped off the saddle onto the ridge which was hard and firm and kept on tugging the pony towards me by the reins. He wallowed in the mud for a while, struggling painfully and giving tugs that nearly pulled the reins out of my hand. He threw himself into an upright position, getting his forelegs above the surface, only to plunge straight down again without making any progress. There were some rotten logs lying half sunk near the ridge towards which I pulled the pony. In each plunge he had gained a few inches only and it looked as if his strength would give way. Fortunately, in one of his plunges his forelegs fell on the logs, and finding them firmer he made his way onto the ridge again. He was panting harder than he ever did after the boar, but now walked on firm ground. I shall never forget the miserable sight which he presented after emerging from the deadly embrace of the bog. I had not only lost the boar but the party as well and had been on the verge of losing my pony also. After taking half-an-hour's rest I made my way back to the camp.

The General and the party, who had killed their boar, came in about an hour later than myself, having spent a good deal of time in searching for me. My Arab was very exhausted and the following day being the last day of the camp, I suggested that we should take the dogs out in the morning to the big ravines and spear pig and panther with their aid.

After a hasty breakfast, we left very early with the pack of hounds. The pack consisted of four greyhounds, two dachs, one fox-terrier 'Ginger' and one Sindhi dog whose name was Moti. Moti was a big brave and strong watch-dog.

We went first among the hills and ravines towards the east, where we released 'Ginger' and the two dachs to search out the game. The dogs ran up and down for a while and within a short time had picked up scent. We let all the dogs go and soon heard them barking round the foot of a tree. This suggested that they had found a panther and had treed him, My cousin suggested that I should shoot the panther up in the tree, but I said it would be more fun to let the dogs kill it. Last time when we were hunting at Kala Pahar the dogs had killed it in this way.

We slowly approached the *neem* tree on which the panther had climbed, whereupon he gathered himself and jumped down the tree. The dogs were anxiously waiting for him, and the moment he touched the ground the big Sindhi was on him catching him by the neck, while the other dogs attacked him from every angle. He was soon seized on every side and could not even put up a fight as his throat was still in the grip of Moti. I got down from my pony and finished him with my spear.

The panther had wounded the two dachs, but luckily the wounds were not of a serious nature. Having loaded the panther on the back of a camel, we proceeded to a pool of water where we rested for a while and them started once again to look for pigs.

After we had been going up and down the ravines for sometime I heard a yelp from 'Ginger', indicating that he had found some game. I let all the dogs go off again and they ran in his direction. We followed on our horses. We soon reached the spot where the dogs were barking and heard a pig grunting. On going nearer, we saw they had surrounded a big boar who stood at bay and was scattering the dogs when they came near. On seeing us approach, the boar made a determined charge, and, finding Gulab in his line, he went for him, jumping clean over the pony, who stood frozen with terror, and knocked down the rider with his snout. The rider and the boar fell together on the ground and the pony, appreciating the situation, bolted away to the camp. As the boar fell on the ground, all the dogs sprang on him and worried him, giving Gulab an opportunity to escape. Gulab had been hit straight on the arm by the snout of the boar without the tushes coming into play and, therefore, received no cut.

All of us were surprised to see the boar make such a jump. So far I had only heard from my father of such instances. One such incident had occurred at Khatipura when father took out Lord Lawrence, the then Viceroy of India, for pig-sticking and the boar had jumped right across the hindquarters of His Excellency's horse, fortunately without hurting the rider.

After scaring off the dogs, the boar entered a deep ravine, one side of which was hollowed out in the quarrying of *kankar* (limestone). The boar entered the hollow portion to face the dogs, thus protecting his sides from the aggressors. He now and again, would dash out to punish the dogs, retreating at once to what was now his stronghold. He knew he could not get rid of the dogs and so must remain in this defensive position.

We watched this fight for a little while and soon realizing that nothing could be done to the boar, but that most of the dogs would be killed or wounded unless we gave them some active help, I dismounted and, having given my reins to Gulab, went to the help of the dogs keeping my spear at the ready with both hands. On seeing me coming, the dogs became much emboldened and the boar, losing interest in them, charged me. I held my spear-point straight at his chest, piercing his body as he came in contact, and quick as lightning the faithful dogs got on the boar from all sides and started tearing him, but still without much effect. The General, who had dismounted now, came forward and finally gave the *coup de grace*.

In places like this where pig-sticking is not possible owing to the nature of the country, I always prefer to hunt the pigs with dogs rather than to shoot them with rifle. There are many animals which can be shot with rifle, and, therefore, why not leave the pig to be hunted from horse or on foot with the aid of dogs?

The two long dogs were wounded by the boar and two others had been mauled by the panther, so we decided that they should be sent back to the camp; but as we had not had much of a run I proposed that we should return and, after some refreshment, should go to the *roond* and stick a pig or two.

The General, who had taken lessons in sabring pig from Father but had not tried it lately, decided to use his sword for the next one. He undoubtedly was the most experienced pig-sticker in our party and was well mounted on his favourite 'Chakrawarti,' a country-bred horse. My cousin and myself mounting our pet horses and taking spears in our hand set out for the *roond*.

It did not take long before we came across a sounder of pigs. The 'master' pig sauntered out of the bush as if offering us a challenge and with every intention of giving us a fight. We stood still because the cover was thick and we preferred him to come out before he became aware that we meant business. He started moving with some other pigs while we followed in the rear, guiding them slowly out of the thicket towards another *roond* about a mile away.

When they were sufficiently far from the cover we broke first into a trot and then into a gentle canter. As we increased our speed the pigs did the same. We did not press them hard yet, because they were not far from the last cover and there was a possibility of their doubling back. When they had gone away we put on more pressure, and the sounder soon scattered in all directions. We kept our eyes on the 'master' pig who had given us the challenge and closed on him. Chawand, who was pulled down from his horse and mauled by the panther a year before, took the lead and dashed at the boar. The boar, who was watching his approach, in the twinkling of an eye, turned round and, cocking his head on one side as if to take aim, attacked with open mouth. The spear glanced off his body and he jumped and caught hold of the rider's foot with his teeth. The pull was so strong that the rider was dragged from the saddle with the boar still holding his foot. By this time the General had turned round and went straight to the rescue of the rider. He slashed with his sword right across the animal's back, severing the spinal cord; the boar sank down on his hind quarters, unable to run any more but still moving about on his front legs and attempting to attack any of us with a murderous look in his eyes. I dismounted from my horse handing over my reins to Gulab, took out my dagger and, holding the boar by the hind leg, put him out of his agony. He was indeed a fighting boar doing battle to the last.

We now turned our attention to Chawand and looked at his injuries. It was very fortunate that when the boar caught his foot the stirrup iron was also caught in his mouth and so he could not crush any bone. The only injury he received was when he landed heavily on his bottom. My cousin was quick in catching his horse, so we mounted him again and suggested that he should ride slowly back to the camp.

The General's leave was now over and my holidays had come to an end, and so the following day we packed up and started for home. It was the most exciting and memorable trip I ever had and one in which I successfully speared and killed a panther.

The Talla Des Man-Eater

Jim Corbett

Probably the best known shikar *writer in this collection, Jim Corbett was born in 1875, the son of the postmaster of Nainital. He grew up in the forests around Kaladhungi, a small village in the terai, where he received his education in jungle lore. He later used his experience of the wild to kill man-eating tigers and leopards which terrorized the villagers of Kumaon. Corbett wrote about his adventures in a series of books which were bestsellers at the time and are now considered classics. His success as a hunter and his fame as a naturalist gained him worldwide recognition. He was given, 'Freedom of the Forests' by the British government in India, received the Kaiser-i-Hind Gold Medal, and was made an officer of the Order of the British Empire. In 1967 a newly discovered race of tiger was named* Panthera Tigris Corbetti. *A commemorative postage stamp was issued by the Indian government in 1976 and a game sanctuary near Kaladhungi bears his name.* The Talla Des Man-Eater *takes place when Corbett was over sixty and reveals his uncanny sensitivity to the jungle.*

Nowhere along the foothills of the Himalayas is there a more beautiful setting for a camp than under the Flame of the Forest trees at Bindukhera, when they are in full bloom. If you can picture white tents under a canopy of orange-coloured bloom; a multitude of brilliantly plumaged red and gold minivets, golden orioles, rose-headed parakeets, golden-backed woodpeckers, and wire-crested drongos flitting from tree to tree and shaking down the bloom until the ground round the tents resembled a rich orange-coloured carpet; densely wooded foothills in the background topped by ridge upon rising ridge of the Himalayas, and they in turn topped by the eternal snows, then, and only then, will you have some idea of our camp at Bindukhera one February morning in the year 1929.

Bindukhera, which is only a name for the camping ground, is on the western edge of a wide expanse of grassland some twelve miles long and ten miles wide. When Sir Henry Ramsay was king of Kumaon the plain was under intensive cultivation, but at the time of my story there were only three small villages, each with a few acres of cultivation dotted along the banks of the sluggish stream that meanders down the length of the plain. The grass on the plain had been burnt a few weeks before our arrival, leaving islands of varying sizes where the ground was damp and the grass too green to burn. It was on these islands that we hoped to find the game that had brought us to Bindukhera for a week's shooting. I had shot over this ground for ten years and knew every foot of it, so the running of the shoot was left to me.

Shooting from the back of a well-trained elephant on the grasslands of the Terai is one of the most pleasant forms of sport I know of. No matter how long the day may be, every moment of it is packed with excitement and interest, for in addition to the variety of game to be shot — on a good day I have seen eighteen varieties brought to bag ranging from quail and snipe to leopard and swamp deer — there is a great wealth of bird life not ordinarily seen when walking through grass on foot.

There were nine guns and five spectators in camp on the first day of our shoot that February morning, and after an early breakfast we mounted our elephants and formed a line, with a pad elephant between each two guns. Taking my position in the centre of the line, with four guns and four pad elephants on either side of me, we set off due south with the flanking gun on the right — fifty yards in advance of the line — to cut off birds that rose out of range of the other guns and were making for the forest on the right. If you are ever given choice of position in a line of elephants on a mixed-game shoot select a flank, but only if you are good with both gun and rifle. Game put up by a line of elephants invariably try to break out at a flank, and one of the most difficult objects to hit is a bird or an animal that has been missed by others.

When the air is crisp and laden with all the sweet scents that are to be smelt in an Indian jungle in the early morning, it goes to the head like champagne, and has the same effect on birds, with the result that both guns and birds tend to be too quick off the mark. A too eager

186

gun and a wild bird do not produce a heavy bag, and the first few minutes of all glorious days are usually as unproductive as the last few minutes when muscles are tired and eyes strained. Birds were plentiful that morning, and, after the guns had settled down, shooting improved and in our first beat along the edge of the forest we picked up five peafowl, three red jungle fowl, ten black partridge, four grey partridge, two bush quail, and three hare. A good *sambhar* had been put up but he escaped before rifles could bear on him.

Where a tongue of forest extended out on to the plain for a few hundred yards, I halted the line. This forest was famous for the number of peafowl and jungle fowl that were always to be found in it, but as the ground was cut up by a number of deep nullahs that made it difficult to maintain a straight line, I decided not to take the elephants through it, for one of the guns was inexperienced and was shooting from the back of an elephant that morning for the first time. It was in this forest — when Wyndham and I some years previously were looking for a tiger — that I saw for the first time a cardinal bat. These beautiful bats, which look like gorgeous butterflies as they flit from cover to cover, are, as far as I know, only to be found in heavy elephant-grass.

After halting the line I made the elephants turn their head to the east and move off in single file. When the last elephant had cleared the ground over which we had just beaten, I again halted them and made them turn their heads to the north. We were now facing the Himalayas, and hanging in the sky directly in front of us was a brilliantly lit white cloud that looked solid enough for angels to dance on.

The length of a line of seventeen elephants depends on the ground that is being beaten. Where the grass was heavy I shortened the line to a hundred yards, and where it was light I extended it to twice that length. We had beaten up to the north for a mile or so, collecting thirty birds and leopard, when a ground owl got up in front of the line. Several guns were raised and lowered when it was realized what the bird was. These ground owls, which live in abandoned pangolin and porcupine burrows, are about twice the size of a partridge, look white on the wing, and have longer legs than the ordinary run of owls. When flushed by a line of elephants they fly low for fifty to a hundred yards before alighting. This I believe they do to allow the line to clear their burrows, for when flushed a second time they invariably fly over the line and back to the spot from where they originally rose. The owl we flushed that morning, however, did not behave as these birds usually do, for after·flying fifty to sixty yards in a straight line it suddenly started to gain height by going round and round in short circles. The reason for this was apparent a moment later when a peregrine falcon, flying at great speed, came out of the forest on the left. Unable to regain the shelter of its burrow the owl was now making a desperate effort to keep above the falcon. With rapid wing beats he was spiralling upwards, while the falcon on widespread wings was circling up and up to get above his quarry. All eyes, including those of the *mahouts*, were now on the exciting flight, so I halted the line.

It is difficult to judge heights when there is nothing to make a comparison with. At a rough guess the two birds had reached a height of 1,000 feet, when the owl — still moving in circles —started to edge away towards the big white cloud, and one could imagine the angels suspending their dance and urging it to make one last effort to reach the shelter of their cloud. The falcon was not slow to see the object of this manoeuvre, and he too was now beating the air with his wings and spiralling up in ever shortening circles. Would the owl make it or would he now, as the falcon approached nearer to him, lose his nerve and plummet down in a vain effort to reach mother earth and the sanctuary of his burrow? Field glasses were now out for those who needed them, and up and down the line excited exclamations — in two languages — were running.

'Oh! he can't make it.'

'Yes he can, he can.'

'Only a little way to go now.'

'But look, look, the falcon is gaining on him.' And then, suddenly, only one bird was to be seen against the cloud. Well done! Well done! *Shabash! Shabash*! The owl had made it, and while hats were being waved and hands were being clapped, the falcon in a long graceful glide came back to the *semul* tree from which he had started.

The reactions of human beings to any particular event are unpredictable. Fifty-four animals had been shot that morning — and many more missed — without a qualm or the batting of an eyelid. And now, guns, spectators, and *mahouts* were unreservedly rejoicing that a ground owl had escaped the talons of a peregrine falcon.

At the northern end of the plain I again turned the line of elephants south, and beat down along the right bank of the stream that provided irrigation water for the three villages. Here on the damp ground the grass was unburnt and heavy, and rifles were got ready, for there was also a possibility of putting up another leopard.

We had gone along the bank of the stream for about a mile, picking up five more peafowl, four cock florican — hens were barred — three snipe, and a hog deer with very good horns when the accidental (please turn your eyes away, Recording Angel) discharge of a heavy high velocity rifle in the hands of a spectator sitting behind me in my howdah, scorched the inner lining of my left ear and burst the ear-drum. For me the rest of the February day was torture. After a sleepless night I excused myself on the plea that I had urgent work to attend to (again, please, Recording Angel) and at dawn, when the camp was asleep, I set out on a twenty-five-mile walk to my home at Kaladhungi.

The doctor at Kaladhungi, a keen young man who had recently completed his medical training, confirmed my fears that my eardrum had been destroyed. A month later we moved up to our summer home at Naini Tal, and at the Ramsay Hospital I received further confirmation of this diagnosis from Colonel Barber, Civil Surgeon of Naini Tal. Days passed, and it became apparent that abscesses were forming in my head. My condition was distressing my two sisters as much as it was distressing me, and as the hospital was unable to do anything to relieve me I decided — much against the wishes of my sisters and the advice of Colonel Barber — to go away.

I have mentioned this 'accident' not with the object of enlisting sympathy but because it has a very important bearing on the story of the Talla Des man-eater which I shall now relate.

*

Bill Baynes and Ham Vivian were Deputy Commissioners of, respectively, Almora and Naini Tal in the year 1929, and both were suffering from man-eaters, the former from the Talla Des man-eating tiger, and the latter from the Chowgarh man-eating tiger.

I had promised Vivian that I would try to shoot his tiger first, but as it had been less active during the winter months than Baynes's I decided, with Vivian's approval, to try for the other first. The pursuit of this tiger would, I hoped, tide me over my bad time and enable me to adjust myself to my new condition. So to Talla Des I went.

My story concerns the Talla Des tiger, and I have refrained from telling it until I had written *Jungle Lore*. For without first reading *Jungle Lore*, and knowing that I had learnt — when a boy and later

189

— how to walk in a jungle and use a rifle, the credulity of all who were not present in Kumaon at that time would have been strained and this, after my previous stories had been accepted at their face value, was the last thing I desired.

My preparations were soon made and on 4 April I left Naini Tal accompanied by six Garhwalis among whom were Madho Singh and Ram Singh, a cook named Elahai, and a Brahmin, Ganga Ram, who did odd jobs and was very keen to go with me. Walking the fourteen miles down to Kathgodam we caught the evening train and, travelling through Bareilly and Pilibhit, arrived at noon next day at Tanakpur. Here I was met by the *peshkar*, who informed me that a boy had been killed the previous day by the Talla Des man-eater, and that under Baynes's orders two young buffalo—to be used as bait—had been dispatched for me via Champawat to Talla Des. After my men had cooked and eaten their food and I had breakfasted at the dak bungalow, we started off in good heart to try to walk the twenty-four miles to Kaladhunga (not to be confused with Kaladhungi) the same night.

The first twelve miles of the road — through Baramdeo to the foot of the sacred Purnagiri mountain — runs through forest most of the way. At the foot of the mountain the road ends, and there is the choice of two tracks to Kaladhunga. One, the longer, goes steeply up the lefthand side of the mountain, to the Purnagiri temples, over a shoulder of the mountain, and down to Kaladhunga. The other track follows the alignment of the tramway line made by Collier when extracting the million cubic feet of *sal* timber that I have already spoken of. Collier's tramline — where it ran for four miles through the Sarda river gorge — has long since been washed away, but portions of the track he blasted across the perpendicular rock face of the mountain still remain. The going over this portion of the track was very difficult for my heavily-laden Garhwalis and night came on when we were only halfway through the gorge. Finding a suitable place on which to camp for the night was not easy, but after rejecting several places made dangerous by falling stones we eventually found a narrow shelf where the overhanging rock offered a measure of safety. Here we decided to spend the night, and after I had eaten my dinner and while the men were cooking their food with driftwood brought up from the river I undressed and lay down on my camp bed, the only article of camp equipment, excluding a washbasin and a forty-pound tent, that I had brought with me.

The day had been hot and we had covered some sixteen miles since detraining at Tanakpur. I was comfortably tired and was enjoying an after-dinner cigarette, when on the hill on the far side of the river I suddenly saw three lights appear. The forests in Nepal are burnt annually, the burning starting in April. Now, on seeing the lights, I concluded that the wind blowing down the gorge had fanned to flame the smoldering embers in some dead wood. As I idly watched these fires two more appeared a little above them. Presently the lefthand one of these two new fires moved slowly down the hill and merged into the central one of the original three. I now realized that what I had assumed were fires, were not fires but lights, all of a uniform size of about two feet in diameter, burning steadily without a flicker or trace of smoke. When presently more lights appeared, some to the left and others farther up the hill, an explanation to account for them presented itself. A potentate out on *shikar* had evidently lost some article he valued and had sent men armed with lanterns to search for it. Admittedly a strange explanation, but many strange things happen on the far side of that snow-fed river.

My men were as interested in the lights as I was, and as the river below us flowed without a ripple and the night was still, I asked them if they could hear voices or any other sounds — the distance across was about 150 yards — but they said they could hear nothing. Speculation as to what was happening on the opposite hill was profitless, and as we were tired out after our strenuous day the camp was soon wrapped in slumber. Once during the night a *ghooral* sneezed in alarm on the cliff above us and a little later a leopard called.

A long march and a difficult climb lay before us. I had warned my men that we would make an early start, and light was just showing in the east when I was given a hot cup of tea. Breaking camp, when only a few pots and pans had to be put away and a camp bed dismantled, was soon accomplished. As the cook and my Garhwalis streamed off in single file down a goat track into a deep ravine, which in Collier's day had been spanned by an iron bridge, I turned my eyes to the hill on which we had seen the lights. The sun was not far from rising and distant objects were not clearly visible. From crest to water's edge and from water's edge to crest I scanned every foot of the hill, first with my naked eyes and then with field glasses. Not a sign of any human being could I see, nor, reverting to my first theory, was there any smouldering wood, and it only needed a glance to see that the vegetation in this area had not been burnt for a year. The hill was rock from top to bottom, a few stunted trees and bushes growing where roothold had been found in crack or cranny. Where the lights had appeared was perpendicular rock where no human being, unless suspended from above, could possibly have gone.

Nine days later, my mission to the hill people accomplished, I camped for a night at Kaladhunga. For a lover of nature, or for a keen fisherman, there are few places in Kumaon to compare with Kaladhunga. From the bungalow Collier built when extracting the timber Nepal gave India, the land slopes gently down in a series of benches to the Sarda river. On these benches, where crops grew in the bygone days, there is now a luxuriant growth of grass. Here sambhar and cheetal are to be seen feeding morning and evening, and in the beautiful forests behind the bungalow live leopards and tigers, and a wealth of bird life including peafowl, jungle fowl, and *kalega* pheasants. In the big pools and runs below the bungalow some of the best fishing in the Sarda river is to be had, either on a spinning rod with plug bait or on a light rod with salmon fly or fly spoon.

At crack of dawn next morning we left Kaladhunga, Ganga Ram taking the mountain track to Purnagiri and the rest of us the shorter way through the Sarda gorge. Ganga Ram's mission — which would entail an additional ten miles' walk — was to present our thank-offerings to the sacred Purnagiri shrine. Before he left me I instructed him to find out all he could, from the priests who served the shrine, about the lights we had seen when on our way up to Talla Des. When he rejoined me that evening at Tanakpur he gave me the following information, which he had gleaned from the priests and from his own observations.

Purnagiri, dedicated to the worship of the Goddess Bhagbatti and visited each year by tens of thousands of pilgrims, is accessible by two tracks. These, one from Baramdeo and the other from Kaladhunga, meet on the northern face of the mountain a short distance below the crest. At the junction of the tracks is situated the less sacred of the two Purnagiri shrines. The more sacred shrine is higher up and to the left. This holy of holies can only be reached by going along a narrow crack, or fault, running across the face of a more or less perpendicular rock cliff. Nervous people, children, and the aged are carried across the cliff in a basket slung on the back of a hillman. Only those whom the Goddess favours are able to reach the upper shrine; the others are struck blind and have to make their offerings at the lower shrine.

Puja (prayer) at the upper shrine starts at sunrise and ends at midday. After this hour no one is permitted to pass the lower shrine. Near the upper and more sacred shrine is a pinnacle of rock a hundred feet high, the climbing of which is forbidden by the Goddess. In the days of long ago a *sadhu*, more ambitious than his fellows, climbed the pinnacle with the object of putting himself on an equality with the Goddess. Incensed at his disregard of her orders, the Goddess hurled the *sadhu* from the pinnacle to the hill on the far side of the snow-fed river. It is this *sadhu* who, banished for ever from Purnagiri, worships the Goddess 2,000 feet above him by lighting lamps to her. These votive lights only appear at certain times (we saw them on 5 April) and are only visible to favoured people. This favour was accorded to me and to the men with me, because I was on a mission to the hill-folk over whom the Goddess watches.

That in brief was the information regarding the lights which Ganga Ram brought back from Purnagiri, and imparted to me while we were waiting for our train at Tanakpur. Some weeks later I received a visit from the Rawal (High Priest) of Purnagiri. He had come to see me about an article I had published in a local paper on the subject of the Purnagiri lights, and to congratulate me on being the only European ever to have been privileged to see them. In my article I gave the explanation for the lights as I have given it in these pages, and I added that if my readers were unable to accept this explanation and desired to find one for themselves, they should bear the following points in mind:

The lights did not appear simultaneously.

They were of a uniform size (about two feet in diameter).

They were not affected by wind.

They were able to move from one spot to another.

The High Priest was emphatic that the lights were an established fact which no one could dispute — in this I was in agreement with him for I had seen them for myself — and that no other explanation than the one I had given could be advanced to account for them.

The following the year I was fishing the Sarda with Sir Malcolm (now Lord) Hailey, who was Governor of the United Provinces at the time. Sir Malcolm had seen my article and as we approached the gorge he asked me to point out the spot where I had seen the lights. We had four *dhimas* (fishermen) with us who were piloting the *sarnis* (inflated skins) on which we were floating down the river from one fishing stand to the next. These men were part of a gang of twenty engaged by a contractor in floating pine sleepers from the high level forests in Kumaon and Nepal to the boom at Baramdeo. This was a long, difficult, and very dangerous task, calling for great courage and a thorough knowledge of the river and its many hazards.

Below the shelf blasted out of the cliff by Collier, on which my men and I had spent the night when on our way up to Talla Des, was a narrow sandy beach. Here the *dhimas* at my request brought the *sarnis* to the bank, and we went ashore. After I had pointed out where the lights had appeared, and traced their movements on the hill, Sir Malcolm said the *dhimas* could possibly provide an explanation, or at least throw some light on the subject. So he turned to them — he knew the correct approach to make to an Indian when seeking information and could speak the language perfectly — and elicited the following information. Their homes were in the Kangra Valley where they had some cultivation, but not sufficient to support them. They earned their living by floating sleepers down the Sarda river for Thakur Dan Singh Bist. They knew every foot of the river as far down as Baramdeo, for they had been up and down it countless times. They knew this particular gorge very well, for there were backwaters in it that hung up the sleepers and gave them a great deal of trouble. They had never seen anything unusual in this part of the river in the way of lights, or anything else.

As he turned away from the *dhimas* I asked Sir Malcolm to put one more question to them. Had they in the years they had been working on the Sarda ever spent a night in the gorge? Their answer to this question was a very emphatic: No! Questioned further they said that not only had they never spent a night in the gorge but that they had never heard of anyone else ever having done so. The reason they gave for this was that the gorge was haunted by evil spirits.

Two thousand feet above us a narrow crack, worn smooth by the naked feet of generations upon generations of devotees, ran for fifty yards across a perpendicular rock cliff where there was no handhold of any kind. In spite of the precautions taken by the priests to safeguard the lives of pilgrims, casualties while negotiating that crack were heavy until H.H. The Maharaja of Mysore provided funds a few years ago for a steel cable to be stretched across the face of the cliff, from the lower shrine to the upper.

So there well might be spirits at the foot of that cliff but not, I think, evil ones.

*

194

Now to get back to my story.

Ganga Ram, who could cover the ground as fast as any man in Kumaon, had stayed back with me to carry my camera, and we caught up with the cook and the six Garhwalis two miles from where we had spent the night. For the next six hours we walked with never a pause, at times through dense forests and at times along the bank of the Sarda river. Our way took us through Kaladhunga and through Chuka to the foot of the mountain, on the far side of which was our objective, the hunting grounds of the Talla Des man-eater. At the foot of the mountain we halted for two hours —to cook and eat our midday meal — before essaying the 4,000-foot climb.

In the afternoon, with the hot April sun blazing down on our backs and without a single tree to shade us, we started on one of the steepest and most exhausting climbs my men and I had ever undertaken. The so-called road was only a rough track which went straight up the face of the mountain without a single hairpin bend to ease the gradient. After repeated and many halts we arrived at sunset at a little hamlet, a thousand feet from the crest.We had been warned at Chuka to avoid this hamlet, for, being the only inhabited place on the southern face of the mountain, it was visited regularly by the man-eater. However, man-eater or no man-eater we could go no farther, so to the hamlet — which was a few hundred yards from the track — we went. The two families in the hamlet were delighted to see us, and after we had rested and eaten our evening meal, my men were provided with accommodation behind locked doors, while I settled down on my camp bed under a tree that sheltered the tiny spring which provided the two families with drinking water, with a rifle and a lantern to keep me company.

Lying on my bed that night I had ample time to review the situation. Instructions had been issued by Bill Baynes to headmen of villages not to disturb any human or other kills, pending my arrival. The boy the *peshkar* of Tanakpur had told me about, had been killed on the fourth and it was now the night of the sixth. Since leaving the train at Tanakpur we had not spared ourselves in an effort to try to get to the scene of the killing with as little delay as possible. I knew the tiger would have eaten out his kill before our arrival and that, if he was not disturbed, he would probably remain in the vicinity for a day or two. I had hoped when leaving camp that morning that we would reach our destination in time to tie out one of the young buffaloes, but the climb up from the Sarda had been too much for us. Regrettable as the loss of one day was, it could not be helped, and I could only hope that, if

195

the tiger had moved away from the scene of his kill, he had not gone far. One of the disadvantages I had to contend with was that I did not know this part of Kumaon. The tiger had been operating for eight years and had made 150 human kills, so it was reasonable to assume he was working over a very large area. If contact with him was once lost it might be weeks before it could again be made. However, worrying over what the tiger had done, or what he might do, was profitless, so I went to sleep.

I was to make an early start and it was still quite dark when Ganga Ram roused me by lighting the lantern which had gone out during the night. While breakfast was being got ready I had a bath at the spring, and the sun was just rising over the Nepal mountains when, having cleaned and oiled my .275 Rigby Mauser rifle and put five rounds in the magazine, I was ready to start. Inter-village communication had been interrupted by the man-eater and the two men in the hamlet had not heard about the tiger's last kill, so they were unable to give me any information as to the direction, or the distance, we would have to go. Not knowing when my men would get their next meal I told them to have a good one now and to follow me when they were ready, keeping close together and selecting open places to sit down in when they wanted to rest.

Rejoining the track up which we had laboured the previous evening, I halted for a spell to admire the view. Below me the valley of the Sarda was veiled in shadow and a wisp of mist showed where the river wound in and out through the foothills to emerge at Tanakpur. Beyond Tanakpur the eye could follow the river as a gleaming silver ribbon, until lost to sight on the horizon. Chuka was in shadow and partly obscured by mist, but I could see the path winding up to Thak, every foot of which I was to know when hunting the Thak man-eater ten years later. Thak village, gifted hundreds of years ago by the Chand Rajas of Kumaon to the priests who serve the Purnagiri shrines, was bathed in the morning sun, as was also the pinnacle of Purnagiri.

Twenty-five years have come and gone since I turned away from that view to complete the last stage of my journey to Talla Des — a long period, in which much has happened. But time does not deface events graven deep on memory's tablets, and the events of the five days I spent hunting the man-eating tiger of Talla Des are as clear-cut and fresh in my memory today as they were twenty-five years ago.

On the far side of the hill I found the track that I was on joined a quite good forest road some six feet wide, running east and west. Here I was faced with a dilemma, for there were no villages in sight and I did not know in which direction to go. Eventually, on the assumption that the road to the east could only take me out of my way as far as the Sarda, I decided to try it first.

Given the option of selecting my own time and place for a walk anywhere, I would unhesitatingly select a morning in early April on the northern face of a wellwooded hill in the Himalayas. In April all nature is at her best; deciduous trees are putting out new leaves, each of a different shade of green or bronze; early violets, buttercups, and rhododendrons are giving way to later primulas, larkspurs, and orchids; and the birds — thrushes, babblers, minivets, tits, and a host of others — that migrated to the foothills for the winter are back on their nesting rounds and vie with each other in their joyous mating songs. Walking carefree and at ease in a forest in which there is no danger, only those objects and sounds which please the senses are looked at and listened to with any degree of attention, and all the other less-arresting sights and sounds blend together to form a pleasing whole. When there is danger from a man-eating tiger, however, the carefree feeling gives way to intense awareness.

Danger not only adds zest to all forms of sport, it also tends to sharpen the faculties and to bring into focus all that is to be seen and heard in a forest. Danger that is understood, and which you are prepared to face, does not detract in any way from pleasure. The bank of violets does not lose any of its beauty because the rock beyond it may shelter a hungry tiger, and the song of the black-headed sibia, poured out from the topmost branch of an oak tree, is none the less pleasing because a scimetar-babbler at the foot of the tree is warning the jungle folk of the presence of danger.

Fear may not be a heritage to some fortunate few, but I am not of their number. After a lifelong acquaintance with wild life I am no less afraid of a tiger's teeth and claws today than I was the day that a tiger shooed Magog and me out of the jungle in which he wanted to sleep. But to counter that fear and hold it in check I now have experience that I lacked in those early years. Where formerly I looked for danger all round me and was afraid of every sound I heard, I now knew where to look for danger, and what sound to ignore or pay special attention to. And, further, where there was uncertainty where a bullet would go, there was now a measure of certainty that it would go in the direction I wanted it to. Experience engenders confidence, and with-

197

out these two very important assets the hunting of a man-eating tiger on foot, and alone, would be a very unpleasant way of committing suicide.

The forest road I was walking on that April morning ran through an area in which a man-eating tiger was operating and had been used by the tiger frequently, as was evident from the scratch marks on it. In addition to these marks, none of which was fresh enough to show the pug marks of the tiger which had made them, there were many tracks of leopard, sambhar, bear, *kakar*, and pig. Of birds there were many varieties, and of flowers there was great profusion, the most beautiful of which was the white butterfly orchid. These orchids hang down in showers and veil the branch or the trunk of the tree to which their roots are attached. One of the most artistic nests I have ever seen was that of a Himalayan black bear, made in a tree on which orchids were growing. A big oak tree had snapped off, either by weight of snow or in a storm, some forty feet above ground. Where the break had taken place a ring of branches, the thickness of a man's arm, had sprouted out at right angles to the trunk. Here moss had grown and in the moss butterfly orchids had found roothold. It was here among these orchids that a bear had made its nest by bending over and pressing down the branches on to the broken-off tree trunk. The trees selected by bears in which to make their nests are of the variety whose branches will bend without snapping. The nests have nothing to do with family affairs and I have seen them at altitudes of from 2,000 to 8,000 feet. At the lower altitude, the nests give protection from ants and flies, and at the higher altitude they enable the animals to bask undisturbed in the sun.

When a road is interesting its length does not register on one's consciousness. I had been walking for about an hour when the forest ended and I came out on a grassy ridge overlooking a village. My approach over the open ground was observed, and when I reached the village the whole population appeared to have turned out to greet me. I often wonder whether in any other part of the world a stranger whose business was not known, arriving unexpectedly at a remote village, would be assured the same welcome and hospitality as he would receive at any village throughout the length and breadth of Kumaon. I was possibly the first white man who had ever approached that village alone and on foot, and yet, by the time I reached the assembled people, a square of carpet had been produced, a *morha* (rush seat) placed on it, and I had hardly sat down before a brass vessel containing milk was placed in my hands. A lifelong association with the hill-folk enables me to understand the different dialects that are spoken in Kumaon and what is just as important, to follow their every thought. As I had arrived armed with a rifle it was taken for granted that I had come to rid them of the man-eater, but what was puzzling them was my arrival on foot at that early hour when the nearest bungalow at which I could have spent the night was thirty miles away.

Cigarettes, passed round while I was drinking the milk, loosened tongues, and after I had answered the many questions put to me I put a few of my own. The name of the village, I learnt, was Tamali. The village had suffered for many years from the man-eater. Some said eight years and others said ten, but all were agreed that the man-eater had made its appearance the year that Bachi Singh had cut off his toes while splitting wood with an axe, and Dan Singh's black bullock, for which he had paid thirty rupees, had fallen down the hill and got killed. The last person killed at Tamali by the man-eater had been Kundan's mother. She had been killed on the twentieth day of the previous month (March), while working with other women in a field below the village. No one knew whether the tiger was a male or a female, but all knew it was a very big animal, the fear of which was now so great that the outlying fields were no longer being cultivated and no one was willing to go to Tanakpur to get the food that was needed for the village. The tiger was never absent from Tamali for long, and if I stayed with them, which they begged me to do, I would have a better chance of shooting it than anywhere else in Talla Des.

To leave people who place implicit trust in you to the tender mercies of a man-eater is not easy. However, my reason for doing so was accepted, and, after I had assured the fifty or more people gathered round me that I would return to Tamali at the first opportunity, I bade them goodbye and set off to find the village where the last kill had taken place.

At the point where the track from the hamlet met the forest road I removed the sign I had placed on the road to indicate to my men that I had gone east, and replaced it on the road to the west, and, to ensure that there would be no mistake, I put a 'road closed' sign on the road to the east. The two signs I have mentioned are known throughout the hills, and, though I had not told my men that I had laid them, I knew they would understand that I had laid them and would interpret them correctly. The first sign consists of a small branch laid in the middle of the road, held in position with a stone or bit of wood, with the leaves pointing in the direction in which it is intended that the person following should go. The second sign consists of two branches crossed, in the form of an X.

The road to the west was level most of the way and ran through a forest of giant oak trees standing knee-deep in bracken and maidenhair fern. Where there were openings in the forest there were magnificent views of hills upon rising hills backed by the snowy range extending to east and west as far as the eye could see.

*

After going for some four miles due west the forest road turned to the north and crossed the head of a valley. Flowing down the valley was a crystal-clear stream which had its birth in the dense oak forest on the hill that towered above me on my left. Crossing the stream on stepping-stones, and going up a short rise, I came out on an open stretch of ground on the far side of which was a village. Some girls coming down from the village on their way to the stream caught sight of me as I came out on the open ground, and they called out in great excitement, 'The *Sahib* has come! The *Sahib* has come!' The cry was caught up from house to house and before I reached the village I was surrounded by an excited throng of men, women, and children.

From the headman I learnt that the name of the village was Talla Kote. That a *patwari* had arrived two days previously (5 April) from Champawat, to meet me and to tell all the people in the district that a sahib was coming from Naini Tal to try to shoot the man-eater. That shortly after the arrival of the *patwari* a woman of the village had been killed by the man-eater, and that in obedience to orders received from the Deputy Commissioner, Almora, the kill had not been disturbed. And finally, that in anticipation of my arrival a party of men had been sent that morning to look for the kill and, if there was anything of it left, to put up a *machan* for me. While the headman was giving me this information the party, numbering some thirty men, returned. These men told me that they had searched the ground where the tiger had eaten its kill and that all they had been able to find were the woman's teeth. Even her clothes, they said, were missing. When I asked where the kill had taken place, a lad of about seventeen who was with the party of men said that if I would accompany him to the other side of the village he would point out to me where his mother had been killed by the man-eater. With the lad leading and the throng of men, women, and children following me, we went through the village to a narrow saddle some fifty yards long connecting two hills. This saddle was the apex of two great valleys. The one on the left, or western side, swept down towards the Ladhya river; the one on the right fell steeply away and down ten or fifteen miles to the Kali river. Halting on the saddle the lad turned and faced the valley on the right. The left-hand, or northern, side of this valley was under short grass with an odd bush scattered here and there, and the right-hand side was under dense scrub and tree jungle. Pointing to a bush on the grassy side 800 to 1,000 yards away and 1,000 to 1,500 feet below us, the lad said his mother had been killed near it while cutting grass in company with several other women. Then pointing to an oak tree in the ravine, the branches of which had been broken by *langurs*, he said it was under that tree that they had found the remains of his mother. Of the tiger, he said, neither he nor any of the party of men with him had seen or heard anything, but that when they were on their way down the hill they had heard first a *ghooral*, and then a little later, a *langur* calling.

A *ghooral* and a *langur* calling. *Ghooral* do occasionally call on seeing human beings, but not *langurs*. Both will call on seeing a tiger, however. Was it possible that the tiger had lingered near the scene of its kill and on being disturbed by the party of men had moved off and been seen, first by the *ghooral*, and then by the *langur*? While I was speculating on this point, and making a mental map of the whole country that stretched before me, the *patwari*, who had been having his food when I arrived, joined me. Questioned about the two young buffaloes for which I had asked Baynes, the *patwari* said he had started out with them from Champawat and that he had left them at a village ten miles from Talla Kote, where a boy had been killed by the man-eater on 4 April within sight of the village. As there was no one on the spot to deal with the man-eater, the body had been recovered, and after a report of the occurrence had been sent to Champawat, from where it had been telegraphed to Tanakpur for my information, he had given orders for the body of the boy to be cremated.

My men had not yet arrived from the hamlet where we spent the night, so, after instructing the headman to have my tent pitched on the open ground near the stream, I decided to go down and have a look at the ground where the tiger had eaten his kill, with the object of finding out if the man-eater was male or female, and if the latter, whether she had cubs. This part of Kumaon was, as I have already said, unknown

201

to me, and when I asked the headman if he could tell me the easiest way to get down into the valley the lad, who had pointed out to me where his mother had been killed and eaten, stepped forward and said very eagerly, 'I will come with you, sahib, and show you the way.'

The courage of people living in an area in which there is danger from a man-eater, and the trust they are willing to place in absolute strangers, has always been a marvel to me. The lad, whose name I learnt was Dungar Singh, was yet another example of that courage and trust. For years Dungar Singh had lived in fear of the man-eater and only an hour previously he had seen the pitiful remains of his mother. And yet, alone and unarmed, he was willing to accompany an absolute stranger into an area in which he had every reason to believe — from the alarm call of a *ghooral* and a *langur* — that the killer of his mother was lurking. True, he had only recently visited that area, but on that occasion he had been accompanied by thirty of his friends, and in numbers there was safety.

There was no way down the steep hillside from the saddle, so Dungar Singh led me back through the village to where there was a goat track. As we went down through scattered bushes I told him that my hearing was defective, that if he wanted to draw my attention to any particular thing to stop and point to it, and that if he wanted to communicate with me to come close and whisper into my right ear. We had gone about four hundred yards when Dungar Singh stopped and looked back. Turning round and looking in the same direction, I saw the *patwari* followed by a man carrying a shotgun hurrying down the hill after us. Thinking they had some important information for me, I awaited their arrival and was disappointed to find that all the *patwari* wanted was to accompany me with his gun-bearer. This, very reluctantly, I permitted him to do for neither he nor his gunbearer — both of whom were wearing heavy boots — looked like men who could move in a jungle without making considerable noise.

We had gone another four hundred yards through dense scrub jungle, when we came out on a clearing a few yards square. Here, where the goat track divided, one arm going towards a deep ravine on the left while the other followed the contour of the hill to the right, Dungar Singh stopped, and pointing in the direction of the ravine whispered that it was down there that the tiger had eaten his mother. As I did not wish the ground on which I wanted to look for pug marks to be disturbed by booted men, I told Dungar Singh to stay on the open ground with the two men, while I went down alone into the ravine. As I stopped talking Dungar Singh whipped round and looked up the hill. When I looked in the same direction I saw a crowd of men standing on the saddle of the hill, where I had stood a little while before. With a hand stretched out towards us to ensure silence, and the other cupped to his ear, Dungar Singh was intently listening, occasionally nodding his head. Then with a final nod he turned to me and whispered. 'My brother says to tell you that in the *wyran* field below you, there is something red lying in the sun.'

A *wyran* field is one that has gone out of cultivation, and below us on such a field there was something red lying in the sun. Maybe the red object was only a bit of dry bracken, or a *kakar* or young samb-har, but it might be a tiger. Anyway, I was not going to risk spoiling what might turn out to be a heaven-sent chance. So, handing my rifle to Dungar Singh, I took the *patwari* and his man, each by an arm, and led them to a medlar tree growing nearby. Unloading the *patwari's* gun and laying it under a bush, I told the two men to climb the tree and on pain of death to remain quietly in it until I ordered them to come down. I do not think any two men ever climbed into a tree more gladly and from the way they clung to the branches after they had climbed as high as it was safe to go, it was evident that their views on man-eater hunting had undergone a drastic change since they followed me from the village.

The goat track to the right led on to a terraced field which had long been out of cultivation, and on which there was a luxuriant growth of oat grass. This field, about a hundred yards long, was ten feet wide at my end and thirty feet wide at the other, where it terminated on a ridge. For fifty yards the field was straight and then it curved to the left. As Dungar Singh saw me looking at it, he said that from the farther end we would be able to see down on to the *wyran* field on which his brother had seen the red object. Bending down and keeping to the inner edge of the field we crept along until we came to the far end. Here we lay down and, crawling on hands and knees to the edge of the field, parted the grass and looked down.

Below us was a small valley with, on the far side, a steep grassy slope fringed on the side farthest from us by a dense growth of oak saplings. Beyond the saplings was the deep ravine in which the man-eater had eaten Dungar Singh's mother. The grass slope was about thirty yards wide and below it was a rock cliff which, judging from the trees growing at the foot, was from eighty to a hundred feet high. On the near side of the slope was a terraced field, a hundred yards long and some ten yards wide. The field, which was in a straight line with us, had a small patch of short emerald-green grass at our end. On the remainder was a dense growth of an aromatic type of weed which grows to a height of four or five feet and has leaves like chrysanthemums, the undersides of which are white. Lying in brilliant sunlight on the patch of grass, and about ten feet apart, were two tigers.

The nearer tiger had its back to us with its head towards the hill, and the farther one had its stomach to us with its tail towards the hill. Both were asleep. The nearer offered the better shot, but I was afraid that on hearing the smack of the bullet the farther one would go straight down the hill into dense cover, in the direction in which its head was pointing. Whereas if I fired at the farther one first, the smack of the bullet—not the crack of the rifle—would either drive the nearer one up the hill where there was less cover or else drive it towards me. So I decided to take the further one first. The distance was approximately 120 yards, and the angle of fire was not so steep that any allowance had to be made for the lift of the bullet, a point to be kept in mind when shooting downhill on the Himalayas. Resting the back of my hand on the edge of the field, to form a cushion, and holding the rifle steady, I took careful aim at where I thought the animal's heart would be and gently pressed the tiger. The tiger never moved a muscle, but the other one was up like a flash and in one bound landed on a five-foot-high bank of earth that divided the field from a rainwater channel. Here the second tiger stood, broadside on to me, looking back over its right shoulder at its companion. At my shot it reared up and fell over backwards into the rainwater channel, and out of sight.

After my second shot I saw a movement in the aromatic weeds which started close to where the dead tiger was lying. A big animal was going at full gallop straight along the field. Having started from so close to where the two tigers had been lying, this third animal could only be another tiger. I could not see the animal, but I could follow its movements by the parting of the weeds, the leaves of which were white on the underside. Flicking up the 200-yard leaf-sight, I waited for the animal to break cover. Presently out on to the grassy slope dashed a tiger. I now noticed that the slope the tiger was on curved to the right, in the same way as the field I was lying on curved to the left. As the tiger was keeping to the contour of the hill this curve in the slope enabled me to get a near broadside shot at it.

I have seen animals fall over at a shot, and I have seen them crumple up, but I have never seen an animal fall as convincingly dead as that tiger fell at my shot. For a few moments it lay motionless and then it started to slide down, feet foremost, gaining momentum as it went. Directly below it, and within a few feet of the brink of the rock cliff, was an oak sapling eight to ten inches thick. The tiger struck this sapling with its stomach and came to rest with its head and forelegs hanging down on one side and its tail and hind-legs hanging down on the other. With rifle to shoulder and finger on trigger I waited, but there was not so much as a quiver in the tiger. Getting to my feet I beckoned to the *patwari*, who from his seat on the medlar tree had obtained a grandstand view of the whole proceedings. Dungar Singh, who had lain near me breathing in short gasps, was now dancing with excitement and from the way he was glancing at the tigers and then up at the crowd of people on the saddle, I knew he was thinking of the tale he would have to tell that night and for many moons thereafter.

When I saw the two tigers lying asleep I concluded that the man-eater had found a mate, but later, when my second shot flushed a third tiger, I knew I was dealing with a tigress and her two cubs. Which of the three was the mother and which the cubs it was not possible to say, for all three looked about the same size when I had viewed them over the sights of my rifle. That one of the three was the man-eater of Talla Des there could be no question, for tigers are scarce in the hills, and these three tigers had been shot close to where a human being had recently been killed and eaten. The cubs had died for the sins of their mother. They had undoubtedly eaten the human flesh their mother had provided for them from the time they were weaned; this, however, did not mean that when they left the protection of their mother they would have become man-eaters themselves. For in spite of all that has been said since *Man-eaters of Kumaon* was published, I still maintain that the cubs of man-eating tigers —in the part of India about which I am writing — do not become man-eaters simply because they have eaten human flesh when young.

Sitting on the edge of the field with my feet dangling down and the rifle resting on my knees, I handed cigarettes to my companions and told them I would go and have a look at the tiger that had fallen into the rainwater channel, after we had finished our smoke. That I would find the tiger dead I had no doubt whatever; even so, nothing would be lost by waiting a few minutes, if for no other reason than to give myself a little time to rejoice over the marvellous luck I had met with. Within an hour of my arrival at Talla Des I had, quite by accident, got in touch with a man-eater that had terrorized an area of many hundreds of square miles for eight years, and in a matter of a few seconds had shot dead the man-eater and her two cubs. To the intense pleasure that all sportsmen feel at having held a rifle steady when every drop of blood in one's body was pounding with excitement, was added the pleasure and relief of knowing that there would be no necessity to follow up a wounded animal, a contingency that has to be faced when hunting tigers on foot.

My men would not ascribe my good fortune to luck. To avoid the possibility of failure they had consulted the old priest at the temple in Naini Tal and he had selected the propitious day for us to start on our journey to Talla Des, and evil omens when we started had been absent. My success would not be ascribed to good luck, therefore; nor, if I had failed to shoot the tigers, would my failure have been ascribed to bad luck, for no matter how well aimed a bullet might be it could do no harm to an animal whose time to die had not come. The superstitions of those whom I have been associated with on *shikar* have always been of interest to me. Being myself unwilling to begin a journey on a Friday, I am not inclined to laugh at a hillman's rooted aversion to begin a journey to the north on Tuesday or Wednesday, to the south on Thursday, to the east on Monday or Saturday, or to the west on Sunday or Friday. To permit those who accompany one on a dangerous mission to select the day for the start of the journey is a small matter, but it makes all the difference between having cheerful and contented companions or companions who are oppressed by a feeling of impending disaster.

The four of us sitting on the edge of the field had nearly finished our cigarettes, when I noticed that the tiger that was resting against the oak sapling was beginning to move. The blood from the body had evidently drained into the forward end of the animal making that end heavier than the tail end, and it was now slowly slipping down head foremost. Once it was clear of the sapling the tiger glissaded down the grassy slope, and over the brink of the rock cliff. As it fell through space I threw up the rifle and fired. I fired that shot on the spur of the moment to give expression to my joy at the success of my mission to Talla Des, and also, I am ashamed to admit, to demonstrate that there was nothing — not even a tiger falling through space — that I would not hit on a day like this. A moment after the tiger disappeared among the tree tops, there was a rending of branches, followed by a dull and heavy thud. Whether or not I had hit the falling tiger did not matter, but what did matter was that the men of the village would have farther to carry it now than if it had remained on the slope.

My cigarette finished, I told my companions to sit still while I went down to look at the tiger in the rainwater channel. The hill was very steep and I had climbed down some fifty feet when Dungar Singh called out in a very agitated voice. 'Look, *sahib*, look. There goes the tiger.' With my thoughts on the tiger below me, I sat down and raised my rifle to meet the charge I thought was coming. On seeing my preparations, the lad called out, 'Not here, but there, sahib, there.' Relieved of the necessity of guarding my front I turned my head and looked at Dungar Singh and saw he was pointing across the main valley to the lower slopes of the hill on which his mother had been killed. At first I could see nothing, and then I caught sight of a tiger going diagonally up towards a ridge that ran out from the main hill. The tiger was very lame and could only take three or four steps at a time, and on its right shoulder was a big patch of blood. The patch of blood showed it was the tiger that had crashed though the trees, for the tiger that had fallen into the rainwater channel had been shot in the left shoulder.

Growing on the hill close to where I was sitting was a slender pine sapling. Putting up the 300-yard leaf-sight I got a firm grip of the sapling with my left hand and resting the rifle on my wrist took a careful and an unhurried shot. The distance was close on 400 yards and the tiger was on a slightly higher elevation than I was, so, taking a very full sight, I waited until it again came to a stand and then gently pressed the trigger. The bullet appeared to take an incredibly long time to cover the distance, but at last I saw a little puff of dust and at the same moment the tiger lurched forward, and then carried on with its slow walk. I had taken a little too full a sight, and the bullet had gone a shade too high. I now had the range to a nicety and all that I needed to kill the tiger was one more cartridge; the cartridge I had foolishly flung away when the tiger was falling through the air. With an empty rifle in my hands, I watched the tiger slowly and painfully climb to the ridge, hesitate for a few moments, and then disappear from view.

Sportsmen who have never shot in the Himalayas will question my wisdom in having armed myself with a light .275 rifle, and only carrying five rounds of ammunition. My reasons for having done so were:

(a) The rifle was one I had used for over twenty years and with which I was familiar.

(b) It was light to carry, accurate, and sighted up to 300 yards.

(c) I had been told by Colonel Barber to avoid using a heavy rifle, and not to fire more shots than were necessary with a light one.

With regard to ammunition, I had not set out that morning to shoot tigers but to find the village where the last human kill had taken place and, if I had the time, to tie out a young buffalo as bait. As it turned out, both the light rifle and the five rounds would have served my purpose if I had not thrown away that vital round.

My men arrived at the village in time to join the crowd on the saddle, and to witness the whole proceedings. They knew that the five rounds in the magazine of the rifle were all the ammunition I had with me, and when after my fifth shot they saw the wounded tiger disappear over the ridge, Madho Singh came tearing down the hill with a fresh supply of ammunition.

The tiger on the patch of green grass, and the tiger in the rainwater channel — which I found lying dead where it had fallen —were both nearly full-grown, and the one that had got away wounded was quite evidently their mother, the man-eater of Talla Des. Leaving Madho Singh and Dungar Singh to make arrangements for the cubs to be carried up to the village, I set out alone to try to get in touch with the wounded tigress. From the bed of bracken on to which she had fallen after crashing through the trees, I followed a light blood-trail to where she had been standing when I fired my last shot. Here I found a few cut hairs clipped from her back by my bullet, and a little extra blood which had flowed from her wound when she lurched forward on hearing my bullet strike the ground above her. From this spot to the ridge there was only an occasional drop of blood, and on the short stiff grass beyond the ridge I lost the trail. Close by was a dense patch of scrub, a hundred yards wide, extending up the side of a steep hill for 300 yards, and I suspected that the tigress had taken shelter in this scrub. But as night was now closing in and there was not sufficient light for accurate shooting, I decided to return to the village and leave the searching of the scrub until the following day.

*

The next morning was spent in skinning the cubs and in pegging out their skins with the six-inch nails I had brought with me from Naini Tal. While I was performing this task at least a hundred vultures alighted on the trees fringing the open ground on which my tent was pitched. It was these that brought to light the missing clothes of the man-eater's victim, for the cubs had torn the bloodsoaked garments into strips and swallowed them.

The men of the village sat round me while I was skinning the cubs and I told them I wanted them to assist my Garhwalis in beating out the patch of scrub in which I thought the wounded tigress had taken shelter. This they were very willing to do. At about midday we set off, the men going through the village and along the saddle to the top of the hill above the cover, while I went down the goat track into the valley and up to the ridge over which I had followed the tigress the previous evening. At the lower edge of the scrub there was an enormous boulder the size of a small house. Climbing to the top of the boulder — from which I was visible to the men at the top of the hill — I waved my hat as a signal for them to start the beat. To avoid the risk of anyone getting mauled, I had instructed the men to stay on the top of the hill and, after clapping their hands and shouting, to roll rocks down the hillside into the scrub I have spoken of. One *kakar* and a few *kalege* pheasants came out of the bushes, but nothing else. When the rocks had searched out every foot of the ground, I again waved my hat as a signal for the men to stop the beat and return to the village.

When the men had gone I searched the cover, but without any hope of finding the tigress. As I watched her going up the hill the previous evening I could see that she was suffering from a very painful wound, and when I examined the blood where she had lurched forward, I knew the wound was a surface one and not internal. Why then had the tigress fallen to my bullet as if poleaxed, and why had she hung suspended from the oak sapling for a matter of ten to fifteen minutes without showing any signs of life? To these questions I could not at the time nor can I now find any reasonable answer. Later I found my softnose, nickel-encased bullet firmly fixed in the ball-and-socket joint of the right shoulder. When the flight of a high-velocity bullet is arrested by impact with a bone the resulting shock to an animal is very considerable. Even so, a tiger is a heavy animal with a tremendous amount of vitality, and why a light .275 bullet should knock such an animal flat and render it unconscious for ten or fifteen minutes is to me inexplicable.

Returning to the ridge, I stood and surveyed the country. The ridge appeared to be many miles long and divided two valleys. The valley to the left at the upper end of which was the patch of scrub was open grass country, while the valley to the right at the upper end of which the tigers had eaten the woman had dense tree and scrub jungle on the right-hand side, and a steep shaly slope ending in a rock cliff on the left.

Sitting down on a rock on the ridge to have a quiet smoke, I reviewed the events of the previous evening, and came to the following conclusions:

(a) From the time the tigress fell to my shot to the time she crashed through the trees, she had been unconscious.

(b) Her fall, cushioned by the trees and the bed of bracken, had restored consciousness but had left her dazed.

(c) In this dazed condition she had just followed her nose and on coming up against the hill she had climbed it without knowing where she was going.

The question that now faced me was: How far and in what direction had the tigress gone? Walking downhill with an injured leg is far more painful than walking uphill, and as soon as the tigress recovered from her dazed condition she would stop going downhill and would make for cover in which to nurse her injury. To get to cover she would have to cross the ridge, so the obvious thing was to try to find out if she had done so. The task of finding if a soft-footed animal had crossed a ridge many miles long would have been a hopeless one if the ridge had not had a knife-edge. Running along the top was a game track, with an ideal surface for recording the passage of all the animals that used it. On the left of the track was a grassy slope and on the right a steep shale scree ending in a sheer drop into the ravine below.

Finishing my smoke I set off along the game track on which I found the tracks of *ghooral*, *sarao*, sambhar, *langur*, porcupine, and the pug marks of a male leopard. The farther I went the more despondent I grew, for I knew that if I did not find the tigress's pug marks on this track there was little hope of my ever seeing her again. I had gone about a mile along the ridge, disturbing two *ghooral* who bounded away down the grassy slope to the left, when I found the pug marks of the tigress, and a spot of dry blood. Quite evidently, after disappearing from my view over the ridge the previous evening, the tigress had gone straight down the grassy slope until she recovered from her dazed condition and then had kept to the contour of the hill, which brought her to the game track. For half-a-mile I followed her pug marks to where the shale scree narrowed to about fifteen yards. Here the tigress attempted to go down the scree, evidently with the intention of gaining the jungle on the far side of the ravine. Whether her injured leg failed her or whether dizziness overcame her, I do not know; anyway, after falling forward and sliding head-foremost for a few yards she turned round and with legs widespread clawed the ground in a desperate but vain effort to avoid going over the sheer drop into the ravine below. I am as sure-footed as a goat, but that scree was far too difficult for me to attempt to negotiate, so I carried on along the track until I came to a rift in the hill. Down this rift I climbed into the ravine.

As I walked up the thirty-yard-wide ravine I noted that the rock cliff below the shale scree was from sixty to eighty feet high. No animal, I was convinced, could fall that distance on to rocks without being killed. On approaching the spot where the tigress had fallen I was overjoyed to see the white underside of a big animal. My joy however, was short lived, for I found the animal was a *sarao* and not the tigress. The *sarao* had evidently been lying asleep on a narrow ledge near the top of the cliff and, on being awakened by hearing, and possibly scenting, the tigress above him had lost his nerve and jumped down, breaking his neck on the rocks at the foot of the cliff. Close to where the *sarao* had fallen there was a small patch of loose sand. On this the tigress had landed without doing herself any harm beyond tearing open the wound in her shoulder. Ignoring the dead *sarao*, within a yard of which she passed, the tigress crossed the ravine, leaving a well-defined blood trail. The bank on the right-hand side of the ravine was only a few feet high, and several times the tigress tried but failed to climb it. I knew now that I would find her in the first bit of cover she could reach. But my luck was out. For some time heavy clouds had been massing overhead, and before I found where the tigress had left the ravine a deluge of rain came on, washing out the blood trail. The evening was now well advanced and as I had a long and a difficult way to go, I turned and made for camp.

Luck plays an important part in all sport, and the tigress had —so far — had her full share of it. First, instead of lying out in the open with her cubs where I would have been able to recognize her for what she was, she was lying out of sight in thick cover. Then, the flight of my bullet had been arrested by striking the one bone that was capable of preventing it from inflicting a fatal wound. Later the tigress had twice fallen down a rock cliff, where she would undoubtedly have been killed had her fall in the one case not been cushioned by branches and bracken and in the other by sand. And finally, when

211

I was only a hundred yards from where she was, the rain came down and washed out the blood trail. However, I too had had a measure of luck, for my fear that the tigress would wander away down the grassy slope where I would lose touch with her had not been realized, and, further, I knew now where to look for her.

*

Next morning I returned to the ravine, accompanied by my six Garh-walis. Throughout Kumaon the flesh of *sarao* is considered a great delicacy, and as the young animal that had broken its neck was in prime condition, it would provide a very welcome meat ration for my men. Leaving the men to skin the *sarao*, I went to the spot from where I had turned back the previous evening. Here I found that two deep and narrow ravines ran up the face of the hill on the right. As it was possible that the tigress had gone up one of these, I tried the nearer one first only to find, after I had gone up it for a few hundred yards, that the sides were too steep for any tiger to climb, and that it ended in what in the monsoon rains must have been a thirty-foot-high water-fall. Returning to my starting point I called out to the men, who were about fifty yards away up the main ravine, to light a fire and boil a kettle of water for my tea. I then turned to examine the second ravine and as I did so I noticed a well-used game track coming down the hill on the left-hand side. On the game track I found the pug marks of the tigress, partly obliterated by the rain of the previous evening. Close to where I was standing was a big rock. On approaching this rock I saw that there was a little depression on the far side. The dead leaves in the depression had been flattened down, and on them were big clots of blood. After her fall into the ravine —which may have been forty hours earlier — the tigress had come to this spot and had only moved off on hearing me call to the men to boil the kettle for tea.

Owing to differences in temperament it is not possible to predict what a wounded tiger will do when approached by a human being on foot, nor is it possible to fix a period during which a wounded tiger can be considered as being dangerous — that is, liable to charge when disturbed. I have seen a tiger with an inch-long cut in a hind pad, received while running away, charge full out from a distance of a hundred yards five minutes after receiving the wound; and I have seen a tiger that had been nursing a very painful jaw wound for many hours allow an approach to within a few feet without making any attempt to attack. Where a wounded man-eating tiger is concerned the situation is a little complicated, for, apart from not knowing

212

whether the wounded animal will attack on being approached, there is the possibility — when the wound is not an internal one — of its attacking to provide itself with food. Tigers, except when wounded or when man-eaters, are on the whole very good-tempered. Were this not so it would not be possible for thousands of people to work as they do in tiger-infested jungles, nor would it have been possible for people like me to have wandered for years through the jungles on foot without coming to any harm. Occasionally a tiger will object to too close an approach to its cubs or to a kill that it is guarding. The objection invariably takes the form of growling, and if this does not prove effective it is followed by short rushes accompanied by terrifying roars. If these warnings are disregarded, the blame for any injury inflicted rests entirely with the intruder. The following experience with which I met some years ago is a good example of my assertion that tigers are good-tempered. My sister Maggie and I were fishing one evening on the Boar river three miles from our home at Kaladhungi. I had caught two small *mahseer* and was sitting on a rock smoking when Geoff Hopkins, who later became Conservator of Forests, Uttar Pradesh, turned up on his elephant. He was expecting friends, and being short of meat he had gone out with a .240 rook-rifle to try to shoot a *kakar* or a peafowl. I had caught all the fish we needed, so we fell in with Geoff's suggestion that we should accompany him and help him to find the game he was looking for. Mounting the elephant we crossed the river and I directed the *mahout* to a part of the jungle where *kakar* and peafowl were to be found. We were going through short grass and plum jungle when I caught sight of a dead cheetal lying under a tree. Stopping the elephant I slipped to the ground and went to see what had killed the cheetal. She was an old hind that had been dead for twenty-four hours, and as I could find no marks of injury on her I concluded that she had died of snake bite. As I turned to rejoin the elephant I saw a drop of fresh blood on a leaf. The shape of the drop of blood showed that the animal from which it had come had been moving away from the dead cheetal. Looking a little farther in the direction in which the splash from the blood indicated the animal had gone, I saw another spot of blood. Puzzled by this fresh blood-trail I set off to see where it led to, and signalled to the elephant to follow me. After going over short grass for sixty or seventy yards the trail led towards a line of thick bushes some five feet high. Going up to the bushes where the trail ended I stretched out both arms — I had left my rod on the elephant — and parted the bushes wide, and there under my outstretched hands was a cheetal stag with horns in velvet, and lying facing me and eating the stag was a tiger. As I parted the bushes the tiger looked up and the expression on its face said, as clearly as any words, 'Well, I'll be damned!' Which was exactly what I was saying to myself. Fortunately I was so surprised that I remained perfectly still—possibly because my heart had stopped beating—and after looking straight into my face for a moment the tiger, who was close enough to have stretched out a paw and stroked my head, rose, turned, and sprang into the bushes behind him all in one smooth graceful movement. The tiger had killed the stag among the plum bushes shortly before our arrival, and in taking it to cover he went past the dead hind, leaving the blood trail that I followed. The three on the elephant did not see the tiger until he was in the air, when the *mahout* exclaimed with horror, '*Khabardar, Sahib. Sher hai.*' He was telling me that it was a tiger and to be careful.

Rejoining my men I drank a cup of tea while they cut up the *sarao* into convenient bits to carry, and returned with them to the depression in which I had found the clots of blood. All six men had been out on *shikar* with me on many occasions, and on seeing the quantity of blood they were of the opinion that the tigress had a body wound which would prove fatal in a matter of hours. On this point we were not in agreement, for I knew the wound was a superficial one from which the tigress, given time, would recover, and that the longer she lived the more difficult it would be to get in touch with her.

If you can imagine a deep and narrow ravine running up the face of a steep hill with the ground on the right sloping towards the ravine and well wooded but free of undergrowth, and the ground on the left-hand side of the ravine sloping upwards and covered with dense patches of *ringal* (stunted bamboo), bracken, and brushwood of all kinds, you will have some idea of the country my men and I worked over for the rest of that day.

My plan was for the men to go up on the right-hand side of the ravine, to keep me in sight by climbing into the highest trees they could find, and, if they wished to attract my attention, to whistle — hillmen, like some boys, are very good at whistling through their teeth. They would be in no danger from the tigress, for there was no cover on their side, and all of them were expert tree-climbers. The tracks of the tigress after she left the depression near the big rock showed that she had gone up the hill on the left-hand side of the ravine. Up this hill I now started to follow her.

I have emphasized elsewhere that jungle lore is not a science that can be learnt from textbooks, but that it can be absorbed a little at a time, and that the absorption process can go on indefinitely. The same applies to tracking. Tracking, because of its infinite variations, is one of the most interesting forms of sport I know, and it can at times be also the most exciting. There are two generally-accepted methods of tracking. One, following a trail on which there is blood, and the other, following a trail on which there is no blood. In addition to these two methods I have also at times been able to find a wounded animal by following blowflies, or by following meat-eating birds. Of the two generally-accepted methods, following a blood-trail is the more sure way of finding a wounded animal. But as wounds do not always bleed, wounded animals have at times to be tracked by their foot-prints or by the disturbance to vegetation caused by their passage. Tracking can be easy or difficult according to the nature of the ground, and also according to whether the animal being tracked has hard hooves or soft pads. When the tigress left the depression — on hearing me calling to my men — her wound had stopped bleeding and the slight discharge that was coming from the wound owing to its having turned septic was not sufficient to enable me to follow her, so I had to resort to tracking her by her foot-prints and by disturbed vegetation. This, on the ground I was on, would not be difficult, but it would be slow, and time was on the side of the tigress. For the longer the trail the better the chance would be of her recovering from her wound and the less chance there would be of my finding her, for the strain of the past few days was now beginning to tell on me.

For the first hundred yards the trail led through knee-high bracken. Here tracking was easy, for the tigress had kept to a more or less straight line. Beyond the bracken was a dense thicket of *ringal*. I felt sure the tigress would be lying up in this thicket, but unless she charged there was little hope of my getting a shot at her, for it was not possible to move silently through the matted *ringals*. When I was halfway through the thicket a *kakar* started barking. The tigress was on the move, but instead of going straight up the hill she had gone out on the left, apparently on to open ground, for the *kakar* was standing still and barking. Retracing my steps I worked round to the left but found no open ground in that direction, nor did I appear to be getting any nearer the barking deer. The *kakar*, soon after, stopped barking and a number of *kalega* pheasants started chattering. The tigress was still on the move, but, turn my head as I would, I could not locate the sound.

Pin-pointing, that is, fixing the exact direction and distance of all sounds heard, is a jungle accomplishment which I have reduced to a fine art and of which I am very proud. Now, for the first time, I realized with a shock that my accident had deprived me of this accomplishment and that no longer would I be able to depend on my ears for safety and for the pleasure of listening intimately to the jungle folk whose language it had taken me years to learn. Had my remaining ear been sound it would not have mattered so much, but unfortunately the drum of that ear also had been injured by a gun 'accident' many years previously. Well, there was nothing that could be done about it now, and handicapped though I was I was not going to admit at this stage of the proceedings that any tiger, man-eater or other, had any advantage over me when we were competing for each other's lives under conditions that favoured neither side.

Returning to the bracken, I started to try to find the tigress, depending on my eyes only. The jungle appeared to be well stocked with game, and I repeatedly heard sambhar, *kakar*, and *langur* giving their alarm calls, and more than once I heard pheasants, jays, and white-capped laughing thrush mobbing the tigress. Paying no attention to these sounds, which ordinarily I would have listened for eagerly, I tracked the tigress foot by foot as, resting frequently, she made her way up the hill, at times in a straight line and at times zigzagging from cover to cover. Near the top of the hill was a stretch of short stiff grass about a hundred yard wide. Beyond this open ground were two patches of dense brushwood divided by a narrow lane which ran up to the top of the hill. On the short stiff grass I lost the tracks. The tigress knew she was being closely followed and would therefore expose herself as little as possible. The patch of brushwood to my right front was thirty yards nearer than the patch to the left, so I decided to try it first. When I was within a yard or two of the cover I heard a dry stick snap under the weight of some heavy animal. I was positive on this occasion that the sound had come from the left, so I turned and went to the patch of brushwood from which the sound appeared to have come. This was the second mistake I made that day — the first was calling to my men to boil the kettle for tea — for my men told me later that I crossed the open stretch of ground on the heels of the tigress, and that when I turned and walked away to the left she was lying on an open bit of ground a few yards inside the bushes, evidently waiting for me.

Finding no trace of the tigress in the brushwood on the left I came back to the open ground, and, on hearing my men whistling, looked in the direction in which I expected them to be. They had climbed to the top of a tree a few hundred yards to my right, and when I lifted my hand to indicate that I had seen them, they waved me up, up, up, and then down, down, down. They were letting me know that the tigress had climbed to the top of the hill, and that she had gone down on the far side. Making what speed I could I went up the narrow lane and on reaching the top found an open hillside. On this the grass had been burnt recently, and in the ashes, which were still damp from the rain of the previous evening, I found the pug marks of the tigress. The hill sloped gently down to a stream, the one that I had crossed several miles higher up on the day of my arrival at Talla Kote. After lying down and quenching her thirst the tigress had crossed the stream and gone up into the thick jungle beyond. It was now getting late, so I retraced my steps to the top of the hill and beckoned to my men to join me.

From the big rock where I took up the tracks of the tigress to the stream where I left them was only some four miles, and it had taken me seven hours to cover the distance. Though it had ended in failure the day had been an interesting and exciting one. Not only for me who, while doing the tracking, had to avoid being ambushed by a wounded man-eating tiger, but also for my Garhwalis who by climbing trees had kept both the tigress and myself in view most of the time. And it had been a long day also, for we had started at daylight, and it was 8 p.m. when we got back to camp.

*

The following morning while my men were having their food I attended to the skins, re-pegging them on fresh ground and rubbing wood ashes and powdered alum on the damp parts. Tiger skins need a lot of care, for if every particle of fat is not removed and the lips, ears, and pads properly treated, the hair slips, ruining the skin. A little before midday I was ready to start, and accompanied by four of my men — I left the other two men in camp to attend to the *sarao's* skin — I set out for the place where I had stopped tracking the tigress the previous evening.

The valley through which the stream flowed was wide and comparatively flat, and ran from west to east. On the left-hand side of the valley was the hill on the far side of which I had followed the tigress

217

the previous day, and on the right-hand side was the hill along which ran the road to Tanakpur. Before the advent of the man-eater the valley between these two hills had been extensively grazed over by the cattle of Talla Kote, and in consequence the ground was criss-crossed by a maze of cattle paths, and cut up with narrow eroded water-channels. Dotted about the valley were open glades of varying sizes surrounded by dense scrub and tree jungle. Good ground on which to hunt sambhar, *kakar*, and bear, all of whose tracks were to be seen on the cattle paths, but not the ground one would select on which to hunt a man-eating tiger. The hill on the left commanded an extensive view of the valley, so I spaced my men in trees along the crest at intervals of two hundred yards to keep a look-out and to be on hand in case they were needed. I then went down to the spot where I had left the tracks of the tigress the previous evening.

I had wounded the tigress on 7 April, and it was now the 10th. As a general rule a tiger is not considered to be dangerous — that is, liable to charge at sight — twenty-four hours after being wounded. A lot depends on the nature of the wound, however, and on the temper of the wounded individual. Twenty-four hours after receiving a light flesh wound a tiger usually moves away on being approached, whereas a tiger with a painful body-wound might continue to be dangerous for several days. I did not know the nature of the wound the tigress was suffering from, and as she had made no attempt to attack me the previous day I believed I could now ignore the fact that she was wounded and look upon her only as a man-eater, and a very hungry man-eater at that, for she had eaten nothing since killing the woman whom she had shared with the cubs.

Where the tigress had crossed the stream there was a channel, three feet wide and two feet deep, washed out by rain water. Up this channel, which was bordered by dense brushwood, the tigress had gone. Following her tracks I came to a cattle path. Here she had left the channel and gone along the path to the right. Three hundred yards along was a tree with heavy foliage and under this tree the tigress had lain all night. Her wound had troubled her and she had tossed about, but on the leaves on which she had been lying there was neither blood nor any discharge from her wound. From this point on I followed her fresh tracks, taking every precaution not to walk into an ambush. By evening I had tracked her for several miles along cattle paths, water channels, and game tracks, without having set eyes on so much as the tip of her tail. At sunset I collected my men, and as we returned to camp they told me they had been able to follow the movements of the tigress through the jungle by the animals and birds that had called at her, but that they too had seen nothing of her.

When hunting unwounded man-eating tigers the greatest danger, when walking into the wind, is of an attack from behind, and to a lesser extent from either side. When the wind is from behind, the danger is from either side. In the same way, if the wind is blowing from the right the danger is from the left and from behind, and if blowing from the left the danger is from the right and from behind. In none of these cases is there any appreciable danger of an attack from in front, for in my experience all unwounded tigers, whether man-eaters or not, are disinclined to make a head-on attack. Under normal conditions man-eating tigers limit the range of their attack to the distance they can spring, and for this reason they are more difficult to cope with than wounded tigers, who invariably launch an attack for a little distance, maybe only ten or twenty yards, but possibly as much as a hundred yards. This means that whereas the former have to be dealt with in a matter of split seconds, the latter give one time to raise a rifle and align the sights. In either case it means rapid shooting and a fervent prayer that an ounce or two of lead will stop a few hundred pounds of muscle and bone.

In the case of the tigress I was hunting, I knew that her wound would not admit of her springing and that if I kept out of her reach I would be comparatively safe. The possibility that she had recovered from her wound in the four days that had elapsed since I had last seen her had, however, to be taken into account. When therefore I started out alone on the morning of 11 April to take up the tracks where I had left them the previous evening, I resolved to keep clear of any rock, bush, tree, or other object behind which the tigress might be lying up in wait for me.

She had been moving the previous evening in the direction of the Tanakpur road. I again found where she had spent the night, this time on a soft bed of dry grass, and from this point I followed her fresh tracks. Avoiding dense cover — possibly because she could not move through it silently — she was keeping to water channels and game tracks and it became apparent that she was not moving about aimlessly but was looking for something to kill and eat. Presently, in one of these water channels she killed a few-weeks-old *kakar*. She had come on the young deer as it was lying asleep in the sun on a bed of sand, and had eaten every scrap of it, rejecting nothing but the tiny hooves. I was now only a minute or two behind her, and knowing that the morsel would have done no more than whet her appetite, I redoubled my precautions. In places the channels and game tracks to which the tigress was keeping twisted and turned and ran through dense cover or past rocks. Had my condition been normal I would have followed on her footsteps and possible been able to catch up with her, but unfortunately I was far from normal. The swelling on my head, face, and neck, had now increased to such proportions that I was no longer able to move my head up or down or from side to side, and my left eye was closed. However, I still had one good eye, fortunately my right one, and I could still hear a little.

During the whole of that day I followed the tigress without seeing her and without, I believe, her seeing me. Where we had gone along water channels, game tracks, or cattle paths that ran through dense cover I skirted round the cover and picked up her pug marks on the far side. Not knowing the ground was a very great handicap, for not only did it necessitate walking more miles than I need have done, but it also prevented my anticipating the movements of the tigress and ambushing her. When I finally gave up the chase for the day, the tigress was moving up the valley in the direction of the village.

Back in camp I realized that the 'bad time' I had foreseen and dreaded was approaching. Electric shocks were stabbing through the enormous abscess, and the hammer blows were increasing in intensity. Sleepless nights and a diet of tea had made a coward of me, and I could not face the prospect of sitting on my bed through another long night, racked with pain and waiting for something, I knew not what, to happen. I had come to Talla Des to try to rid the hill people of the terror that menaced them and to tide over my bad time, and all that I had accomplished so far was to make their condition worse. Deprived of the ability to secure her natural prey, the tigress, who in eight years had only killed 150 people would now, unless she recovered from her wound, look to her easiest prey — human beings — to provide her with most of the food she needed. There was therefore an account to be settled between the tigress and myself, and that night was as suitable a time as any to settle it.

Calling for a cup of tea — made hill-fashion with milk — which served me as dinner, I drank it while standing in the moonlight. Then, calling my eight men together, I instructed them to wait for me in the village until the following evening, and if I did not return by then to pack up my things and start early the next morning for Naini Tal.

Having done this I picked up my rifle from where I put it on my bed, and headed down the valley. My men, all of whom had been with me for years, said not a word either to ask me where I was going or to try to dissuade me from going. They just stood silent in a group and watched me walk away. Maybe the glint I saw on their cheeks was only imagination, or maybe it was only the reflection of the moon. Anyway, when I looked back not a man had moved. They were just standing in a group as I had left them.

*

One of my most pleasant recollections — of the days when I was young — are the moonlight walks along forest roads that ten or a dozen of us used to take during the winter months, and the high teas we consumed on our return home. These walks tended to dispel all the fears that assail a human being in a forest at night, and, further, they made us familiar with the sounds to be heard in a forest by night. Later, years of experience added to my confidence and to my knowledge. When therefore I left my camp on the night of 11 April — in brilliant moonlight — to try conclusions with the Talla Des man-eating tigress, I did not set out with any feeling of inferiority on what might appear to have been a suicidal quest.

I have been interested in tigers from as far back as I can remember, and having spent most of my life in an area in which they were plentiful I have had ample opportunities of observing them. My ambition when I was very young was to see a tiger, just that, and no more. Later my ambition was to shoot a tiger, and this I accomplished on foot with an old army rifle which I bought for fifty rupees from a seafaring man, who I am inclined to think had stolen it and converted it into a sporting rifle. Later still, it was my ambition to photograph a tiger. In the course of time all three of these ambitions were fulfilled. It was while trying to photograph tigers that I learnt the little I know about them. Having been favoured by Government with the 'freedom of the forests,' a favour which I very greatly appreciate and which I shared with only one other sportsman in India, I was able to move about without let or hindrance in those forests in which tigers were most plentiful. Watching tigers for days or weeks on end, and on one occasion for four-and-a-half months, I was able to learn a little about their habits and in particular their method of approaching and of killing their victims. A tiger does not run down its prey; it either lies in wait or stalks it. In either case contact with its victim is made by a single spring, or by a rush of a few yards followed by a spring. If

221

therefore an animal avoids passing within striking distance of a tiger, avoids being stalked, and reacts instantly to danger whether conveyed by sight, scent, or by hearing, it has a reasonable chance of living to an old age. Civilization has deprived human beings of the keen sense of scent and hearing enjoyed by animals, and when a human being is menaced by a man-eating tiger he has to depend for his safety almost entirely on sight. When restlessness and pain compelled me to be on the move that night, I was handicapped to the extent that I only had one effective eye. But against this handicap was the knowledge that the tigress could do me no harm if I kept out of her reach, whereas I could kill her at a distance. My instructions therefore to my men to go back to Naini Tal if I failed to return by the following evening, were not given because I thought I could not cope with the tigress, but because I feared there was a possibility of my becoming unconscious and unable to defend myself.

One of the advantages of making detailed mental maps of ground covered is that finding the way back to any given spot presents no difficulty. Picking up the pug marks of my quarry where I had left them, I resumed my tracking, which was now only possible on game tracks and on cattle paths, to which the tigress was, fortunately, keeping. Sambhar and *kakar* had now come out on to the open glades, some to feed and others for protection, and though I could not pinpoint their alarm calls they let me know when the tigress was on the move and gave me a rough idea of the direction in which she was moving.

On a narrow, winding cattle path running through dense cover I left the pug marks of the tigress and worked round through scattered brushwood to try to pick them up on the far side. The way round was longer than I had anticipated, and I eventually came out on an open stretch of ground with short grass and dotted about with big oak trees. Here I came to a halt in the shadow of a big tree. Presently, by a movement of this shadow, I realized that the tree above me was tenanted by a troop of *langurs* . I had covered a lot of ground during the eighteen hours I had been on my feet that day, and here now was a safe place for me to rest awhile, for the *langurs* above would give warning of danger. Sitting with my back against the tree and facing the cover round which I had skirted, I had been resting for half-an-hour when an old *langur* gave his alarm call; the tigress had come out into the open and the *langur* had caught sight of her. Presently I, too, caught sight of the tigress just as she started to lie down. She was a hundred yards to my right and ten yards from the cover, and she lay down broadside on to me with her head turned looking up at the calling *langur*.

I have had a lot of practice in night shooting, for during the winter months I assisted our tenants at Kaladhungi to protect their crops against marauding animals such as pig and deer. On a clear moonlight night I can usually count on hitting an animal up to a range of about a hundred yards. Like most people who have taught themselves to shoot, I keep both eyes open when shooting. This enables me to keep the target in view with one eye, while aligning the sights of the rifle with the other. At any other time I would have waited for the tigress to stand up and then fired at her, but unfortunately my left eye was now closed and a hundred yards was too far to risk a shot with only one eye. On the two previous nights the tigress had lain in the one spot and had possibly slept most of the night, and she might do the same now. If she lay right down on her side — she was now lying on her stomach with her head up — and went to sleep I could either go back to the cattle path on which I had left her pug marks and follow her tracks to the edge of the cover and get to within ten yards of her, or I could creep up to her over the open ground until I got close enough to make sure of my shot. Anyway, for the present I could do nothing but sit perfectly still until the tigress made up her mind what she was going to do.

For a long time, possibly half-an-hour or a little longer, the tigress lay in the one position, occasionally moving her head from side to side, while the old *langur* in a sleepy voice continued to give his alarm call. Finally she got to her feet and very slowly and very painfully started to walk away to my right. Directly in the line in which she was going there was an open ravine ten- to fifteen-feet deep and twenty- to twenty-five yards wide, which I had crossed lower down when coming to the spot where I now was. When the tigress had increased the distance between us to 150 yards, and the chances of her seeing me had decreased, I started to follow her. Slipping from tree to tree, and moving a little faster than she, I reduced her lead to fifty yards by the time she reached the edge of the ravine. She was now in range, but was standing in shadow, and her tail end was a very small mark to fire at. For a long and anxious minute she stood in the one position and then, having made up her mind to cross the ravine, very gently went over the edge.

As the tigress disappeared from view I bent down and ran forward on silent feet. Bending my head down and running was a very stupid mistake for me to have made, and I had only run a few yards when I was overcome by vertigo. Near me were two oak saplings, a few feet apart and with interlaced branches. Laying down my rifle I climbed up the saplings to a height of ten or twelve feet. Here I found a branch to sit on, another for my feet, and yet other small branches for me to rest against. Crossing my arms on the branches in front of me, I laid my head on them, and at that moment the abscess burst, not into my brain as I feared it would, but out through my nose and left ear.

'No greater happiness can man know, than the sudden cessation of great pain,' was said by someone who had suffered and suffered greatly, and who knew the happiness of sudden relief. It was round about midnight when relief came to me, and the grey light was just beginning to show in the east when I raised my head from my crossed arms. Cramp in my legs resulting from my having sat on a thin branch for four hours had roused me, and for a little while I did not know where I was or what had happened to me. Realization was not long in coming. The great swelling on my head, face, and neck had gone and with it had gone the pain. I could now move my head as I liked, my left eye was open, and I could swallow without discomfort. I had lost an opportunity of shooting the tigress, but what did that matter now, for I was over my bad time and no matter where or how far the tigress went I would follow her, and sooner or later I would surely get another chance.

When I last saw the tigress she was heading in the direction of the village. Swinging down from the saplings, up which I had climbed with such difficulty, I retrieved my rifle and headed in the same direction. At the stream I stopped and washed and cleaned myself and my clothes as best I could. My men had not spent the night in the village as I had instructed them to, but had sat round a fire near my tent keeping a kettle of water on the boil. As, dripping with water, they saw me coming towards them they sprang up with a glad cry of 'Sahib! sahib! You have come back, and you are well.' 'Yes,' I answered, 'I have come back, and I am now well.' When an Indian gives his loyalty, he gives it unstintingly and without counting the cost. When we arrived at Talla Kote the headman put two rooms at the disposal of my men, for it was dangerous to sleep anywhere except behind locked doors. On this my bad night, and fully alive to the danger, my men had sat out in the open in case they could be of any help to me, and to keep a kettle on the boil for my tea — if I should return. I cannot remember if I drank the tea, but I can remember my shoes being drawn off by willing hands, and a rug spread over me as I lay down on my bed.

Hours and hours of peaceful sleep, and then a dream. Someone was urgently calling me, and someone was as urgently saying I must not be disturbed. Over and over again the dream was repeated with slight variations, but with no less urgency, until the words penetrated through the fog of sleep and became a reality. 'You must wake him or he will be very angry.' And the rejoinder, 'We will not wake him for he is very tired.' Ganga Ram was the last speaker, so I called out and told him to bring the man to me. In a minute my tent was besieged by an excited throng of men and boys all eager to tell that the man-eater had just killed six goats on the far side of the village. While pulling on my shoes I looked over the throng and on seeing Dungar Singh, the lad who was with me when I shot the cubs, I asked him if he knew where the goats had been killed and if he could take me to the spot. 'Yes, yes,' he answered eagerly, 'I know where they were killed and I can take you there.' Telling the headman to keep the crowd back, I armed myself with my .275 rifle and, accompanied by Dungar Singh, set off through the village.

My sleep had refreshed me, and as there was now no need for me to put my feet down gently — to avoid jarring my head — I was able for the first time in weeks to walk freely and without discomfort.

*

The day I arrived at Talla Kote, Dungar Singh, the lad who was with me now, had taken me through the village to a narrow saddle from where there was an extensive view into two valleys. The valley to the right fell steeply away in the direction of the Kali river. At the upper end of this valley I had shot the cubs and wounded the tigress. The other valley, the one to the left, was less steep and from the saddle a goat track ran down into it. It was in this valley that the goats had been killed. Down the goat track the lad now started to run, with me close on his heels. After winding down over steep and broken ground for five or six hundred yards, the track crossed a stream and then continued down the valley on the left bank. Close to where the track crossed the stream there was an open bit of comparatively flat ground. Running from left to right across this open ground was a low ridge of rock, on the far side of which was a little hollow, and lying in the hollow were three goats.

On the way down the hill the lad had told me that round about midday a large flock of goats in charge of ten or fifteen boys was feeding in the hollow, when a tiger — which they suspected was the man-eater — suddenly appeared among them and struck down six goats. On seeing the tiger the boys started yelling and were joined by some men collecting firewood nearby. In the general confusion of goats dashing about and human beings yelling, the tiger moved off and no one appeared to have seen in which direction it went. Grabbing hold of three dead goats the men and boys dashed back to the village to give me the news, leaving three goats with broken backs in the hollow.

That the killer of the goats was the wounded man-eater there could be no question, for when I last saw her the previous night she was going straight towards the village. Further, my men told me that an hour or so before my return to camp a *kakar* had barked near the stream, a hundred yards from where they were sitting, and thinking that the animal had barked on seeing me they had built up the fire. It was fortunate that they had done so, for I later found the pug marks of the tigress where she had skirted round the fire and had then gone through the village, obviously with the object of securing a human victim. Having failed in her quest she had evidently taken cover near the village, and at the first opportunity of securing food had struck down the goats. This she had done in a matter of seconds, while suffering from a wound that had made her limp badly.

As I was not familiar with the ground, I asked Dungar Singh in which direction he thought the tigress had gone. Pointing down the valley he said she had probably gone in that direction, for there was heavy jungle farther down. While I was questioning him about this jungle, with the idea of going down and looking for the tigress, a *kalege* pheasant started chattering. On hearing this the lad turned round and looked up the hill, giving me an indication of the direction in which the bird was calling. To our left the hill went up steeply, and growing on it were a few bushes and stunted trees. I knew the tigress would not have attempted to climb this hill, and on seeing me looking at it Dungar Singh said the pheasant was not calling on the hill but in a ravine round the shoulder of it. As we were not within sight of the pheasant, there was only one thing that could have alarmed it, and that was the tigress. Telling Dungar Singh to leave me and run back to the village as fast as he could go, I covered his retreat with my rifle until I considered he was clear of the danger zone and then turned round to look for a suitable place in which to sit.

The only trees in this part of the valley were enormous pines which, as they had no branches for thirty or forty feet, it would be quite impossible to climb. So of necessity I would have to sit on the ground. This would be all right during daylight, but if the tigress delayed her return until nightfall, and preferred human flesh to mutton, I would need a lot of luck to carry me through the hour or two of darkness before the moon rose.

On the low ridge running from left to right on the near side of the hollow was a big flat rock. Near it was another and smaller one. By sitting on this smaller rock I found I could shelter behind the bigger, exposing only my head to the side from which I expected the tigress to come. So here I decided to sit. In front of me was a hollow some forty yards in width with a twenty-foot-high bank on the far side. Above this bank was a ten-to twenty-yard-wide flat stretch of ground sloping down to the right. Beyond this the hill went up steeply. The three goats in the hollow, which were alive when the boys and men ran away, were now dead. When striking them down the tigress had ripped the skin on the back of one of them.

The *kalege* pheasant had now stopped chattering, and I speculated as to whether it had called at the tigress as she was going up the ravine after the lad and I had arrived or whether it had called on seeing the tigress coming back. In the one case it would mean a long wait for me, and in the other a short one. I had taken up my position at 2 p.m., and half-an-hour later a pair of blue Himalayan magpies came up the valley. These beautiful birds, which do a lot of destruction in the nesting season among tits and other small birds, have an uncanny instinct for finding in a jungle anything that is dead. I heard the magpies long before I saw them, for they are very vocal. On catching sight of the goats they stopped chattering and very cautiously approached. After several false alarms they alighted on the goat with the ripped back and started to feed. For some time a king vulture had been quartering the sky, and now, on seeing the magpies on the goat, he came sailing down and landed as lightly as a feather on the dead branch of a pine tree. These king vultures with their white shirt-fronts, black coats, and red heads and legs, are always the first of the vultures to find a kill. Being smaller than other vultures it is essential for them to be first at the table, for when the others arrive they have to take a back seat.

I welcomed the vulture's coming, for he would provide me with information I lacked. From his perch high up on the pine tree he had an extensive view, and if he came down and joined the magpies it would mean that the tigress had gone, whereas if he remained where he was it would mean that she was lying up somewhere close by. For the next half hour the scene remained unchanged — the magpies continued to feed, and the vulture sat on the dead branch — and then the sun was blotted out by heavy rain-clouds. Shortly after, the *kalege* pheasant started chattering again and the magpies flew screaming down the valley. The tigress was coming, and here, sooner than I had expected, was the chance of shooting her that I had lost the previous night when overcome by vertigo.

A few light bushes on the shoulder of the hill partly obstructed my view in the direction of the ravine, and presently through these bushes I saw the tigress. She was coming, very slowly, along the flat bit of ground above the twenty-foot-high bank and was looking straight towards me. With only head exposed and my soft hat pulled down to my eyes, I knew she would not notice me if I made no movement. So, with the rifle resting on the flat rock, I sat perfectly still. When she had come opposite to me the tigress sat down, with the bole of a big pine tree directly between us. I could see her head on one side of the tree and her tail and part of her hindquarters on the other. Here she sat for minutes, snapping at the flies that, attracted by her wound, were tormenting her.

*

Eight years previously, when the tigress was a comparatively young animal, she had been seriously injured in an encounter with a porcupine. At the time she received this injury she may have had cubs, and unable for the time being to secure her natural prey to feed herself in order to nourish her cubs, she had taken to killing human beings. In doing this she had committed no crime against the laws of nature. She was a carnivorous animal, and flesh, whether human or animal, was the only food she could assimilate. Under stress of circumstances an animal, and a human being also, will eat food that under normal conditions they are averse to eating. From the fact that during the whole of her man-eating career the tigress had only killed 150 human beings — fewer than twenty a year — I am inclined to think that she only resorted to this easily-procured form of food when she had cubs

228

and when, owing to her injury, she was unable to get the requisite amount of natural food needed to support herself and her family.

The people of Talla Des had suffered and suffered grievously from the tigress, and for the suffering she had inflicted she was now paying in full. To put her out of her misery I several times aligned the sights of my rifle on her head, but the light, owing to the heavy clouds, was not good enough for me to make sure of hitting a comparatively small object at sixty yards.

Eventually the tigress stood up, took three steps, and then stood broadside on to me, looking down at the goats. With my elbows resting on the flat rock I took careful aim at the spot where I thought her heart would be, pressed the trigger, and saw a spurt of dust go up on the hill on the far side of her. On seeing the dust the thought flashed through my mind that not only had I missed the tigress's heart, but that I had missed the whole animal. And yet, after my careful aim, that could not be. What undoubtedly had happened was that my bullet had gone clean through her without meeting any resistance. At my shot the tigress sprang forward, raced over the flat ground like a very frightened but unwounded animal, and before I could get in another shot disappeared from view.

Mad with myself for not having killed the tigress when she had given me such a good shot, I was determined now that she would not escape from me. Jumping down from the rock, I sprinted across the hollow, up the twenty-foot bank and along the flat ground until I came to the spot where the tigress had disappeared. Here I found there was a steep forty-foot drop down a loose shale scree. Down this the tigress had gone in great bounds. Afraid to do the same for fear of spraining my ankles, I sat down on my heels and tobogganed to the bottom. At the foot of the scree was a well-used footpath, along which I felt sure the tigress had gone, though the surface was too hard to show pug marks. To the right of the path was a boulder-strewn stream, the one that Dungar Singh and I had crossed farther up, and flanking the stream was a steep grassy hill. To the left of the path was a hill with a few pine trees growing on it. The path for some distance was straight, and I had run along it for fifty or more yards when I heard a *ghooral* give its alarm sneeze. There was only one place where the *ghooral* could be and that was on the grassy hill to my right. Thinking that the tigress had possibly crossed the stream and gone up this hill, I pulled up to see if I could see her. As I did so, I thought I heard men shouting. Turning round I looked up in the direction of the village and saw a crowd of men standing on the saddle of the hill. On seeing me look round they shouted again and waved me on, *on*, straight along the path. In a moment I was on the run again, and on turning a corner found fresh blood on the path.

The skin of animals is loose. When an animal that is standing still is hit in the body by a bullet and it dashes away at full speed, the hole made in the skin does not coincide with the hole in the flesh, with the result that, as long as the animal is running at speed, little if any blood flows from the wound. When, however, the animal slows down and the two holes come closer together, blood flows and continues to flow more freely the slower the animal goes. When there is any uncertainty as to whether an animal that has been fired at has been hit or not, the point can be very easily cleared up by going to the exact spot where the animal was when fired at, and looking for cut hairs. These will indicate that the animal was hit, whereas the absence of such hairs will show that it was clean missed.

After going round the corner the tigress had slowed down, but she was still running, as I could see from the blood splashes, and in order to catch up with her I put on a spurt. I had not gone very far when I came to a spur jutting out from the hill on my left. Here the path bent back at a very acute angle, and not being able to stop myself, and there being nothing for me to seize hold of on the hillside, I went over the edge of the narrow path, all standing. Ten to fifteen feet below was a small rhododendron sapling, and below the sapling a sheer drop into a dark and evil-looking ravine where the stream, turning at right angles, had cut away the toe of the hill. As I passed the sapling with my heels cutting furrows in the soft earth, I gripped it under my right arm. The sapling, fortunately, was not uprooted, and though it bent it did not break. Easing myself round very gently, I started to kick footholds in the soft loamy hill-face which had a luxuriant growth of maidenhair fern.

The opportunity of catching up with the tigress had gone, but I now had a well-defined blood-trail to follow, so there was no longer any need for me to hurry. The footpath which at first had run north now ran west along the north face of a steep and well-wooded hill. When I had gone for another two hundred yards along the path, I came to flat ground on a shoulder of the hill. This was the limit I would have expected a tiger shot through the body to have travelled, so I approached the flat ground, on which there was a heavy growth of bracken and scattered bushes, very cautiously.

A tiger that has made up its mind to avenge an injury is the most terrifying animal to be met with in an Indian jungle. The tigress had a very recent injury to avenge and she had demonstrated — by striking down six goats and by springing and dashing away when I fired at her — that the leg wound she had received five days before was no handicap to rapid movement. I felt sure, therefore, that as soon as she became aware that I was following her and she considered that I was within her reach, she would launch an all-out attack on me, which I would possibly have to meet with a single bullet. Drawing back the bolt of the rifle, I examined the cartridge very carefully, and satisfied that it was one of a fresh lot I had recently got from Manton in Calcutta, I replaced it in the chamber, put back the bolt, and threw off the safety catch.

The path ran through the bracken, which was waist high and which met over it. The blood trail led along the path into the bracken, and the tigress might be lying up on the path or on the right or the left-hand side of it. So I approached the bracken foot by foot and looking straight ahead for, on these occasions, it is unwise to keep turning the head.When I was within three yards of the bracken I saw a movement a yard from the path on the right. It was the tigress gathering herself together for a spring. Wounded and starving though she was, she was game to fight it out. Her spring, however, was never launched, for, as she rose, my first bullet raked her from end to end, and the second bullet broke her neck.

Days of pain and strain on an empty stomach left me now trembling in every limb, and I had great difficulty in reaching the spot where the path bent back at an acute angle and where, but for the chance dropping of a rhododendron seed, I would have ended my life on the rocks below.

The entire population of the village, plus my own men, were gathered on the saddle of the hill and on either side of it, and I had hardly raised my hat to wave when, shouting at the tops of their voices, the men and boys came swarming down. My six Garhwalis were the first to arrive. Congratulations over, the tigress was lashed to a pole and six of the proudest Garhwalis in Kumaon carried the Talla Des man-eater in triumph to Talla Kote village. Here the tigress was laid down on a bed of straw for the women and children to see, while I went back to my tent for my first solid meal in many weeks. An hour later with a crowd of people round me I skinned the tigress.

My first bullet, a .275 soft-nose with split nickel case fired on 7

April, was bushed and firmly fixed in the ball-and-socket joint of the tigress's right shoulder. The second and third bullets, fired as she was falling through the air and climbing up the hill, had missed her. The fourth, fired on 12 April, had gone clean through without striking any bones, and the fifth and sixth had killed her. From her right foreleg and shoulder I took some twenty porcupine quills, ranging in length from two to six inches, which were firmly embedded in muscle and were undoubtedly the cause of the tigress's having become a man-eater.

I spent the following day in partly drying the skin, and three days later I was safely back in my home with my bad time behind me. Baynes very kindly sent for Dungar Singh and his brother, and at a public function at Almora thanked them for the help they had given me and presented them with my token of gratitude. A week after my return to Naini Tal, Sir Malcolm Hailey gave me an introduction to Colonel Dick, a ear specialist, who treated me for three months in his hospital in Lahore and restored my hearing sufficiently for me to associate with my fellow men without embarrassment, and gave me back the joy of hearing music and the song of birds.

Epilogue

The story of the Talla Des man-eater — which I refrained from telling until I had written *Jungle Lore* — has now been told. I am aware that to many the story will seem incredible, and to none more so than to those who have themselves hunted tigers. None knows better than I that the hunting of tigers on foot is not a popular sport, and that the hunting of man-eaters on foot is even less so. I also know that the following-up of a wounded tiger on foot is a task that is sought by none and dreaded by all. And yet, knowing these things, I have told of the hunting of a man-eating tiger on foot, not only by day but also by night, and the chasing on foot of a wounded tiger. Small wonder, then, if my story to many should seem incredible.

There are few places in Kumaon where a fortnight's holiday could be more pleasantly spent than along the eastern border of the Almora district. Hiking in the Himalayas is becoming a very popular pastime, and I could suggest no more pleasant hike for a sportsman or for a party of a young army men or students than the following:

Start from Tanakpur, but before doing so get the *peshkar* to give you a *tahsil peon* to show you where the epic fight took place between the elephant and the two tigers. From Tanakpur go via Baramdeo to

Purnagiri. Here, after doing *darshan* at the temple, learn all you can from the High Priest and the temple *pujaris* about the lights that appear on the far side of the Sarda, and similar manifestations, as for example the fire with an old man sitting near it telling his beads that is to be seen at certain seasons at the foot of the Pindari Glacier. From Purnagiri a track used by the priests will take you to Thak village. This is beautifully situated, and while you rest and admire the view, get the headman or any of the other men sitting round to give you his version of the shooting of the Thak and of the Chuka man-eating tigers.Tewari, a relative of the headman and as fine a type of a hill Brahmin as you will see, will then show you where his brother whose body he helped me to find was killed, the mango tree with a spring at its roots, and the rock on the way down to Chuka where I shot the Thak man-eater. He will also, if you have the time, show you the *ficus* tree from which I shot the Chuka man-eater. At Chuka inquire for Kunwar Singh, and hear his story of the hunting of the two tigers.

From Chuka to Talla Kote is a long march, and it will be advisable to start at crack of dawn. Having forded the Ladhya near its junction with the Sarda, you will come to Sem. The headman of Sem, who was a boy when I knew him, will show you where the man-eater killed his mother while she was cutting grass near their home. With Sem behind you and a stiff climb accomplished, you will pass the small hamlet where I spent a night under a mango tree, After going over the ridge you will come to a forest road. Take the turn to the left and follow the road until you come to a stream. Cross the stream and the small patch of open ground on which my 40-pound tent was pitched, and you have reached your destination, Talla Kote.

Dunger Singh, *malguzar* (land-holder) of Talla Kote, will now be about forty years of age. Give him my *salams* and ask him to take you to the saddle from which there is an extensive view into two valleys. Face first the valley to the east and get Dungar Singh to point out the bush where his mother was killed, the oak tree under which she was eaten, the *wyran* field on which the young tigers were shot, and the grassy hill up which the wounded tigress went. Then turn round, walk a few steps, and face the valley to the west. Dungar Singh will now point out where the six goats were killed, where the tigress was standing when my bullet went through her, and the footpath along which she dashed and along which I ran after her.

The hunting of no other tiger has ever been witnessed by a greater

233

number of non-participants than witnessed the hunting of the Talla Des man-eating tiger. Some of those will have passed away, but many will still remain and they will not have forgotten my visit or the thrilling events of the week I spent with them.

The Man-Eater of Jowlagiri

Kenneth Anderson

Kenneth Anderson was one of the most prolific shikar *writers of his time. Eight of his books are presently in print, including* Nine Man-Eaters And One Rogue *and* The Black Panther of Sivana-palli. *Much of his work seeks to emulate Jim Corbett, though he set his stories in the forests of South India, around Bangalore and Mysore. Kenneth Anderson was born near Hyderabad, in 1910, the son of a Scotsman and 'Descendant of Scots' who had lived and worked there for six generations. Anderson lived his whole life in India and only visited Britain once. He died in 1974. In* The Man-Eater of Jowlagiri *he survives several close encounters with the tigress and finally lures her into range of his rifle by imitating the mating call of a male tiger.*

Those who have been to the tropics and to jungle places will not need to be told of the beauties of the moonlight over hill and valley, that picks out in vivid relief the forest grasses and each leaf of the giant trees, and throws into still greater mystery the dark shadows below, where the rays of the moon cannot reach, concealing perhaps a beast of prey, a watchful deer or a lurking reptile, all individually and severally in search of food.

All appeared peaceful in the Jowlagiri Forest Range, yet there was danger everywhere, and murder was afoot. For a trio of poachers, who possessed between them two matchlocks of ancient vintage, had decided to get themselves some meat. They had cleverly constructed a hide on the sloping banks of a water-hole, and had been sitting in it since sunset, intently watchful for the deer which, sooner or later, must come to slake their thirst.

The hours wore on. The moon, at the full, had reached mid-heaven and the scene was as bright as day. Suddenly, from the thicket of ever-green saplings to their left, could be heard the sound of violently rustling leaves and deep-throated grunts. What could be there? Wild-pig undoubtedly! A succulent meal, and flesh in addition that could be sold! The poachers waited, but the beasts, whatever they were, did not break cover. Becoming impatient, Muniappa, the marksman of the trio, decided to risk a shot. Raising his matchlock, he waited till a dark shadow, deeper than its surroundings, became more evident, and fired. There was a snarling roar and a lashing of bushes, followed by a series of coughing 'whoofs' and then silence.

Not pigs, but a tiger! Fearfully and silently the three poachers beat a hasty retreat to their village, there to spend the rest of the night in anxiety as to the result of their act.

But morning revealed that all was apparently well, for a male tiger just in his prime lay dead, the chance shot from the ancient musket having sped straight to his heart. So Muniappa and his friends were, for that day, the unsung and whispered heroes of the village.

But the next night produced a different story. With sunset came the urgent, angry call of a tigress seeking her dead mate. For it was the mating season, and this tigress, which had only just succeeded in finding her companion the night before, was decidedly annoyed at his unaccountable absence, which she quite rightly connected with the interference of human beings.

Night after night for a week she continued her uneasy movements, calling by day from the depths of the forest and in darkness roaring almost at the outskirts of the village itself.

Young Jack Leonard, who was keen to secure a trophy, and who had been summoned to the village by an urgent letter, arrived on the morning of the eighth day, and acquainted himself with the situation. Being told that the tiger wandered everywhere, and seeing her many pug-marks on the lonely path to the forest-bungalow, he decided to try his luck that evening, concealing himself by five o'clock behind an ant-hill that stood conveniently beside the path.

The minutes passed, and at 6.15 p.m. dusk was falling. Suddenly there was a faint rustle of leaves and a loose stone rolled down the bank a little to his right. Leonard strained his eyes for the first sight of the tigress, but nothing happened. The minutes passed again. And then, rapidly moving along the edge of the road towards him, and on the same side as himself, he could just discern the form of the tigress.

Hastily transferring the stock of his rifle to his left shoulder, and leaning as far out from his sheltering bush as possible, so that he might see more of the animal, Leonard fired at her chest what would have been a fatal shot had it carried a little more to the right.

As it was, Leonard's bullet ploughed deeply into the right shoulder, causing the beast to roar loudly before crashing away into the jungle. Bitterly disappointed, Leonard waited till morning to follow the trail. There was abundance of blood everywhere, but due to the rocky and difficult country, interspersed with densely wooded ravines and close, impenetrable shrubbery, he failed to catch up with his quarry.

Months passed, and the scene changes to Sulekunta, a village deeper in the forest and about seven miles from Jowlagiri, where there was a little temple occasionally visited by pilgrims from the surrounding region. Three of these had finished their devotions and were returning to their home; a man, his wife and son aged sixteen. Passing under a wild tamarind tree, hardly a quarter-mile from the temple, the boy lingered to pick some of the half-ripe acid fruit. The parents heard a low growl, followed by a piercing, agonized scream, and looked back to see their son carried bodily in the jaws of a tiger, as it leapt into a nullah bordering the lonely path. The aged couple bravely turned back and shouted abuse at the marauder as best they could, only to be answered by two more shrieks from their only son, then all was silent again.

· Thereafter, death followed death over a wide area, extending from Jowlagiri in the extreme north to the cattle-pen of Gundalam, thirty miles to the south; and from the borders of Mysore State, twenty miles to the west, to the main road to Denkanikota, for about forty-five miles of its length. Some fifteen victims, including three girls, one just married, had fallen a prey to this monster, when I received an urgent summons from my friend, the Sub-Collector of Hosur, to rid the area of the scourge.

Journeying to Jowlagiri, where the Sub-Collector had told me the trouble had begun, I pieced together the facts of the story, deducing that this was no tiger but a tigress, and the one that had been robbed of her mate by the poachers and later wounded by Leonard's plucky but unfortunate shot. From Jowlagiri I tramped to Sulekunta in the hope of coming across the fresh pug marks of the marauder, but I was unlucky, as no kills had occurred at that place in recent days, and what tracks there were had been obliterated by passing herds of cattle. Moving on to Gundalam, twenty-three miles away at the southern

237

limit of the affected area, I decided to pitch camp, since it was at this cattle-pen that the majority of kills had been reported, seven herdsmen being accounted for in the last four months.

Three fat buffalo calves had been very thoughtfully provided as bait by my friend the Sub-Collector; I proceeded to tie them out at likely spots in the hope of securing a kill. The first I tethered a mile down the river bordering Gundalam — at that time of the year a mere trickle of water — at a point where the river was joined by a tributary named Sige Halla, down which the tigress was reported to keep her beat; the second I tied along the path to the neighbouring village of Anchetty, four miles away; the remaining calf I secured close to the watershed, whence both herdsmen and cattle obtained their daily supply of drinking water.

Having myself attended to the securing and comfort of these three baits, I spent the next two days in tramping the forest in every direction, armed with my .405 Winchester, in the hope of picking up fresh pug marks, or perhaps of seeing the man-eater herself.

Early in the morning of the second day I located the foot-prints of the tigress in the soft sand of the Gundalam river. She had descended in the night, walked along the river past the watershed — and my buffalo bait, which, as was evident by her foot-prints, she had stopped to look at but had not even touched — and up and across a neighbouring hill on her way to Anchetty. Here the ground became too hard for further tracking.

The third morning found me searching again, and I had just returned to camp, preparatory to a hot bath and early lunch, when a group of men, accompanied by the headman of Anchetty, arrived to inform me that the tigress had killed a man early that morning at a hamlet scarcely a mile south of Anchetty. Apparently a villager, hearing restless sounds from his penned cattle, had gone out at dawn to investigate and had not returned. Thereafter his brother and son had followed to find out the cause of his absence and at the outskirts of the cattle-pen had found the man's blanket and staff, and, indistinct in the hard earth, the claw marks of the tigress' hind-feet as she reared to attack her victim. Being too alarmed to follow, they had fled to the hamlet and thence to Anchetty, where, gathering strength in numbers and accompanied by the head-man they had hastened to find me.

Foregoing the bath and swallowing, a quick lunch, we hastened to Anchetty and the hamlet. From the spot where the tigress had attacked and — as was evident by the fact that no sound had been made by the unfortunate man — had killed her victim, tracking became arduous and slow owing to the hard and stony nature of the ground. In this case, the profusion of thorny bushes among the shrubbery assisted us; for, on casting around, we found shreds of the man's loincloth impaled on the thorns as the tigress carried him away. Had the circumstances not been so tragic, it was instructive to learn how the sagacious animal had endeavoured to avoid such thorns and the obstruction they would have offered.

Some 300 yards away she had dropped her burden beneath a thicket at the foot of a small fig-tree, probably intending to start her meal. Then she had changed her mind, or perhaps been disturbed, for she had picked her victim up again and continued her retreat towards a deep nullah that ran southwards towards the main Cauvery river, some thirty miles away.

Thereafter, tracking became easier, for the tigress had changed her hold from the man's neck and throat; this had accounted for the lack of blood-spoor. Now she held him by the small of his back. Drops of blood, and smears across the leaves of bushes and thickets, now made it comparatively easy for us to follow the trail, and in another hundred yards we had found the man's loincloth, which had completely unwound itself and was hanging from a protruding sprig of 'wait-a-bit' thorn.

Continuing, we reached the nullah where, in the soft dry sand, the pugs of the tigress were clearly imprinted, with a slight drag-mark to one side, evidently caused by one of the man's feet trailing downwards as he was carried.

As there was no need of a tracker, and numbers would create disturbance, apart from needless risk, I crept cautiously forward alone, after motioning to the rest to remain where they were. Progress was of necessity very slow, for I had carefully to scan the heavy undergrowth on both banks of the nullah, where the tigress might have been lurking, waiting to put an end to her pursuer. Thus I had traversed two bends in the nullah when I sighted a low outcrop of rock jutting into the nullah-bed itself. Keeping as far as possible to the opposite side of the rock, I increased the stealth of my approach. Closer scrutiny revealed a dark object on the far side of the rock, and this duly proved to be the body of the unfortunate victim.

The tigress had already made a fair meal, having consumed about half her prey in the process, severing one leg from the thigh and one arm. Having assured myself that she was nowhere in the vicinity, I returned to the men, whom I summoned to the spot to help construct some sort of place where I might sit up and await the return of the assassin to its gruesome meal, which I was confident would be before sunset that day.

A more unsuitable spot for sitting-up could hardly be imagined. There was a complete absence of trees on which a hide or *machan* could be constructed, and it soon became evident that there were only two possibilities. One was to sit close to the opposite bank of the nullah, from where the human victim was clearly visible. The other was to ascend the sloping outcrop of rock to a point some ten feet above the bed of the nullah, where a natural ledge was formed about forty feet from its upper edge. The first plan I rejected, as being too dangerous in the case of a man-eater, and this left me with the prospect of sitting upon the rock-ledge, from where I could not only view the cadaver but the whole length of the nullah up to its bend in the direction from which we had come, and for about twenty yards in the other direction, where it swung abruptly to the right.

Working silently and quickly, at a spot some distance up the nullah, whence the sound of lopping would not be heard, the men cut a few thorny branches of the same variety as grew in the immediate vicinity of the rock, so as not to cause a contrasting background. These they deftly and cunningly arranged below the ledge, so that I would not be visible in any direction from the nullah itself. Fortunately I had had the forethought to bring my blanket, water-bottle and torch, although there would not be much use for the last of these during the major portion of the night, as the moon was nearing full and would rise comparatively early. By 3 p.m. I was in my place and the men left me, having been instructed to return next morning with a flask of hot tea, and sandwiches for a quick snack.

The afternoon wore slowly on, the heat from the blazing sun beating directly on the exposed rock and bathing me in sweat. Looking down the nullah in both directions, all was still and nothing disturbed the rays of shimmering heat that arose from the baked earth. Absence of vultures could be accounted for by the fact that, in the position the tigress had left it beneath the sharply-sloping rock, the body was hidden from the sky. About 5 p.m. a crow spotted it, and by its persistent cawing soon attracted its mate. But the two birds were too nervous of the human scent actually to begin pecking the kill. Time wore on, and the sun set as a fiery ball beneath the distant rim of forest-clad hills. The crows flapped away, one after the other, to roost in readiness on some distant tree in expectation of the morrow when, overcome by hunger, they would be more equal to braving the feared smell of human beings. The cheering call of the jungle-cock broke forth in all directions as a farewell to the dying day, and the strident *a-ow* of a peacock sounded from down the dry bed of the stream. I welcomed the sound, for I knew that in the whole forest no more alert watchman than a peacock could be found and that he would warn me immediately of the tigress' approach, should he see her. Now was the expected time, and with every sense intently alert I awaited the return of the man-killer. But nothing happened, the peacock flapped heavily away and dusk rapidly followed the vanquished day.

Fortunately the early moon had already risen and her silvery sheen soon restored a little of my former range of vision. The birds of the day had gone to roost by now, and their places had been taken by the birds of the night. The persistent *chuck-chuck-chuckoo'* of night-jars resounded along the nullah, as these early harbingers of the night sought their insect prey along the cooling banks. Time passed again, and then a deathly silence fell upon the scene. Not even the chirrup of a cricket disturbed the stillness, and my friends, the night-jars, had apparently gone elsewhere in their search for food. Glancing downwards at the human remains it seemed that one arm reached upwards to me in supplication or called perhaps for vengeance. Fortunately the head was turned away, so that I could not see the frightful contortion of the features, which I had noticed earlier that afternoon.

All at once the strident belling of an alarmed sambar broke the silence and was persistently followed by a succession of similar calls from a spot I judged to be about half-a-mile away. These were followed by the sharp cry of spotted-deer, and echoed up the nullah by a restless brain fever bird in his weird call of 'brain-fever,brain-fever,' repeated in rising crescendo. I breathed a sigh of relief and braced my nerves and muscles for final action. My friends,the night-watchmen of the jungle, had faithfully accomplished their task and I knew the tigress was approaching and had been seen.

The calls then gradually died away. This meant that the tigress had passed out of the range of the callers and was now close by. I strained my eyes on the bend to the right,twenty yards down the nullah, around which, at any moment, I expected the man-eater to appear. But nothing happened. Thirty minutes passed, then forty-five, by the hands of my wrist-watch, clearly visible in the moonlight.Strange, I thought; the tigress should have appeared long ago. She would not take forty-five minutes to cover half-a-mile.

And then a horrible feeling of imminent danger came over me. Many times before had that obscure sixth sense which we all possess but few develop, stood me in good stead in my many wanderings in the forests of India and Burma, and on the African veldt. I had not the slightest doubt that somehow, in spite of all my precautions, complete screening and absolute stillness, the tigress had discovered my presence and was at that moment probably stalking me preparatory to a final spring.

In moments of danger, we who know the jungle think quickly. It is not braveness that goads the mind to such quick thinking, for I confess that at this moment I was very afraid and could feel beads of cold sweat trickling down my face. I knew the tigress could not be on the nullah itself, or below me, or I would have seen her long before. She might have been on the opposite bank, hidden in the dense undergrowth and watching my position, but somehow I felt that her presence there would not account for the acutely-growing sense of danger that increasingly beset me. She could only be above and behind me. Suddenly it was borne home to me that the four-foot wall of rock behind me prevented me from looking backwards unless I raised myself to a half-crouching, half-kneeling position, which would make a steady shot almost impossible, apart from completely giving away my position to any watcher on the opposite bank, or on the nullah-bed itself. Momentarily, I cursed myself for this lack of forethought, which now threatened to become my undoing. As I hesitated for another second, a thin trickle of sand slid down from above, probably dislodged by the killer, now undoubtedly very close above me, and gathering herself for a final spring.

I hesitated no longer; I forced my numbed legs to raise me to a half-crouching position, simultaneously slewing the cocked .405 around, till the end of the muzzle was in line with my face. Then I raised myself a fraction higher, till both my eyes and the muzzle, came above the ledge.

A fearful sight revealed itself. There was the tigress, hardly eight feet away and extended on her belly, in the act of creeping down the sloping rock towards me. As our eyes met in surprise, we acted simultaneously, the tigress to spring with a nerve-shattering roar, while I ducked down again, at the same moment contracting my trigger finger.

The heavy blast of the rifle, level with and only a few inches from my ears, mingled with that demoniacal roar to create a sound which often till this day haunts me in my dreams and causes me to awaken, shivering with fear.

The brute had not anticipated the presence of the ledge behind which I sheltered, while the blast and blinding flash of the rifle full in her face evidently disconcerted her, deflecting her aim and deviating her purpose from slaughter to escape. She leapt right over my head, and in passing her hind foot caught the muzzle of the rifle a raking blow, so that it was torn from my grasp and went slithering, butt-first, down the sloping rock, to fall dully on the soft sand below, where it lay beside the half-eaten corpse. Quicker than the rifle, the tigress herself reached the nullah-bed, and in two bounds and another coughing roar was lost to view in the thickets of the opposite bank.

Shocked and hardly aware of what had happened, I realized I was unarmed and helpless, and that should the tigress return on her tracks, there was just nothing I could do. At the same time, to descend after the rifle would undoubtedly single me out for attack, if the animal were lying wounded in the bushes of the opposite bank. But anything seemed preferable to indecision and helplessness, and I dived down the slope to retrieve the rifle and scramble back, expecting at each second to hear the awful roar of the attacking killer. But nothing happened, and in less time that it takes to tell I was back at the ledge.

A quick examination revealed that no harm had come to the weapon in its fall, the stock having absorbed the shock. Replacing the spent cartridge, I fell to wondering whether I had hit the tigress at all, or if I had missed her at ridiculously close range. Then I noticed something black and white on the ledge behind me and barely two feet away. Picking it up, I found it was the major portion of the tigress' ear, which had been torn off by my bullet at that close range. It was still warm to my touch, and being mostly of skin and hair, hardly bled along its torn edge.

To say that I was disappointed and chagrined could not describe one-tenth of my emotions. I had failed to kill the man-eater at a point-blank range, failed even to wound her in the true sense. The tearing-off of her ear would hardly inconvenience her, beyond causing slight local pain for a few days. On the other hand, my foolish miss would teach her never to return to a kill the second time. This would make her all the more cunning, all the more dangerous and all the more destructive, because now she would have to eat when she killed, and then kill again when she felt hungry, increasing her killings beyond what would have been normally necessary. She might even alter her sphere of activities and remove herself to some other part of the country, where the people would not be aware of the arrival of a man-eater and so fall still easier prey. I cursed myself throughout that night, hoping against hope that the tigress might show up again, but all to no purpose. Morning, and the return of my men, found me chilled to the marrow, disconsolate and disappointed beyond expression. The hot tea and sandwiches they brought, after my long fast since the previous forenoon, followed by a pipeful of strong tobacco, somewhat restored my spirits and caused me to take a slightly less critical view of the situation which, after all, might have been far worse. Had it not been for my sixth sense, I would undoubtedly have been lying a partially devoured corpse beside that of the previous day's unfortunate victim. I had something to be really thankful for.

Approaching the spot into which the tigress had leapt, we cast about for blood-spoor, but, as I had expected, found none, beyond a very occasional smear from the damaged ear against the leaves of bushes, as the tigress had retreated from what had turned out for her a very surprising situation. Even these we eventually lost some distance away, so that it was an unhappy party of persons that returned to the hamlet and Anchetty, and eventually Gundalam, to report complete failure.

I remained at Gundalam for a further ten days, persistently tying out my buffalo baits each day, although I had little hope of success. Whole mornings and afternoons I devoted to scouring the forest in search of tracks, and nights were spent in sitting over water-holes, game-trails and along the bed of the Gundalam River in the hope of the tigress showing up, but all to no avail. Parties of men went out in the daytime in all directions to secure news of further kills, but nothing had happened. Apparently the tigress had deserted her haunts and gone off to healthier localities.

On the eleventh day I left Gundalam, tramping to Anchetty and Denkanikota. From there I travelled to Hosur, where I told my friend the Sub-Collector of all that had happened and extracted from him a promise that he would tell me immediately of further kills, should they occur, as I now felt myself responsible for the welfare of the people of the locality. Then, leaving Hosur, I returned to my home at Bangalore.

Five months passed, during which time I received three letters from the Sub-Collector, telling of vague rumours of human tiger-kills from distant places, two being from across the Cauvery River in the Coimbatore District, one from Mysore State territory, and the fourth from a place still further away.

Then suddenly came the bad news I feared, but had hoped would not eventuate. A tiger had struck again at Gundalam, killing her eighth victim there, and the next evening had snatched, from the very door of the little temple at Sulekunta, the old priest who had attended to the place for the last forty years. The letter concluded with the request to come at once.

Such urgent invitation was unnecessary, for I had been holding myself in readiness for the worst; within two hours I was motoring to Jowlagiri.

Arriving there I was fortunate in being able to talk to one of the party of pilgrims who had almost been eye-witnesses to the death of the old priest of the temple at Sulekunta. Apparently a party of men had been on pilgrimage and, as they approached the temple itself, were horrified to hear the low growl of a tiger, which then leapt into the forest from the roots of a giant *pepul* tree that grew some thirty yards away. Bolting for shelter into the temple itself, they were surprised to find it tenantless, and looking out were aghast to see the body of the old priest lying within the folds of the gnarled roots of the old *pepul* tree that directly faced them. After some time, and very timidly, they approached in a group, to find that the old man had apparently been attacked in, or very near, the temple, and then been carried to this spot to be devoured. The tiger had already begun its meal, consuming part of the skinny chest, when it had been disturbed by the pilgrim party.

I particularly inquired as to whether my informant, or his companions, had noticed anything wrong with the tiger's ears, but obviously they had all been too frightened to observe any defects.

I hurried to Sulekunta with my party of three and arrived near dusk; I must confess that the last two miles of the journey had been very uncomfortable, traversing a valley between two steeply sloping hills that were densely clothed with bamboo. But we heard and saw nothing, beyond the sudden trumpeting of a solitary elephant, which had been inhabiting these parts for some time and had been a considerable annoyance to pilgrims, whom he apparently delighted to chase if they were in small parties. But that is another story.

There was no time to make a proper camp, so we decided to sleep in the deserted front portion of the temple itself, a proceeding which I, and very decidedly my followers, would have declined to do under normal circumstances. But nightfall and the proximity of a man-eater are apt to overcome all scruples and principles. I stood guard with the loaded rifle, while my three men frenziedly gathered brush-wood and rotting logs that lay in plenty nearby, to build a fire for our warmth and protection, for on this occasion there was no friendly moon and it would soon be dark. Under such circumstances, attempting to sit-up for the man-eater, in the hope of its passing near the temple, would have been both highly dangerous and futile.

Soon we had a bright fire blazing, on the inner side of which we sat, away from the pitch-black jungle night, which could easily have sheltered the murderer, all unknown to us, within a distance of two feet. Listening intently, we occasionally heard the deep belling boom of sambar, and I could discern the harsher note of a stag, but these did not follow in persistent repetition, showing that the animals had not been unduly alarmed by any such major foe as the king of the Indian jungle. After midnight we arranged to keep watch in twos, three hours at a time, and I elected, with one of my companions, to take first turn. The other two were soon asleep. Nothing untoward happened, however, beyond the fact that the solitary tusker, who had approached near enough to catch a sudden sight of the fire, trumpeted once again and crashed away. A kakur, or barking-deer, uttered its sharp cry around 2 a.m., but as this was not continued, I decided it had been disturbed by a wandering leopard. Three o'clock came, I awoke the two sleeping men, and in turn fell into a dreamless sleep, to awaken to the early and spirited cry of a grey jungle cock, saluting the rising sun.

Hot tea, made with water from the well nearby, and some food gave us new life and heart, after which I walked across to the giant *pepul* tree and inspected the remains of the old priest. The vultures by day, and hyenas and jackals by night, had made a good job of him, for nothing remained but a few cleanly-picked bones, at the sight of which I fell to reminiscing about the old man who had tended this temple for the past 40 years, looking daily upon the same view as the one I now saw, hearing the same night-sounds of sambar, kakur and elephant as I had heard that night, and was now but a few bones, folded in the crevices of the hoary *pepul* tree.

For the next hour we cast around in the hope of finding pug marks and perhaps identifying the slayer, but although we saw a few old trails, I could not with any certainty classify them as having been made by my tigress.

By 9 a.m. we left on the long 23-mile trek to Gundalam, where we arrived just after 5 p.m. Here, upon making inquiries about the recent killing, I gleaned the first definite information about the slayer from a herdsman who had been attending to his cattle at the same watershed where I had tied my buffalo bait on my last visit. This man stated that he had had a companion with whom he had been talking, and who had then walked across to a nearby bush to answer a call of nature. He had just squatted down when, beyond the bush, the devilish head of a tiger arose, with only one ear, soon to be followed by an evil, striped body. The man had shrieked once when the fangs sank into the face and throat, and the next instant tiger and victim had disappeared into the jungle.

Here at last was the information I had been dreading, but somehow wanting, to hear. So, after all, it was now confirmed that the killer was none other than my old enemy, the tigress, who had returned at last to the scene of her former depredations, and for whose return and now vastly increased cunning I was myself responsible.

Everywhere I had heard reports that no cattle or buffaloes had been killed by this beast, so I did not waste time, as on the previous occasion, in setting live baits, realizing that I had an adversary to deal with whom I could only hope to vanquish in a chance encounter, face-to-face.

For the next two days I again searched the surrounding jungle, hoping by luck to meet the killer, but with fear and dread of being attacked from behind at any moment. Pugmarks I came across in plenty, especially on the soft sands of the Gundalam River, where the familiar tracks of the Jowlagiri tigress were plainly in view, adding confirmation to the thought that by my poor shot, some five months ago, I had been responsible for several more deaths.

At midday on the third day, a party of men arrived in a lather, having covered the thirty miles from Jowlagiri to tell me of a further kill — this time the watchman of the Jowlagiri Forest Bungalow — who had been killed and half-eaten within a hundred yards of the bungalow itself, the previous afternoon.

Hoping that the tigress might retrace her steps towards Sulekunta and Gundalam, as she was rumoured never to stay in the same place for more than a day after making a human kill, I left with my men at once, augmented by the party from Jowlagiri, who, although they had practically run the thirty miles to Gundalam, preferred the return tramp of twenty-five miles to Sulekunta protected by my rifle rather than return by themselves.

Again we reached the temple of Sulekunta as daylight was fading and, as the nights were still dark, repeated our camp-fire procedure within the temple itself. Our party had now been increased to twelve, including myself, a number which, although it made us feel safer, was far too many for my personal comfort.

This time, however, we were not to spend a peaceful night. The sambar and kakur were restless from night-fall, and at 8.30 p.m. we heard a tiger calling from a spot I judged to be half-a-mile away. This was repeated an hour later from quite close, and I could then easily distinguish the intonations of a tigress calling for a mate. The tigress had also seen the camp-fire and become aware of the proximity of humans and, obviously hoping for a meal, she twice circled the temple, her repeated mating calls being interspersed by distinctly audible grunts of anticipation.

All this gave me an idea by which I might possibly succeed in keeping her in the vicinity till daylight, at which time only could I hope to accomplish anything. Twice I gave the answering call of a male tiger, and received at once the urgent summons of this imperious female. Indeed, she came to the edge of the clearing and called so loudly as almost to paralyze us all. I was careful, however, not to call while she was in the immediate vicinity, which might have aroused her suspicions. At the same time I instructed the men to talk rather loudly, and not over-stoke the already blazing fire, instructions which were doubtlessly most unwelcome. I hoped by these means, between mating urge and appetite, to keep the tigress in the vicinity till daylight.

She called again, shortly before dawn and, congratulating myself on my ruse, as soon as it became light enough to see I hastened down the path towards Jowlagiri where, but a quarter mile away, stood the tamarind tree beneath which the boy had been killed over a year ago, and which I had already mentally noted as an ideal sitting-up place, requiring no preparation.

Reaching the tree in safety, I clambered up some twelve feet to a crotch, which was reasonably comfortable and provided a clear view of the path at both ends. Then, expanding my lungs, I called lustily in imitation of a male tiger. Nothing but silence answered me, and I began to wonder if after all the tigress had moved on at dawn. A new anxiety also gripped me. Perhaps she was near the temple, waiting for one of the men she had marked down the night before to come out of the building.

Before departing I had very strictly enjoined my companions not, on any account, to leave the temple, but I felt anxious lest any of them disobey me, perhaps in answer to a call of nature, or to get water from the well that was temptingly near.

I called a second time. Still no answer. After a short interval, and expanding my lungs to bursting-point, I called again. This time I was successful, for my voice penetrated the intervening forest and was picked up by the tigress, who immediately answered from the direction of the temple. I had been right in my surmise; the wily animal had gone there to look for a meal.

After a few minutes I called a fourth time and was again answered by the tigress; I was overjoyed to find that she was coming in my direction in search of the mate she thought was waiting.

I called twice more, my last call being answered from barely a hundred yards. Levelling the rifle, I glanced along the sights to a spot on the path about twenty-five yards away. I judged she would take less than thirty seconds to cover the intervening distance. I began to count, and as I reached twenty-seven the tigress strode into full view, inquiringly looking for her mate. From my commanding height in the tree her missing ear was clearly visible, and I knew that at last, after many tiring efforts, the killer was within my power. This time there would be no slip. To halt her onward movement, I moaned in a low tone. She stopped abruptly and looked upwards in surprise. The next second the .405 bullet crashed squarely between the eyes, and she sank forward in a lurching movement and lay twitching in the dust. I placed a second shot into the crown of her skull, although there was no need to have done so; actually this second shot did considerable damage to the head and gave much unnecessary extra work to the taxidermist.

The dreaded killer of Jowlagiri had come to a tame and ignominious end, unworthy of her career, and although she had been a murderer, silent, savage and cruel, a pang of conscience troubled me as to my unsporting ruse in encompassing her end.

There is not much more to tell. My eleven followers were elated at the sight of the dead marauder. Soon a stout sapling was cut, to which her feet were lashed by strong creeper vines, and we commenced the seven mile walk to Jowlagiri, staggering beneath the burden. Because of the man-eater's presence, no humans were afoot until we practically entered the village itself. Then word went round and throngs surrounded us. I allowed the people a short hour in which to feast their eyes on their onetime foe, while I retired to a tree some distance away, where hot tea soon refreshed me, followed by some food, and two comforting pipes of tobacco. Then I returned to the village, where willing hands helped me to lash the tigress across the rear seat of my two-seater Studebaker, to begin my homeward journey with the comforting thought that I had lived down my error and avenged the deaths of many humans.

The Kanchinda Panther

Augustus Somerville

This story is taken from the collection, At Midnight Comes the Killer *by Augustus Somerville. There is little biographical information available on the author but from his stories it would appear that he worked in the railways and made his home in Calcutta. The story of* The Kanchinda Panther *is told in the words of Somerville's close friend John Upshon, who was a Permanent Way Inspector in a small princely state. Upshon tells a remarkable story about how he follows a wounded panther into its cave and grapples with it, literally with his bare hands.*

On the south east of Peninsular India and not far from the sea-front, is a vast tract of land consisting mainly in forest clad mountains, deep valleys and broad rivers, whose waters are fed by innumerable shallow streams, practically dry during the winter months, but rushing torrents during the rains. In these dense forests once roamed herds of elephants, bison, deer and buffalo, which, although sadly depleted in recent years, still provide some of the finest hunting for local sportsmen. This vast area during the period of British occupation was the sole property of the Raja of Mayurbhanj, who had his palace at Baripada. As the main revenue of the state came from timber, the Raja had built a light railway, meter-gauge, from Rupsa on the main line to Talbund at its extreme end. It was on this line, at the little station Betnoti, that I first met Mr. John Upshon and his charming wife. Mr. Upshon was at the time employed as a Permanent Way Inspector and the very nature of his duties compelled him to travel up and down this line frequently, so that there was no part of this dense forest, through which this line penetrated, that was not familiar to

251

him.

It was while I was at Betnoti, enjoying the hospitality of this young couple, that I noticed the deep lacerations that Mr. Upshon had on his chest and arms and on enquiry learned of the terrible experience he had had with a Panther. The story he told me, which is true in every respect, I give in his own words.

It was on the 25 April 1955, he said. That the events I am about to narrate occurred. I remember the date well. It was my first Wedding Anniversary and we had arranged to have a few friends over and enjoy a pleasant evening. Imagine then my feelings when one of my trollymen, named Leppu, arrived at the bungalow to inform me that a leopard had killed a goat in the vicinity of one of our gang huts at Kanchinda. He further added that *machans* had been tied and every preparation made for sitting up that night. I am a keen *shikari* and the longing to take advantage of this excellent opportunity was irresistible, but I remembered the occasion and determined to forego the shoot, but as I told Leppu, I would not be able to come, my voice and face must have betrayed my disappointment. Now my wife is one of those women who have been blessed with the sublimest of all human virtues, an understanding mind. Instantly she countermanded the order and when I reminded her of the occasion, she brushed the objection aside. "You will have an anniversary every year John, but this Panther will not wait. Besides it is your duty to your workmen to protect their property." This last argument decided me and issuing immediate orders to get the car ready, I selected both my .405 rifle and my .12 bore and by two P.M. set out for Baripada, where the necessary petrol could only be obtained. Now Baripada is sixteen miles from my bungalow. The road is excellent and presents no difficulties, but at Baripada I discovered that I would have to travel another thirty-three miles to a small station called Banjriposi. The road was bad but not impassable and I arrived at Banjriposi within a couple of hours only to discover that my journey was not yet over as the 'kill' had occurred at a small station on this same line called Kanchinda. However, as it was getting dark I had no alternative but to set out immediately. The road to Kanchinda led through dense forest and was nothing more than a forest path, hacked out by wood-cutters and consisted in a succession of hollows and ruts and I would have to negotiate seven miles of this before reaching my destination. Eventually, just as night was falling I reached my gangmen's hut and proceeded across the fields to where the 'kill' was lying. The goat was an exceptionally large animal and, judging from the way its throat had been lacerated, must have put up a determined fight before it was finally overcome. Very little of the carcass had been eaten and the chances of the animal returning that night were excellent.

Hurrying to the *machan*, which had been tied on the only tree overlooking the 'kill,' I took up my position and as I was pretty sure that all our movements had been carefully noted by the Panther, I instructed the gangmen to return to the hut, talking loudly but on no account to return should I fire.

Settling myself as comfortably as possible, I prepared for a long and tiresome vigil. There was no moon as darkness fell, Venus, her brightness undimmed by any rival star, hung like a jewel in the western sky. Slowly the forest sank into silence. An occasional night-jar called mournfully, while from the direction of the hut came the voices of the crewmen as they gathered round the fire. After a while even this died down and I was left in complete silence. I had noted the direction of the 'kill' carefully and strained my eyes watching the spot for evidence of the Panther's return. Towards midnight, exhausted with the long drive and the strain of watching, I fell into a fitful doze, from which I was suddenly awakened by hearing a sharp crack from the direction of the 'kill.' With every faculty now thoroughly alert, I watched the spot where the goat was lying and after a time seemed to see a larger body worrying the carcass. In that uncertain light I could take no chances, so carefully aligning my sights I switched on my torch. In the brilliant beam I could see the Panther distinctly. He was lying with his back to me, tearing at the stomach of the goat, but although I switched the torch, on and off, several times, he refused to turn and look at me. Lying as he was the narrow width of his body offered a most difficult target, and by switching my torch I had hoped to make him turn his head so that I could have sighted between his eyes, gleaming in the torch-light, for a head shot. There being no alternative, I laid down the rifle and took up the .12 bore, which I had loaded with L.G.. Once again I depressed the switch and sighting along the middle of his spine, pressed the trigger. Simultaneously with the shot the Panther bounded into the air and then made off across the fields in the direction of the forest. For a while I followed him with the torch, but never had an opportunity to fire again, and I was forced to admit I had either missed the animal completely or had only wounded him slightly.

From the direction of the hut I heard Leppu's voice enquiring if they should come; but I shouted back telling the men to wait till morning, as I had wounded the animal and it would be dangerous for them to come at that time.

Thereafter I tried to sleep but could not and it was with relief that with the first light of dawn I saw Leppu and the crewmen, reinforced by several villagers, coming towards me.

Later, examining the ground in the vicinity of the 'kill' we came on the blood trail and as the animal appeared to have bled freely I came to the conclusion that it must have been badly wounded and determined to take up the tracking at once, before the village cattle, wandering all over the area, obliterated the trail.

By this time it was getting quite light and after a hasty cup of coffee and a few sandwiches, we set out. With Leppu leading and carrying my rifle, I followed, with Kalia, another crewman and the rest of the party trailing behind.

The trail led directly through the forest and a large outcrop of rocks, standing like sentinels a short way up the hill. Here we came to a single rock, some ten feet high, which rose sheer out of the ground. Cracked in the centre and worn smooth by the action of wind and water, was a large hole into which the animal had crawled. Hurrying round this rock we discovered that it was backed by an equally large rock that leaned over it, forming a large, natural cave. Of the two exits on either side, the one on the right showed that this had been the usual exit by which the animal left the cave, but careful survey all round showed no further signs of recent use.

'He is still inside, *Sahib*,' Leppu shouted, 'Let us smoke him out.'

Acting on this advice we collected a large quantity of leaves and straw and thrust this into both entrances, as well as the crack in the rock. Being slightly damp the straw threw off dense clouds of smoke when lit, but although the men shouted and threw rocks into the cave, nothing emerged and after half-an-hour or so, when the fire had died down I determined that the animal had either sneaked out from some secret exit or had died in the cave.

'Leppu,' I informed my crewman, 'I am going inside the cave to have a look. The rest of you stand back and shout Panther coming out.' But to this Leppu would not agree. 'If you are going in *Sahib*, I am coming with you,' and fired by his example Kalia announced his intention of coming with me as well. I tried to dissuade them but without success and it was finally decided that I would enter first, carrying the .12 bore, loaded with L. G. Kalia would come directly behind me carrying the torch as the cave was pitch dark within, while Leppu would bring up the rear with my rifle. The rest of the men would stand outside and warn us if the animal was escaping.

I can assure you I was not happy at the thought of entering that cave. It was against all my experience and my knowledge of the ways of wild animals and the thought that I was leading others into the some danger as myself was not very heartening. However, there was no way of backing out now. To have done so would have lowered me in the eyes of the men, who would immediately have concluded that I was afraid.

Holding the .12 bore carefully before me, I forced myself between the rocks at the entrance and entered. Once I was in the cave itself, I found a natural hollow, about four feet wide, ten feet long and sufficiently high to stand up in. Taking the torch from Kalia, who had followed immediately after me, I swung the beam round and saw that the floor on which we stood, was a foot or two lower than the entrance. About three feet from where we stood, was a deep crevice in the rock, which ran the whole length of the cave to where the opposite entrance could be seen. Of the Panther there was not a sign.

I was about to leave the cave when happening to cast the beam of the torch on the floor, I noticed a patch of blood at the very entrance to this crevice. Immediately I concluded that the animal had entered the cave, forced its way into the crevice and there died. Anxious to test the truth of my supposition, I stepped up to the entrance and was about to shine the torch into the cleft in the rocks, when I noticed a high spider crouched at the entrance, watching me. Now I have an inborn horror of these insects and would rather face a tiger than one of these creatures, so I handed the torch to Kalia, instructing him to shine the torch into the crevice, to see if the body of the Panther was lying there. Advancing cautiously, Kalia did as he was told, but no sooner had the light entered the cleft in the rocks, than with a savage roar the Panther was on him. Taken completely by surprise I had no opportunity to fire nor could I have done so without injuring the man as well, so I did the next thing automatically. As there was no room to swing the gun, I jabbed the barrel into the Panther's ribs with all my strength. In an instant it had released its victim and jumped back into the crevice.

Shouting to Leppu to help me lift the injured man, we soon got Kalia out of the cave and into the open, where I left Leppu to attend to his wounds, returning to retrieve my gun which had fallen to the ground in the melee.

As I entered the cave I discovered the torch, still alight, lying on the ground, while my gun lay a few feet away. Swiftly I entered and as swiftly returned to the entrance. With my legs half-way through, I turned to see if the Panther was anywhere about and noticed the tip of his tail, which he was obviously holding erect, moving in the direction of the opposite exit from the cave. This gave me an idea. The exit was small and for a little while the panther would be silhouetted against the light. At that distance it was impossible to miss, so stepping back I levelled my gun and waited. What caused the animal to abandon the idea I do not know, but once he reached the end of the crevice, he paused a moment and then returned. The tables were now reversed and I was the target silhouetted against the light. The panther was taking no chances. He must have spotted me before he had traversed half the distance, for with a sudden roar, he raced along the passage and sprang. No sooner did his face appear, than I fired, but unable to raise the gun in that confined space, I fired from the hip and the L. G. intended for his face and chest, hit him in the stomach, and the next instant he was on me, burying his teeth in my right shoulder. One hundred and fifty pounds of bone and muscle is not easily supported and his charge flung me back against the rock. Fortunately I still retained my balance and bracing myself against the rock at my back, I struck out with all my strength at his head, using the butt of the gun to augment my blows. Partially stunned, he released his hold for an instant and I took advantage of this brief respite to force the gun between us, holding the barrel in one hand and the stock in the other, so as to form a barrier with which I was able to ward off his next attack. But my advantage was short-lived. With one vicious stroke of his paw, he severed the stock just below the trigger guard, wrenching the barrel out of my hand. I was now completely at his mercy. As he came in for the kill, I made one desperate lunge at his head, but succeeded only in forcing my hand into his gaping jaws and I felt his teeth slipping past the bones of my palm as he bit fiercely on my hand, but this also gave me a slight advantage. Seizing his tongue with my partially paralyzed fingers, I strove desperately to force my fist further and further down his throat. In this position he was unable to do me any further damage with his teeth, but his claws raked me unmercifully, tearing the shirt and coat from my shoulders. Fortunately for me, his hind legs were partially paralyzed from the two gun-shot wounds he had received or he would have disemboweled me.

All this while, although I was myself unaware of it, I had been shouting to Leppu to shoot. It was now for the first time I saw this gallant fellow forcing his way into the cave. As he entered he cocked the hammer on my rifle and I distinctly heard the click as the hammer fell on the empty chamber and I realized with a sick feeling of despair, that I had forgotten to load the rifle. Leppu, I knew, was unable to work the bolt to force a cartridge from the magazine into the chamber and with that realization I probably went mad with fear, agony and frustration. Releasing the animal's tongue, I started lashing out wildly with hands and feet, in a frantic effort to drive the animal from me. By some lucky accident my boot drove straight into the gun-shot wound in his stomach and so great must have been the pain, that the Panther fell back gasping with agony. This was my opportunity and seizing the rifle from Leppu, I wrenched open the bolt, driving a cartridge into the chamber and with my crippled hand presented the rifle in the direction of the Panther and pulled the trigger. A good woman's prayers must have been my salvation that day, for the bullet crashed into the Panther's body, hurling it to the ground and I fainted. I must have regained consciousness in a few minutes, for when I came to I discovered Leppu using the barrel of my rifle to prise open the Panther's jaws, where in its death struggles it had bitten through the calf of my leg. Once free I wasted no time in getting out of the cave, but so weak had I become that Leppu had to practically carry me out. Once in the open a cup of the still warm coffee in my flask helped to revive me and tearing slips of cloth from Leppu's turban I bound my wounds as best I could and the men carried me back to the car.

Now you can imagine the quandary I was in. Once the excitement died down, reaction set in and I was trembling all over. My shoulder and right hand were lacerated and crippled and to make matters worse, blood from a scalp wound where the Panther's claws had inflicted a nasty wound on my head, kept seeping down my forehead and entering my eyes. In this state I was obliged to drive my car down a country road, through ditches and nullahs and around fallen logs, a distance of seven miles to the main road. How I ever completed this nightmare journey I have no idea. I must have blacked out on several occasions for when I came to it was to find Leppu clinging desperately to the wheel to prevent me from going off the road. However, at last we made it and arriving at Banjriposi, I drove to the only dispensary the town boasted. Here I was patched up, the meagre resources of this dispensary being wholly inadequate for the job, and returned to the car for the thirty mile drive to Baripada.

But here I came up against a real obstacle. The Doctor would not hear of it. 'Mr. Upshon,' he exclaimed, 'you are in a state of shock. You have lost a lot of blood and you are physically unfit to undertake a thirty mile drive. Wait here and I will make other arrangements to drive you in.'

An old Sikh driver who happened to be at Banjriposi, awaiting some minor repairs to his truck, came up just at this time and hearing the discussion, very sportingly offered to drive the car to Baripada.

At the Baripada Hospital I received expert attention and sixteen stitches. Four hours later I was back at my bungalow at Betnoti, where my wife, although considerably upset when she heard of my narrow escape, promptly had me removed to the Railway Hospital at Kharagpur, from whence I returned three weeks later, perfectly cured.

The Panther's skin now hangs in the place of honour in my Hall and whenever I look at it I am filled with a deep sense of respect for a very brave animal, who gallantly defended his home and his life against a weaker but far better equipped foe.

Eight Annas a Tail

Hugh Allen

After receiving a head wound in the second World War, Hugh Allen came to India and bought a farm in Madhya Pradesh. In the introduction to his book, The Lonely Tiger, *he writes of how his friends thought that he was crazy to be coming to India just when the British were leaving. It is difficult to tell why exactly Hugh Allen came to India but it must have been partly his passion for wildlife and hunting. Allen was truly a reluctant predator for all his stories contain a wistful note of regret when he talks of hunting.* Eight Annas a Tail *refers to the government 'bounty' for killing a monkey, something which Allen strongly opposed. He tells of the poachers who trap and shoot monkeys on his land and his efforts to drive them away. When his dog 'Jumbo' is killed and eaten by a leopard, Allen takes up his rifle again and sets out to destroy the leopard. No other* shikar *story depicts the struggle between man and the forest with such tragedy and pathos.*

It was six o'clock of a May morning and already unpleasantly warm. As Babs and I sipped our early tea under the shade of the trees near the house we told each other quite unnecessarily that it was going to be another scorching day. Speaking for myself I did not really mind: the hot month of May is a slack one and I was going to spend the morning on a cool verandah with a new book; after lunch I might raise the energy to answer some letters.

Jumbo, one of the dogs, was feeling lazy too and lay stretched at my feet, a shaggy and rather oversized cocker spaniel. He had always hated the heat, and unless I took him down to the river to bathe he would not stir out until the cool of evening for he was a wise old man of twelve summers.

Those were our plans at six in the morning and for a hot day they were sound. Unfortunately they did not last very long; for even as we made them fate and the jungle were decreeing that our day should be very different indeed. For me it was to be a day that is still branded across my memory; for poor old Jumbo it was to mark the end of the road . . .

Bandarwallahs! Bandarwallahs! It was Kalu racing up through the orchards and shouting as he came. I knew at once what he was coming to tell me, another raid by the 'monkey-men' who had already visited us twice before. As soon as Kalu had caught up with his breath I asked him where he had seen them. When he had told me I gulped down my tea and then went in to dress.

This time I was really going to catch them and discourage further visits; for these are cruel devils that come armed with nets, clumsy traps and old muzzle-loading guns. The live monkeys — and they prefer them to be very young — are for export and vivisection; the ones they cannot catch in their traps are shot down for the new government reward of eight annas a tail.

Now you might well imagine that as a farmer with large orchards I should be only too happy to let these men go over the estate as often as they pleased. That, however, would be a wrong idea because by now I have the monkey situation pretty much under control whenever any fruits are on the trees. The monkeys of course always do some damage, but this is more than offset by the help these little animals give you about the jungles. Indeed, they might even save your life for they will often tell where a tiger or a leopard is hiding after a badly placed bullet.

Besides, the business of protecting orchards developed long ago into an exciting game which I believe is enjoyed by the monkeys just as much as by us. I play it often for it takes me back to those early days when I was a senior member of the Black Hand and known over a widish area as 'That bloody little horror with the catapult.' Now, alas, most of that puerile cunning with this weapon has gone, but some of the old magic of those times still returns when I pull back an elastic. But my own accuracy is no longer important as it is more than made up for by a little band of dusky 'sure-shots' — eager volunteers from the kids on the estate.

These young rustics know nothing of space-suits and ray-guns, and even cowboys and Indians are as yet unknown. They are thoroughly old-fashioned kids and so content with a simple 'catty' and a pocketful of smooth pebbles — and the red bottoms of the monkeys in the tree-tops . . .

That morning, as soon as I was dressed, I set off after the monkey-men with Jumbo at my heels. We walked fast for I was hoping to find them before they could do much damage. I was carrying a rifle while Jumbo had his old red and blue ball bulging from his mouth. Somewhere, he hoped, we should stop by water and play his favourite game.

I was making for a deep and shady nullah which runs diagonally through the estate and divides it into two almost equal halves. The banks of this are lined with magnificent trees, most of them tall stately *kohas*, which are loved by the monkeys for the cool shade of their topmost branches. So it was somewhere along here that I expected to find the monkey-men at work because this nullah is more than three miles long and the trees above it 'home' for at least six troops of monkeys.

The estate is roughly square, so I started the search at the far north-eastern corner and intended to stalk along the nullah until I found the raiders. By now the morning was really hot. There was little breeze and even under the shade of the trees the fierce heat from the sun was unpleasant. During the rains this nullah is a raging torrent, but now the flow of water had dried up leaving along the winding bed a series of crystal-clear pools with little fish darting above the pepper-and-salt of their sandy bottoms. By the side of most of these pools, at the foot of the high bank, are small ledges a foot or two wide and a few inches above the surface of the water. These are paths that have been beaten out by game and are much used at night by all kinds of animals. At the days grow warmer and the smaller pools elsewhere dry up, tigers and leopards begin to haunt the banks of this nullah.

For the first mile I found no sign of the raiders. Then I picked up what were almost certainly their tracks: five pairs of human feet, the prints fresh and over the marks of the hooves and pads left by last night's visitors. At one spot these men had stopped to rest. The ground here was littered with *bidis*, the Indian leaf cigarette; and in one place against the bank some heavy bundles had been thrown down, one of them leaving on the sand a criss-crossed pattern like a net.

If those signs had not been enough to tell me that the monkey-men were not far ahead, the next pool two hundred yards down the nullah left no doubt of it. The grey bodies of two *langur* monkeys lay just by the water's edge. One was dead and nearly cold, the other still lived though its life was flowing rapidly away into a pool of blood seeping into the sand. Both bodies were peppered with red-brown spots where the shot that had brought them tumbling from the trees had slammed in. Neither of the monkeys had a tail.

I had known the troop from which these monkeys came for many years and had always regarded its little members as some of my best jungle friends. In many ways this was the most useful troop of all along the whole stretch of the nullah. The ground here is tricky; beyond the banks it is covered with heavy forest and to the north rises steeply to several hundred feet. Towards the summit of this high ground are patches of open rocky scrub. These places are difficult to reach: the way up to them is over large boulders which have between them a mass of 'wait-a-bit' thorns and other rampageous weeds; these hide deep crevices so completely that a false step can mean a heavy fall; end up at the bottom of one of these with a broken limb and you might never be found.

All these high places are loved by leopards. They come up in the early morning to take the sun and stretch out on the flat-topped rocks. As the day gets warmer they move to some shady spot to doze away the drowsy hours until night; but although they appear to sleep one eye is always cocked towards the nullah below. Long stretches of it are laid bare from these high places and anything moving on the sandy bed can be seen plainly. It is seldom that there is not a leopard somewhere about here, and whenever one of these sneaking brutes becomes a nuisance, this is the spot I come to first. Then it was that the monkeys used to help, for if a leopard was indeed about they would tell me — sooner or later —where it was.

As I looked up from the bodies of the two monkeys a cold anger took hold of me. The whole troop seemed to have been wiped out for there was no sign of the others anywhere. No swaying branches up in the trees as they swung from bough to bough, and in the air were none of their usual cries as they quarrelled and played above the pool. For the next fifteen minutes my anger mounted and there was but one thought in my mind: to catch these men, free whatever captives they had, and — but that could wait until I caught them.

That morning, however, I was not to catch them. Indeed, that satisfaction only came many years later when I surprised a big camp of them one morning just before dawn. But on that occasion I got them all: men, women and children, all their monkeys and all their goods and chattels. The chattels included the skins of buck, chital and barking deer, as well as an enormous bundle of peacock feathers. The skins and the feathers were a lucky find; for although those rascals had no licence to trap I could not have touched them for the monkeys alone.

All that, however, was still in the future and not known to me that morning when I set off after finding the dead monkeys to track their killers. In the sand I could see that two men had stayed in the nullah while the other three had probably worked the banks. At two places they had stopped to smoke again; then, at a spot where a game-path crosses the nullah, the footsteps of all five led away to the left and were lost on the harder surface of the track up on the bank. Now, I suspected, they were making for the river half-a-mile away where they would find a lot more monkeys.

I was about to go after them when I noticed that Jumbo was no longer at my heels. I whistled softly to bring him up from the pool in the nullah below. He was probably there wallowing like a buffalo with his beloved ball near his nose waiting for me to come and play. But there was no time for that now, so I sent down another and more urgent whistle when he did not come up to the first one.

I felt the first tinge of anxiety when a third call failed to bring him up. In a flash every other thought was swept from my mind and I raced back to the pool. Jumbo was not in sight, and when I started back the way I had come I saw none of his pug marks following mine. Now I was really worried. He was an obedient dog who without word to break would not have gone far on his own affairs.

From the pool I had just left to the one where we had found the two monkeys was just over a quarter of a mile with the nullah between them shaped like the letter S. Slowly I worked back scanning the sand for sign of Jumbo. But there was none, the soft surface showed only my own boots, the feet of the monkey-men and the tracks of wild animals.

There was still no trace of him when at last I was standing by the pool on the far side of which were the two monkeys. Across that placid surface was the last spot where I positively remembered Jumbo at my heels. So, from somewhere between where I stood now and the other end of the water — a distance of only eighty yards — that faithful old dog had vanished into thin air.

My eyes went to the little ledge running along by the water at the foot of the bank. A feeling of sick apprehension was churning inside me and every instinct was warning of what I should find when I went along that ledge.

For five minutes more I stood still and listened to the jungle. Nothing was excited; all the birds were going about their business in a calm way, and from nowhere around me came the slightest sign that anything was wrong. What I needed to tell me the truth was monkeys, but when I scanned the trees again there was still not one in sight. Slowly I started towards the ledge by the side of the pool.

Half-way along it I stopped. In the firm clay at my feet was the whole story and it told me that Jumbo was dead.

Almost at the water's edge was the single imprint of a leopard's paw. The pad had rammed hard into the clay with the toes wide-cleft and the claws straining out. A little to the left of the pug a small patch on the ledge had been swept clean of the debris and dead leaves fallen from the trees above. The leopard had sprung down from the bank, seized Jumbo by the neck, and then shaken him so violently that his body had swept that patch. And about a yard from the ledge, motionless and just showing above the surface of the pool, a spot of faded red and blue that was Jumbo's old ball.

Of the attack I had heard nothing, and why Jumbo had stayed so far behind me I shall never know. I can only think that he must have lingered about the bodies of the two monkeys and then, when he set out to follow me, he had picked up the leopard's scent. That would have stopped him, for he was well aware of the danger from these sneaking cats. By then I must have been round the first bend of the S in the nullah.

From the swept patch the leopard had gone on along the ledge carrying Jumbo with his legs trailing through the dead leaves by the water's edge. Then, a few yards beyond the pool, Jumbo — still alive — had broken the leopard's grip and shaken free. For a few glorious seconds, for he was a fighting man, he had kept the leopard off. The sand here had been wildly churned by both the leopard's pugs and Jumbo's in what had been a short but furious melee. Then sheer brute force had driven Jumbo back against the bank where he had been seized again. From here the leopard had gone on down the nullah and then had bounded up the bank towards that rocky and difficult ground.

I followed slowly, the trail made easy by frequent spots of blood. After climbing steeply for about fifteen minutes I stopped. From a dense patch of scrub farther up the slope I had suddenly heard the leopard.

I am not going to try to describe my feelings. All I can say, passing over the agony, is that a burning fury was urging me on to rush forward and stop those dreadful sounds by any means. But I fought the urge back. To rush forward now would probably send the leopard flying from the back of the scrub and leave him free to operate another day. It might have been very unwise, too, and no help to Jumbo now, to rush straight at an unsuspecting leopard on a fresh kill. Patience was the only thing. If I held my hand and waited I might get the revenge I wanted.

But not from here. When I had looked around me again I soon saw that I could get no nearer to the leopard without giving myself away. The ground was too difficult: the fifty or so yards I still had to climb before I stood the slightest chance were strewn with rocks and crackling leaves. The leopard had picked his spot with instinctive cunning and from no side could he be surprised; the only thing was to leave him where he was and then set a trap on ground of my own choosing.

The morning by now was so hot that there was one place the leopard was sure to come to when he had finished. That place was the pool immediately below me. When he came down to drink, as he must, I could kill him from the other side of the nullah.

With the greatest care I crept away from those heart-rending sounds, back down the rocks, then across the nullah and up the opposite bank where I found some cover to hide me.

The leopard took his time. It was over half-an-hour before I heard him moving on the hill— an animal unsuspicious of any danger. About half-way down he started to roll in the dead leaves; then he spent some time cleaning his claws, tearing them through the bark of a tree with sharp, plucking little jerks. All at once I saw him weaving through the trees at the foot of the high ground across the nullah — a comparatively small animal as his pugs had shown. When he reached the bank above the pool he paused and looked to his right and left. A moment later he came down the bank in a gracefully controlled slide to stand on the ledge beside the water.

He gave me a beautiful broadside shot as he bent to drink with the points of his elbows sharp above his back. But I was a little too eager to see him dead and raised the rifle a shade too quickly. The leopard saw the movement from the corner of his eye. In a flash his head was up and looking straight towards me. As he braced for the spring that would take him away to safety I snatched at the trigger.

I heard the bullet strike and saw the leopard leap into the air. At the top of his jump he twisted and clawed for the bank. For one uncertain moment he hung there fighting for a hold with a blur of scrabbling paws. As I ripped back the bolt I thought he was going to drop; but with a sudden effort he was up and racing away through the trees. The bullet I sent after him hit a rock well behind his tail.

Although the first shot had been poorly placed he was nevertheless a badly wounded animal and that mad rush would not take him far. Or so I thought, but when I went to look for him I sought in vain for over an hour. There was no sign of him anywhere about the spot where I thought he should have fallen; nor on the high ground was there any trace of his passing; and nowhere was there a single drop of blood. At last I came to the conclusion that I must have left him somewhere behind me and so decided to go back to the beginning —the claw marks at the top of the nullah bank.

From here, as I had seen before, his first wild rush had taken him about a hundred yards. Then all trace of him was lost as the ground began to rise and became rocky. I started to search around the end of this trail again, and I had only been going for about a minute when I suddenly found a clue. Across the side of a rock was a heavy smear of blood. As I bent down to examine it I was wondering how I could have missed it the first time.

But had I missed It? The rock had been catching the full rays of the sun for some time and was burning hot when I touched it. Now my follow-up had started more than an hour before, yet this blood was still wet and just beginning to trickle down the rock. *I've walked right into it*! As the thought hit me I froze beside the rock: the leopard had been here within the last few minutes and now was probably watching me from somewhere close by.

Any sudden movement now might bring the enraged beast on top of me. He might come even if I did not move, but it was safer to stay crouched by the rock and let my eyes search as far as they could from under the brim of my hat. There was no sign of him in front of me, so fervently hoping that he was not somewhere close behind I started slowly to my feet. A few breathless moments later, after I had looked all round, the tension slackened. The sudden rush would have come before now if the leopard had been really near.

It had been a nasty scare and I now started off much more cautiously. Not far from the blood-smeared rock a game-path led towards the nullah. That was the way I thought the leopard would have gone. The heat now was like a furnace and a burning thirst had probably driven him back to the pool. I was, however, taking no more chances; for it was just as possible that he had moved on from the rock because he had heard me coming and might now be waiting in ambush somewhere ahead.

As I moved slowly towards the pool I found more blood on the path. This certainly was the way he had gone and I doubled my precautions. Every bit of cover likely to conceal a leopard was now suspect indeed and had to be scrutinized carefully before going on. After I had stalked forward for another hundred yards the ground in front of me rose in a gentle fold before it rolled down to the nullah on the other side. If the leopard was planning mischief, just over the crest of that was a likely place for him to spring it.

A little before the fold started to rise I left the game-path and went thirty yards to the right of it. From this new position I began to creep up the slope as carefully as I could. At the top of it I paused with my finger on the trigger and my eyes everywhere at once. Suddenly I knew that the leopard was not here. Of that I was perfectly sure, for on one of the topmost branches of a *koha* tree almost above my head was a monkey.

From where it sat it could take in a sizable piece of the surrounding jungle. Yet it was calm and quiet, and from the ground appeared to be dozing. That told me that no leopard was or recently had been anywhere near here; for if that monkey had caught even a glimpse of its spotted hide it would now be racing round the tree and screaming in high alarm.

With the tension suddenly slackened and the leopard heaven knew where, I fished out a pipe. Why, I wondered as I filled it, had the leopard so abruptly changed his mind and avoided the nullah? The most probable answer was that he had either seen or heard me close behind him and had realized the danger of going down to the pool. If that was true, then he had for a certainty doubled back to the high ground. One thing, however, was sure: the leopard knew where I was and so it would be unwise to go back from my present position. The safest thing was to let him think I had lost his trail by going on to the nullah. Then, once I was by the pool and out of sight, I could fool him by working round to the high ground from behind.

As I started towards the path leading down to the pool I was thinking again of Jumbo. Once more I was living through the agony of hearing the leopard at his meal. So it happened that as I reached the path the memory of that ordeal was undoubtedly dulling my mind and in some odd way splitting it into two differently thinking parts. I was half-way down the path when I came abruptly into the deep shadow cast by the trees along the bank. Just beyond this and straight ahead of me was a patch of blinding sunlight and the dazzling reflection from the pool. The two together were so bright that for a moment I closed my eyes.

When I opened them again it seemed that one part of my mind showed me the spotted back of a leopard crouched half behind the root of a tree and a small bush on the path six feet ahead. At the same time the other part of my mind was assuring me that no leopard could be there while a monkey sat silent overhead. A little confused but nevertheless sure that this could not be a leopard I walked on expecting to see that spotted back resolve into the litter of dead leaves it had to be.

It was only one pace short of the bush that my confusion vanished when the full length of the leopard leapt into view. For a second that seemed eternity I looked down at him. Neither of us moved and for one brief moment I thought he was dead. But he was alive, and an instant later, with a snarl of rage, he reared up in a blur of flailing paws. I tried to leap clear and went crashing into the bank. As I fought to keep my balance sharp claws raked down my left leg. I raised my foot to kick them off and the leopard's jaws snapped shut round the heel of my boot. I slammed it down with his head still clamped to it. But with my foot caught tight I lost the last of my balance and fell heavily to the path.

Now he had me. A quick spring and the game was his. But he did not move. He might have been dead except for his furious eyes screaming hate into mine. I knew then that he was at his last gasp, but even though his strength was failing fast I could feel his jaws straining tighter round my boot. By now I had found and grabbed up the rifle. The next second I jammed the muzzle into his mouth and pulled the trigger.

He died at once. But although I had felt the blast through my boot it was some little time before I had prised his fangs from the rubber heel. Reaction hit me as soon as my foot was free. I was trembling with shock and my heart was pounding at top speed while the deep claw marks down my leg were streaming blood. I should have liked to lie down beside the dead leopard, but before I could move a wild scream of terror ripped through the air. It came so abruptly and held such a chilling note that I was on my feet in a flash and grabbing for the rifle expecting I knew not what.

All at once I remembered the monkey. It had to be that for the scream had come from high above me. From where I was I could not see it through the leaves of the trees, but the scream had startled me so much that I began to run towards the top of the bank. Just as I reached it and was looking up the scream came again and stopped me in utter amazement.

What sort of monkey was this? It didn't call at leopards and seemed so bad at climbing trees that it was about to fall off the one it was on; for it was hanging from a branch with its arms at full stretch and kicking its legs feebly in the air. Without warning the scream rent the air again. Then before my startled eyes the monkey let go its hold. It dropped like a stone, a sudden twisting flash of grey that hurtled down thumping from branch to branch until it hit the ground with a sickening thud sixty feet below.

I was still surprised, but as I made my way down to it an idea was forming in my mind. The monkey had fallen by the water's edge with its face upwards and one quick look was enough to tell me why it had not called at the leopard and why it had fallen off the tree. It was a young male monkey and it had been dying for hours. Its body was peppered with the shot from a muzzle-loading gun and it had been blinded in both eyes. It would have fallen from the tree in any case, but I believe that the sudden report of my shot at the leopard had so terrified it anew that it slipped from its perch; then, weak from loss of blood and hanging over a sixty-foot drop in a strange and frightening world of blackness and pain — well, who wouldn't scream?

At last I slung the rifle and started to limp up the slope towards home. As I stepped out a whistle instinctively formed on my lips to call up Jumbo before I remembered. At the top of the slope I paused and looked down at the dead monkey. Its little face seemed slightly ashamed and saying, 'I couldn't really help it, you know.'

MORE ABOUT PENGUINS

For further information about books available from Penguins in India write to Penguin Books (India) Ltd, B4/246, Safdarjung Enclave, New Delhi 110 029.

In the UK: For a complete list of books available from Penguins in the United Kingdom write to Dept. EP, Penguin Books Ltd, Harmondsworth, Middlesex UB7 0DA.

In the U.S.A.: For a complete list of books available from Penguins in the United States write to Dept. DG, Penguin Books, 299 Murray Hill Parkway, East Rutherford, New Jersey 07073.

In Canada: For a complete list of books available from Penguins in Canada write to Penguin Books Canada Ltd, 2801 John Street, Markham, Ontario L3R 1B4.

In Australia: For a complete list of books available from Penguins in Australia write to the Marketing Department, Penguin Books Australia Ltd, P.O. Box 257, Ringwood, Victoria 3134.

In New Zealand: For a complete list of books available from Penguins in New Zealand write to the Marketing Department, Penguin Books (N.Z.) Ltd, Private Bag, Takapuna, Auckland 9.

THE LONELY TIGER
Hugh Allen

Ever since he was old enough to use a catapult, Hugh Allen dreamed of hunting big game. When he decided to settle down in India, a country he had been hospitalized in during WWII, his dreams were finally fulfilled.....

In the gripping true life stories in this book, the author recounts his encounters with man-eating tigers, love-sick tigresses, laughing leopards, killer boars and deadly snakes.

'One of the best books on tigers and hunting I've read'—*Stephen Alter*